Introduction to HUMAN ANATOMY

A LABORATORY MANUAL

FIFTH EDITION

JAMES E. CROUCH
CALIFORNIA STATE UNIVERSITY, SAN DIEGO

MAYFIELD PUBLISHING COMPANY

I dedicate this manual to my friend Leon Gardner, M.D. for his help and inspiration, and to my students who have taught me much through the years and have given me hope for the future.

CONTENTS

LIST OF FIGURES

LIST OF PLATES

PREFACE TO THE FIFTH EDITION

The fifth edition of this manual incorporates the more recent suggestions of those who have used it in their teaching. It also reflects the comments and suggestions of the students with whom I have worked.

The amount of material presented in this edition remains much as before. Changes and additions have been made which I believe will aid greatly the learning process. These are mostly in the form of new and improved illustrations, many of which are borrowed from Crouch, TEXT-ATLAS OF CAT ANATOMY, published by Lea & Febiger. A few copies of this reference work should be available in the laboratory. Some of the descriptive material has been expanded, not to increase the amount of work required, but to give further aid in dissection and recognition of structures.

The format of the manual has been modified by placing the plates and figures closer to the descriptive material rather than grouping them at the ends of chapters as in previous editions. Sample examinations have been provided as an appendix to aid the students in their studies and for self-testing. An index is also an added feature of this edition.

A few of the illustrations are completely labeled. Some have no labels but do have leaders to indicate what structures the students should identify and label; others are partially labeled and the students are expected to complete them. Many of the illustrations go beyond the material required of the students, and to make it clear what structures must be learned, lists of muscles, nerves, and blood vessels are provided. I feel that many laboratory manuals leave the students with a false impression of the anatomy. They see it as simple as the diagrams provided. The method used here makes a reasonable requirement for learning but shows also the true nature and complexity of the structure of these animals. For the highly motivated student who feels he wants to go beyond the minimal requirements of the course, the material is there to aid him.

The nomenclature has been brought up to date and an effort made to clarify for the student the relationship between the terminology for a quadruped mammal such as the cat and that for the biped man.

New outline drawings of the human skeleton have been added in the hope that students will draw on them the most important muscles. This exercise should aid them in visualizing origins and insertions as well as understanding muscle action.

In the chapter on the nervous system, drawings of spinal nerve plexuses and spinal nerves have been provided along with the necessary descriptive material. These nerves are shown in their relationship to muscles and blood vessels and should aid the student in the review of these three systems. It is suggested that the students color the nerves yellow, the arteries red, and the veins blue to test their knowledge and to further enhance the illustrations.

I believe the laboratory manual remains as adaptable as before for courses involving greater or lesser amounts of lecture and laboratory time.

Again I acknowledge the work of Mrs. Janet Julian in preparing the new outline drawings of the human skeleton; Mrs. Martha B. Lackey for several new drawings on the respiratory, excretory, and circulatory systems; Dr. Roger Marchand for new and improved photomicrographs. I appreciate the courtesy granted by Lea & Febiger, publishers, for the use of a number of illustrations from Crouch, TEXT-ATLAS OF CAT ANATOMY and FUNCTIONAL HUMAN ANATOMY, and by the American Optical Company for the drawing and descriptive material on the microscope. Thanks go also to Mrs. Helen Morris who typed the manuscript. Finally, I have enjoyed working with Michelle Hogan and Richard Bare of National Press Books and have appreciated their advice, help, confidence and support.

San Diego, California   James E. Crouch
September, 1972   Professor of Zoology
                                                         San Diego State University

PREFACE TO THE SECOND EDITION

Since the printing of the first edition, the manual has been adopted by numerous schools. I have had the advantage of suggestions from those who use it. In this revision some of those ideas and suggestions have been incorporated.

The materials covered in this edition are essentially those used in the first edition; the amount of work required of the students has not been increased. An effort has been made, however, to give the students greater assistance than previously, so that they can learn quicker and with better understanding.

Since some students have difficulty in using the microscope, additional instructions are included in the introductory chapter. The sections of the introduction pertaining to cells, tissues, and systems are expanded. Man's relationship to the other Chordate animals is briefly stated, in the belief that this might aid the students in correlating knowledge, gained from laboratory dissections of the cat, with man himself.

Terms of position and direction and planes of reference are briefly defined. The anatomical position is described. Although this material is included in text-books, repeating it in the laboratory manual gives needed emphasis.

Students find the language of anatomy very difficult. With this in mind, a list of common prefixes used in anatomy has been included in the introduction. Word lists have also been added at the end of most chapters. These should aid the students in their pronunciation of terms as well as with their meanings.

The introductory part of the section on the skeletal system has been expanded in that a brief description of the kinds of articulations has been added.

Many of the illustrations have been replaced by improved ones, and new ones have been added. Of particular importance are the numerous photomicrographs. It is anticipated that these will aid the students greatly in orienting and identifying tissues.

While more labeled drawings are included in this second edition, the majority still remain for students to label in accordance with the printed directions. Instructors and students differ, of course, in their opinions as to the educational value of labeling drawings; if the instructor prefers not to have the drawings labeled, they can be used for testing purposes by the instructor or in self-testing by the students. The drawings can be easily torn from the manual for grading.

Assuming that each class will set its own pace, no effort has been made to divide the manual into separate lessons. It is organized on the body system plan, and includes enough material for a one-semester course with two lectures and one three-hour laboratory per week. The material and organization are such, however, that the manual is useful for courses with more or fewer hours of laboratory experience.

The first laboratory might be used for orientation. Students taking human anatomy, though we assume that they have had one course in high school or college biology, actually vary widely in their knowledge. Starting with a relatively simple study of the cell, involving as it does the use of the microscope, gives the instructor an opportunity to evaluate the background of the class. Students knowing the cell and not needing help in the use of the microscope may go directly to the study of the integumentary system.

Acknowledgement is due to Miss Jane Richey, Miss Sandra Woolf, Mrs. Joan McClintic, Mr. Joseph Stowers, Dr. Harry Plymale, Mr. Al Rowen, Mrs. Martha B. Lackey, and Mr. Joseph Yuhasz for help with the illustrations. Special appreciation is extended to Mrs. Janet Julien for her drawings, to Mr. Bruce Lighthart for the photomicrographs, and to Dr. Edward Huffman for technical advice. I am indebted to the American Optical Company for permission to use the drawing of the microscope, and to L. L. Woodruff and the Macmillan Company for the illustration, Schematic Diagram of a Chordate. A special "thank you" is given to all of the students whose suggestions and interest have been a guide and inspiration to me in the development of this manual and to the people of N-P Publications whose help, confidence, and generosity are deeply appreciated.

San Diego, California   James E. Crouch
July, 1964   Professor of Zoology
                                                                                      San Diego State College

INTRODUCTION

When Nature, her great masterpiece design'd
And fram'd her last, best work, the human mind,
Her eye intent on all the wondrous plan,
She form'd of various stuff, the various Man.

Burns

LABORATORY SUPPLIES AND EQUIPMENT

The following items are recommended for the laboratory work, and must be furnished by each student:

1. Textbook and laboratory manual
2. 3-H pencil
3. Colored pencils
4. Lens paper
5. Eraser
6. Dissecting instruments including scalpel, scissors, forceps, flexible probe, needles
7. Laboratory coat or apron

THE LABORATORY

Attendance in the laboratory is essential, and all assigned work should be completed on schedule. If a laboratory period is missed because of illness or other reasons beyond your control, you may arrange with your laboratory instructor for making up your work.

Every effort to be punctual should be made, and you are expected to work for the entire period. If you complete your work early, have it checked by your instructor—there may be ways to improve it. Ordinarily the laboratory work, if done carefully and thoroughly, will occupy the full time. Your attitude and performance in the laboratory will contribute toward evaluating your competence as a student of anatomy.

It is essential to be able to read and follow directions carefully. Start at the beginning of the directions for each laboratory exercise, and follow them through in orderly sequence. Avoid the error of starting in the middle of an exercise.

You should feel free at all times to ask questions but, before doing so, be sure that your questions are not already answered in the laboratory directions.

Care should be exercised in the handling of charts, models, skeletal materials and microscope slides. These are costly items and are essential aids in the study of anatomy. Repair and replacement costs place a great burden on the budget. Too often the carelessness of one student handicaps another.

Wet specimens should be protected from drying by covering them with moist paper towels when not in use or by returning them to their proper containers.

The cats usually come from the supplier in plastic bags with some liquid preservative. The bag should be opened and the liquid drained into the sink before taking the specimen to your table. It is important to prevent the drying out of the cat as it will be used UNTIL THE END OF THE SEMESTER. When you have finished your work on the cat, moisten some paper towels and wrap them around the animal and return it to the plastic bag which may be closed with a rubber band. Place it in the container provided by the laboratory, BEING CERTAIN THAT YOUR NAME IS ON IT.

Human cadavers are used when available for demonstration and comparison with the anatomy of the cat.

Before leaving the laboratory, be certain that all equipment and supplies have been cleaned and put away. The laboratory tables should be cleaned and all waste paper placed in the waste baskets. Place only liquids in the sinks. Covered cans are available for animal remains.

DRAWINGS

Drawings are due at the end of the laboratory period unless otherwise directed by the instructor.

Drawings should be labeled fully.

Labels should be printed at the ends of straight or angular guide lines, and parallel to the top of the page.

Guide lines should never cross one another.

The student's name, section number, and date should be placed in the upper right hand corner of each page.

LABORATORY TESTS

Laboratory tests will be given at frequent intervals during the course, the number depending on the teaching methods and philosophy of individual instructors. These are generally "practical" tests requiring identification of structures on models, charts and especially from your dissections and microscope slides.

Some instructors may choose to give oral tests on your dissections or other aspects of the laboratory work.

In a sense you are being tested at all times in the laboratory; if not by direct questioning by the instructor, at least by his observation of your work habits, your interest, motivation, independence, capacity for following directions, and quality of dissections. The professor may be the center of focus in the lectures but in the laboratory it is the student who performs.

All tests, lecture or laboratory, should be considered not only as a part of the evaluating process but of the learning process as well.

MICROSCOPE (See Plate 1-1)

Your success in performing laboratory work will depend in part upon the physical equipment at your disposal and your capacity to use it intelligently. The most valuable and complex instrument that you will use is the microscope. If you learn to use it well and to care for it properly, it will be a source of great help to you. If you have not used one before, the first laboratory period should be devoted to its study and use. Since your microscope is a costly instrument and because it will be used by other students, you are obligated to leave it in good condition and in its proper place.

The labeled diagram of the microscope and related material should be studied. Practice using the microscope under the direction of the instructor.

The following suggestions should be kept in mind at all times:

1. Get your microscope from the cabinet, carrying it with one hand on the pillar or arm and the other under the base.
2. Place the microscope on the table with the arm toward you.
3. Clean the lenses of ocular (eyepiece) and objectives with lens paper.
4. Place 10X (16 mm.) objective in place under the body tube. Adjust the tube so that the end of the objective is about one-half inch above the stage.
5. Adjust the light until you see a clear field of light when you look into the ocular.
6. Always keep both eyes open when looking through the microscope even though you may be using a monocular instrument. It helps to avoid eyestrain.
7. Place the slide to be studied on the stage being sure the coverglass is up. Move the slide so that the material to be observed is directly under the objective. Fasten the slide in place with the stage clips.
8. Move the body tube down until it is about one-eighth inch above the slide. Now look through the ocular and, using the coarse adjustment knob, slowly raise the body tube until the material comes into focus.
9. On some microscopes the stage moves rather than the body tube. You may need to readjust the light for best definition; make your focus critical with the fine adjustment knob.

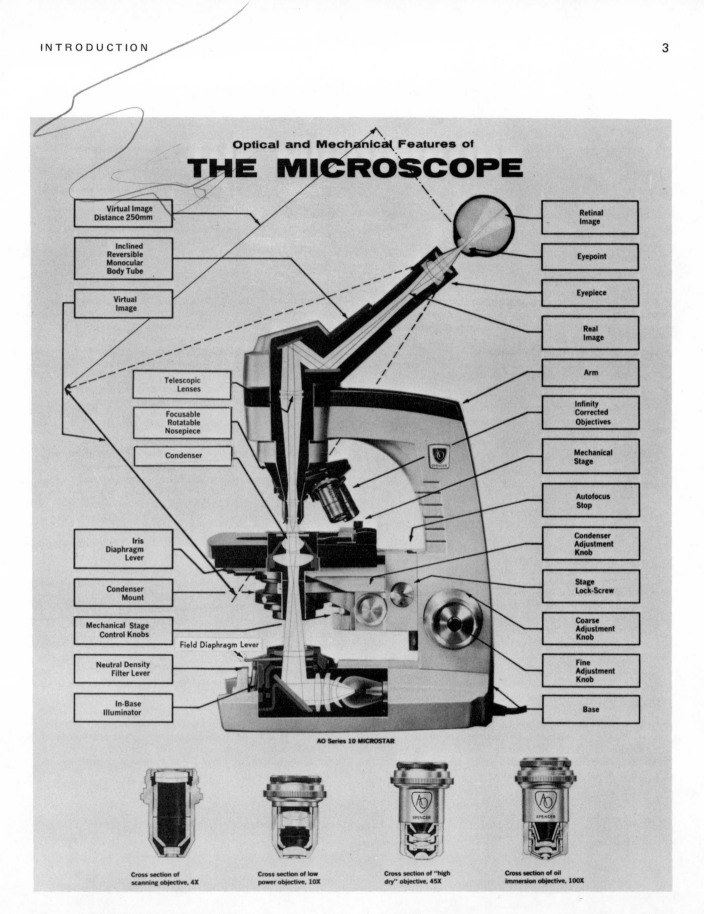

Optical and Mechanical Features of
THE MICROSCOPE

Virtual Image Distance 250mm

Inclined Reversible Monocular Body Tube

Virtual Image

Telescopic Lenses

Focusable Rotatable Nosepiece

Condenser

Iris Diaphragm Lever

Condenser Mount

Mechanical Stage Control Knobs

Field Diaphragm Lever

Neutral Density Filter Lever

In-Base Illuminator

Retinal Image

Eyepoint

Eyepiece

Real Image

Arm

Infinity Corrected Objectives

Mechanical Stage

Autofocus Stop

Condenser Adjustment Knob

Stage Lock-Screw

Coarse Adjustment Knob

Fine Adjustment Knob

Base

AO Series 10 MICROSTAR

Cross section of scanning objective, 4X

Cross section of low power objective, 10X

Cross section of "high dry" objective, 45X

Cross section of oil immersion objective, 100X

Courtesy of American Optical Corporation

Plate 1-1. Optical and Mechanical Features of the Microscope

Terms Used in Microscopy

The three photomicrographs show the relationship of numerical aperture to resolving power, and the failure of magnification to provide increased detail. All three specimens are magnified 650X. The one at the left was taken with a 10X, N.A. 0.25 objective and enlarged photographically. The center picture was taken with a 45X, N.A. 0.66 objective and also enlarged photographically. The one at the right was taken with a 100X, N.A. 1.25 objective. Note the superiority of contrast and sharpness of image in the right hand picture.

Illumination: The full capabilities of a microscope cannot be realized unless the illuminator is efficient. Microscopes may be illuminated in several ways. Daylight, but not direct sunlight, can be used with a mirror tilted and adjusted to reflect the light uniformly into the condenser and through the specimen. Daylight is of variable quality and not always available. Consequently, artificial light is more reliable than daylight.

The In-Base or On-Base illuminator is ideally suited for good results because it is an integral part of the instrument... assures correct alignment and fully illuminates the field of view... also satisfies the numerical aperture requirements of all available objectives 4X, 10X, 45X and 100X. If multiple electrical outlets are not conveniently available, a table globe type microscope illuminator is also suitable and, if centrally located, can be used for four microscopes simultaneously.

Virtual Image: The apparent size and position of the object specimen. See chart on opposite page. This image (not a real or retinal image) seen through the microscope appears to be about 10" away from the eye... approximately the same distance at which average print is read.

Magnification: The ratio of the apparent size of an object as seen through the microscope (virtual image) to the size of the same object as it appears to the unaided eye at a distance of 10". The ratio is linearly expressed in terms of "diameters," "power," "X," or "times."

The total resultant magnification of an eyepiece-objective combination equals the product of the initial magnifications of the two. For example — the 10X eyepiece used in combination with a 10X objective produces a linear resultant magnification of 100X.

Magnification alone is not the aim of the finest microscope. The amplified or enlarged image isn't helpful unless more detail ... resolution ... becomes apparent. Therefore, always use the lowest practical power objective which effectively reveals the detail in which you are interested.

Numerical Aperture (N. A.): A designation, usually engraved on objectives and condensers, expressing mathematically the solid cone of light delivered to the specimen by the condenser and gathered by the objective. It is a criterion of resolving power. The higher the numerical aperture of an objective, the greater its resolving power, provided the N.A. of the condenser is equal to or greater than the N.A. of the objective. For example, a stained preparation of bacteria can be most effectively resolved if viewed with a 100X N.A. 1.25 oil immersion objective used in combination with an Abbe condenser having a corresponding N.A. of 1.25.

Resolving Power (Resolution): The ability of a microscope to reveal fine detail. It is stated as the least distance between two points or lines at which they are seen as two, rather than as a single blurred object. Resolving power is a function of numerical aperture and serves as an indication of which objective should be used to depict any degree of detail.

Definition: The faithfulness with which the instrument magnifies and reproduces specimen detail. The brilliance, clarity, distinctness and sharpness of the microscope image.

Working Distance: The distance between the front mount of the objective, when the microscope is focused on a thin specimen preparation, and the top of the cover glass. The greater the initial magnification of the objective... the shorter the working distance. Most objectives are corrected for use with a cover glass thickness of 0.18mm. For this reason, as well as to prevent specimen liquids from touching the objective, such cover glasses should always be applied to the specimen preparation.

Depth of Focus: The thickness of the specimen which may be seen in focus at one time. The lower powered objectives, because of their longer focal lengths and greater depth of focus, are usually more suitable for the study of the general arrangement of the specimen... also, the field of view is larger and the image brighter.

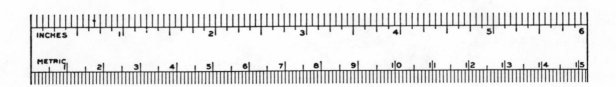

Plate 1-1. Continued

10. If you wish to use a higher magnification (43X), center in the field that part of the material which you wish to observe. Then carefully turn the high power objective into position. Readjust your lighting and focus, if this is necessary.

11. It is important to follow the above procedure for efficient use of the microscope. Especially, do not try to use the high power without first getting the material under low power.

12. If your microscope has an oil immersion lens (97X), place a drop of immersion oil on the coverslip before using this lens.

13. Do not focus down when using high power. Many slides and lenses are damaged in this way.

14. Avoid getting water in contact with the lenses.

15. When returning the microscope to the case, be sure to remove the slide, and have the low power objective in place under the body tube.

16. The microscope should be left in good condition for the next person who uses it. Responsibility is of prime importance in laboratory work.

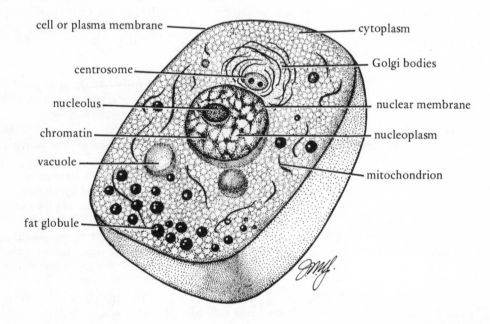

Figure 1-1. An Animal Cell

THE CELL (Figure 1-1)

The cell is the unit of structure and function in living organisms. To review some of the components of the cell, study the surface cells lining the inside of the cheek.

1. Scrape the inside of the cheek GENTLY with a toothpick.

2. Place the material obtained in this way in a drop of water or methylene blue, on a slide, and cover it with a coverglass.

3. Observe the material, picking out some of the large flat cells for careful study.

4. Draw and label one of these cells. Do not expect to see all of the cell components shown on Figure 1-1.

5. Examine some of the prepared slides and note the variety in size and form among cells of the animal body.

TISSUES

Similar cells are grouped together to form tissues. Besides the living cells, tissues contain greater or lesser amounts of intercellular materials. The various tissues will be studied in some detail with the appropriate organs and systems.

There are four groups of tissues in the human body: (1) epithelial, (2) connective and supporting, (3) muscular, and (4) nervous.

Epithelial tissues are those which cover the free surfaces of the body and its organs. They have a minimum of intercellular material. Connective and supporting tissues have a maximum of intercellular material, and their name suggests their principal functions. They include also the blood and lymph which have a fluid intercellular mass. Muscle tissue is specialized in contractility and is responsible for movements of the body. Nervous tissue is specialized in the properties of irritability and conductivity.

ORGANS AND SYSTEMS

ORGANS are composed of two or more tissues which are associated in performing some special function or functions. The HEART, for example, contains epithelium, muscle, and connective tissues. It pumps the blood to the body and is involved in the regulation of blood pressure and blood flow. The ARTERIES contain epithelium, connective tissue, and smooth muscle, and carry blood away from the heart. They, too, are organs involved in blood flow and in blood pressure regulation. Veins, capillaries, lymphatic vessels, lymph nodes, and other ORGANS in turn constitute the remainder of this SYSTEM—the CIRCULATORY SYSTEM. We would thus define a SYSTEM as a group of organs involved in carrying out some particular functions of the body—in our example, circulation. The systems of the human body are as follows:

INTEGUMENTARY SYSTEM. Consists of the skin and its derivatives such as glands, hair, and nails. Among its functions are protection, secretion, temperature regulation, and sensory.

SKELETAL SYSTEM. Composed of bones and cartilage and the connective tissues which bind these organs to form the articulations of the body. It is involved in support, protection, movement and blood formation.

MUSCULAR SYSTEM. Has as organs the skeletal muscles of the body. Like the skeletal system, it is involved in body movements. The muscles are the active organs in movement; the skeleton is passive (but necessary), providing as it does the levers (bones) and the joints around which and through which meaningful movements are possible.

CIRCULATORY SYSTEM. Consists of the heart, blood vessels, and blood, and the lymphatic vessels and nodes. It is essentially a transportation system, and maintains the tissue fluids in a constant state. It is involved in temperature regulation and protection of the body.

ENDOCRINE SYSTEM. Also known as the ductless glands or the glands of internal secretion. These glands contribute their specific secretions, the hormones, to the body fluids where they affect the activity of the various parts of the body. Such organs as the pituitary gland, pineal body, thymus, thyroid, parathyroid, adrenal glands, and parts of other organs such as the testes, ovaries, and pancreas make up this system. We do not consider it in the laboratory as a separate system, although in our dissection and tissue studies we do see most of its component parts.

DIGESTIVE SYSTEM. Composed of the alimentary tract and the various glands derived from it. It carries out the functions of ingestion, digestion, absorption, and egestion.

RESPIRATORY SYSTEM. Includes the lungs and various air passageways. It provides oxygen for the body and rids it of carbon dioxide.

EXCRETORY SYSTEM. Consists of kidneys and accessory organs such as ureters, urinary bladder, and urethra. This system removes wastes and aids in the regulation of the internal environment of the body.

REPRODUCTIVE SYSTEM. Serves to perpetuate the species. Its essential organs—the testes and ovaries—also produce hormones.

NERVOUS SYSTEM. Consists of central, peripheral, and autonomic parts. It is the important orienting and coordinating unit of the body. Intelligence is a part of its functioning. The organs of sense are its receptors, the muscles and glands its effectors.

MAN'S PLACE AMONG ANIMALS

Man belongs to that large subdivision of the animal kingdom, the PHYLUM CHORDATA. This means that he must at some time in his development have a notochord, a dorsal hollow nerve cord, and pharyngeal pouches (Plate 1-2). The notochord is a flexible, supporting rod which runs lengthwise of the body ventral to the nerve cord. It remains in the adult only as a mass of tissue inside the intervertebral discs and is called the nucleus pulposus. The pharyngeal pouches also lose identity as the individual develops, but they leave contributions in the adult such as the auditory tube, middle ear cavity, and parts of various glands. The dorsal hollow nerve cord is represented in the central canal of the spinal cord and the ventricles in the brain.

To narrow the field a little more, man is a VERTEBRATE animal—a distinction which he shares with the fish, amphibians, reptiles, birds, and mammals. Among the vertebrates he is placed with MAMMALS, having, as diagnostic characteristics, hair and mammary glands. Other less obvious features of his anatomy also place him in this group. The cat (the animal used most in our laboratory work) is also a mammal. Finally, man is a PRIMATE mammal, as are the monkeys and apes. Man, however, has as his unique characteristic a highly evolved brain which gives him a level of intelligence found in no other organism. Korzybski[1] has called plants the chemistry-binders; animals—including man—the space-binders; and men alone, the time-binders. He bases this on the fact that most plants are stationary but can manufacture their own food; animals move about in space to find a living; man likewise moves about in space but in addition he builds his present upon the experience of past generations and upon his speculations into the future.

To summarize, we see man in the following relationship with other animals:

Kingdom Animal
  Phylum Chordata
    Subphylum Vertebrata
      Class Mammalia
        Order Primates
          Suborder Anthropoidea
            Family Hominidae
              Genus Homo
                Species sapiens
                  Scientific name: Homo sapiens

TERMS OF POSITION AND DIRECTION

In order that our descriptions be significant, we always assume the human body to be in the ANATOMICAL POSITION. This position is standing erect with the eyes forward, arms hanging at the sides with the palms turned forward (Plate 1-3).

There is some confusion of terms as applied to man, a biped, and to an animal such as the cat which walks on all four feet. The term POSTERIOR in human anatomy refers to that side of the body containing the backbone, while in the cat or in comparative anatomy we would call it DORSAL. ANTERIOR in human anatomy refers to the belly side of the body, while the comparative anatomist would call it VENTRAL. To the comparative anatomist ANTERIOR refers to the head or CEPHALIC (cranial) end of the animal, and posterior to the tail or CAUDAL end. The terms SUPERIOR and INFERIOR, in human anatomy, mean upper or higher and under or lower, respectively. Hence we speak of the superior surface of the diaphragm as its upper surface and its under surface as inferior. In the cat the corresponding surfaces would be anterior (cranial) and posterior (caudal), respectively (Plate 1-5).

The MEDIAL structures of the body are those nearer the midline of the body, and those farthest to the side are LATERAL. The terms DISTAL and PROXIMAL are used mostly in reference to limbs. The distal end of a limb is at the hand or foot; the proximal end, at shoulder or hip. Or, one may speak of the distal end of the ulna where it attaches to the hand, or its proximal end where it articulates with the humerus (Plates 1-3 and 1-4).

The terms EXTERNAL and INTERNAL are used mostly in reference to body cavities and the hollow organs. SUPERFICIAL and DEEP refer to relative distances from the surface of the body or its various structures.

We sometimes substitute for the -al ending of the above words the -ad ending which means to or toward. For example, we say that the hand is distad the radius and ulna, or the aortic arch turns dorsad to become the descending aorta, or the radius is laterad the ulna.

[1] See section on Reference at end of book.

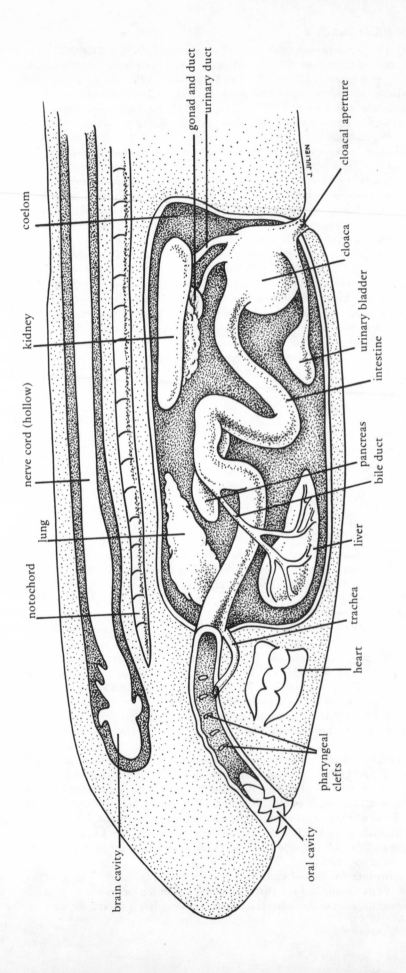

gonad and duct
urinary duct
coelom
cloacal aperture
J. JULIEN
cloaca
kidney
urinary bladder
intestine
nerve cord (hollow)
pancreas
bile duct
lung
liver
notochord
trachea
heart
brain cavity
oral cavity
pharyngeal clefts

Plate 1-2. Schematic Diagram of a Chordate

Modified from L. L. Woodruff, *Animal Biology*, Macmillan Company

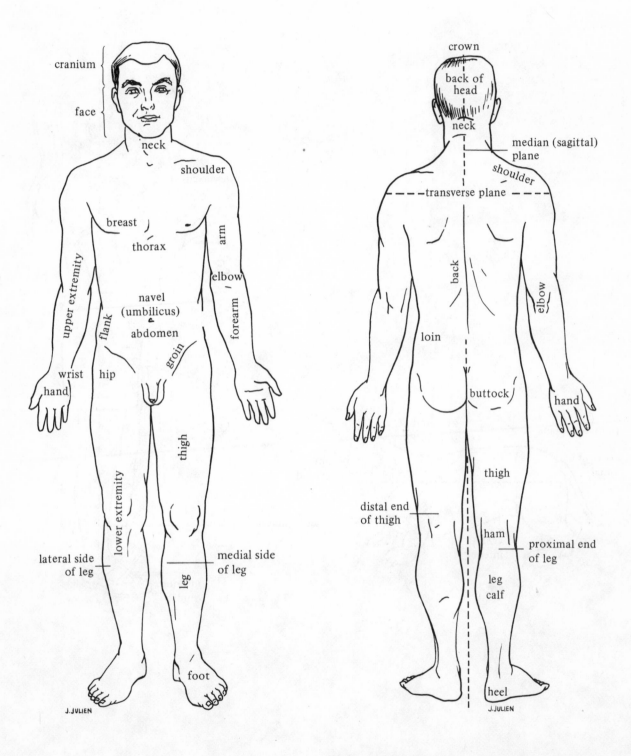

cranium

face

neck

shoulder

breast

thorax

arm

upper extremity

elbow

navel
(umbilicus)

flank

forearm

abdomen

groin

wrist

hip

hand

thigh

lower extremity

lateral side
of leg

leg

medial side
of leg

foot

J. JULIEN

crown

back of
head

neck

median (sagittal)
plane

shoulder

transverse plane

back

elbow

loin

buttock

hand

thigh

distal end
of thigh

ham

proximal end
of leg

leg
calf

heel

J. JULIEN

Plate 1-3. Human Figure in the Anatomical Position

Plate 1-4. Human Figure—Posterior View

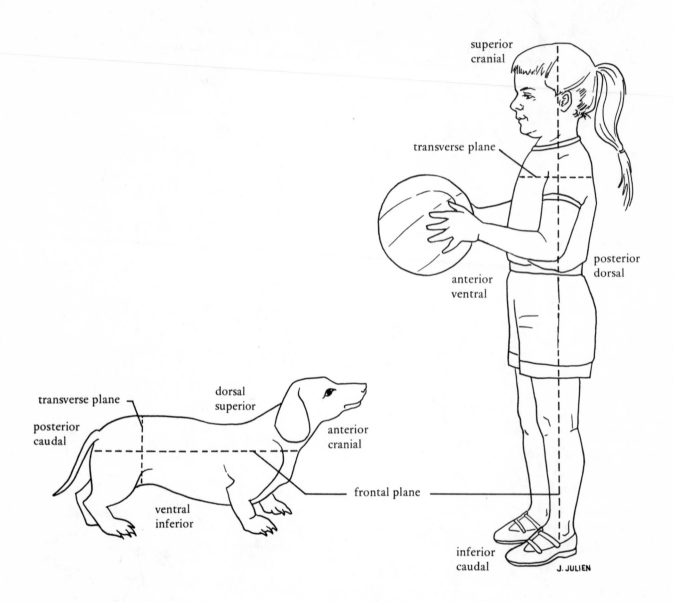

Plate 1-5. Terminology for Quadruped and Biped

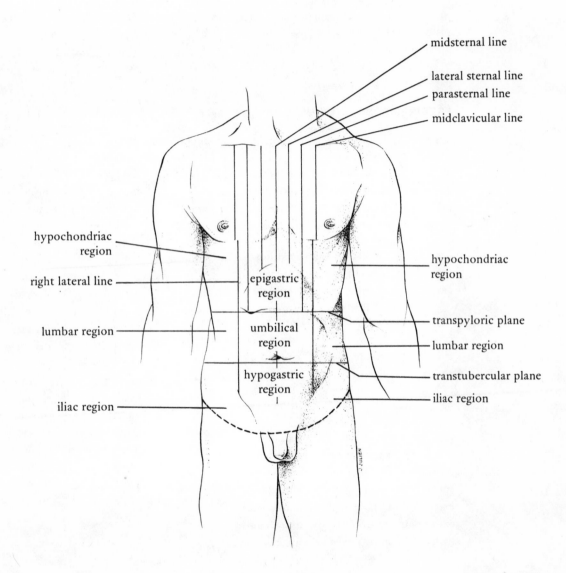

midsternal line

lateral sternal line

parasternal line

midclavicular line

hypochondriac
region

hypochondriac
region

right lateral line

epigastric
region

lumbar region

transpyloric plane

umbilical
region

lumbar region

hypogastric
region

transtubercular plane

iliac region

iliac region

Plate 1-6. Surface Lines and Regions of the Anterior Thorax and Abdomen

PLANES OF REFERENCE

The MEDIAN plane is a vertical plane dividing the body into right and left halves. This plane, or any plane parallel to it may be called a SAGITTAL plane. Sometimes we use the term MIDSAGITTAL for the median plane, and the planes parallel to this would be called PARASAGITTAL.

A FRONTAL plane is one that is at right angles to the median plane and divides the body into anterior and posterior parts. It is sometimes called the CORONAL plane.

A TRANSVERSE plane is at right angles to both the median and frontal planes, and divides the body into superior and inferior portions. It is sometimes called a HORIZONTAL plane (Plates 1-4 and 1-5).

PREFIXES COMMONLY USED IN ANATOMY

a, an	G.	lacking, without	asexual	hypo	G.	under, deficient, below	hypothalamus
ab	L.	away from	abduction	im, in	L.	not	immature
ad	L.	to, toward	adduction	infra	L.	below	infraorbital
af	L.	to, toward	afferent	inter	L.	between	intervertebrae
amphi	G.	on both sides, about	amphibious	intro	L.	within, into	introspection
ana	G.	up, back, again	anatomy	meta	G.	change, after	metamorphosis
ante	L.	forward, before	anteorbital	opistho	G.	behind	opisthocoelous
anti	G.	against, opposed to	antibody	para	G.	by the side of	parabasal
				peri	G.	around	periosteum
bi	L.	twice, double	bifid	post	L.	after, behind	postaxial
cata	G.	down	catabolism	pre	L.	before	preanal
circum	L.	around, about	circumscribe	pro	G.	before, for	procoelous
co, com, con	L.	together, with	commensal	re	L.	again, back	reflex
				retro	L.	backward	retroperitoneal
de	L.	away from, down	decerebrate	semi	L.	half	semilunar
				sub	L.	under	substratum
di	G.	double, twice	digastric	supra	L.	above	supraspinatous
dis	L.	apart, away	disarticulate	sym, syn	G.	together, with	synapse, symphysis
ecto	G.	on outer side	ectoderm	trans	L.	across	transfer
epi	G.	upon, over	epithelium	ultra	L.	in excess, beyond	ultrasonic
exo	G.	outside	exoskeleton				
extra	L.	outside	extracellular				
hyper	G.	over, above, excessive	hypertension				

2

INTEGUMENTARY SYSTEM

THE SKIN

The integumentary system is made up of the skin and its accessory organs.

The skin is composed of two layers, an outer EPIDERMIS and an inner CORIUM (dermis or true skin). The accessory organs of the skin are derived from the epidermis but in their growth push into the underlying corium and subcutaneous tissue (superficial fascia). The subcutaneous tissue is not considered a part of the skin, but does tie the skin loosely to the underlying muscles.

A. Gross examination

By examination of your own skin, note the variations in texture, thickness, looseness, and tightness from one part of the body to another. Observe the large heavy lines on the palms of the hands and opposite the joints of the fingers. These are called FLEXION CREASES.

Finer lines, best seen on the fingertips, are characteristic for each individual and are used for FINGERPRINT identification. Accessory organs of the skin are the HAIR, NAILS, and GLANDS. Note the unequal distribution and abundance of the hair.

B. Microscopic examination

Examine, under the microscope, slides of the skin from different areas of the body. Compare these as to thickness and variations in the different layers of the skin. Choose a section of thick skin from the PALM or SOLE and identify the following, labeling as many as possible of the parts on Plate 2-1.

1. Epidermis—stratified squamous epithelium; nonvascular
   a. Stratum corneum—surface layers of flattened, plate-like cells. No nuclei.
   b. Stratum lucidum—homogeneous or dimly striated layer.
   c. Stratum granulosum—two or three layers of flattened cells containing granules.
   d. Stratum spinosum—several layers of cells, the lowermost being columnar in shape and called stratum basale (STRATUM GERMINATIVUM).
   e. Stratum basale—the cells for this layer multiply by mitosis and provide replacements for the outer layers of cells as they gradually move outward, die off and are shed.

2. Corium or derma—dense connective tissue
   a. Papillary layer—fits into the under surface of the epidermis. Some of the papillae contain tactile corpuscles (Meissner's corpuscles), end bulbs of Krause, and free nerve endings.
   b. Reticular layer—contains many collagenous fibers, some elastic fibers, and is continuous with the SUBCUTANEOUS TISSUE or SUPERFICIAL FASCIA.

3. Accessory organs of the skin—derivatives of the epidermis
   a. Hair—examine a section of skin from the scalp or abdomen and label the following: shaft, root, papilla, hair follicle, arrector pili muscle (Plate 2-1, figure 1).

    b. Sebaceous glands—observe these on the above slide, and label them on the diagram (Plate 2-1).

    c. Sweat glands—examine a slide of the skin and find a sweat gland. Note its tubular form and the way it is coiled at its lower end. Label one on diagram (Plate 2-1).

    d. Nails—study a slide of a longitudinal section of a finger. Notice the nail in its relationship to the epidermis and dermis. Label Plate 2-2, figures 4 and 5.

QUESTIONS

1. What are the functions of the skin?

2. What kind of connective tissue is found in the corium?

3. What is the relationship between the hair and the sebaceous glands?

4. What are the functions of sweat glands?

5. What kind of tissue is the superficial fascia?

6. What is "deep fascia"?

7. What are the lunula, eponychium, and hyponychium?

8. How many of the structures named above can you identify on Plate 2-2?

9. Can you locate a Pacinian corpuscle on your slides of the skin? What is their function?

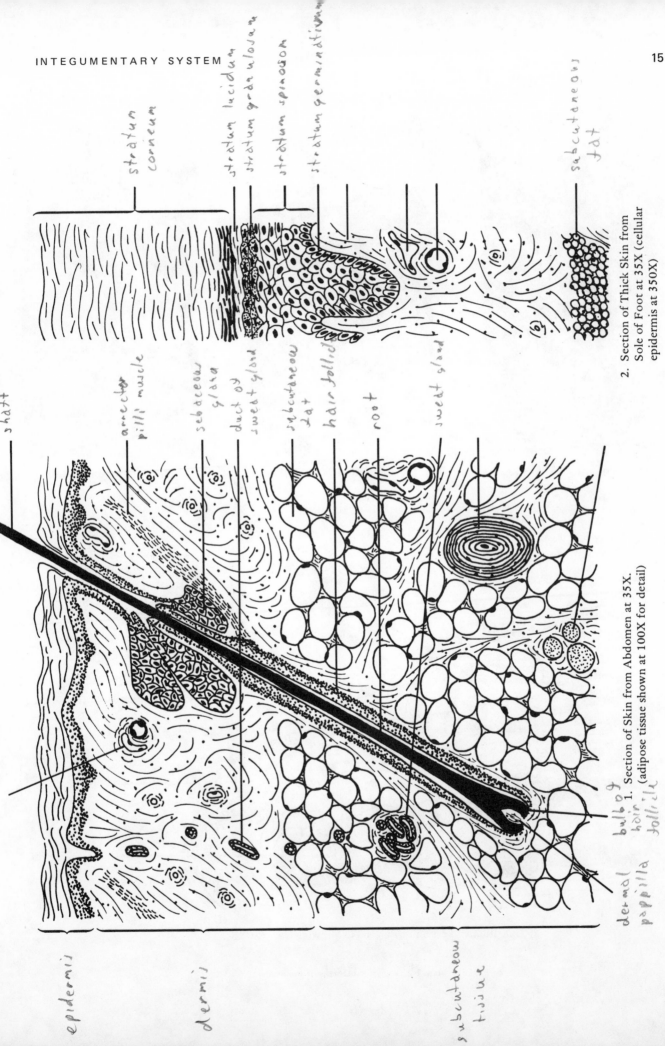

stratum corneum

stratum lucidum
stratum granulosum
stratum spinosum
stratum germinativum

subcutaneous fat

2. Section of Thick Skin from Sole of Foot at 35X (cellular epidermis at 350X)

shaft

arrector pilli muscle

sebaceous gland

duct of sweat gland

subcutaneous fat

hair follicle

root

sweat gland

dermal papilla

bulb of hair follicle

1. Section of Skin from Abdomen at 35X. (adipose tissue shown at 100X for detail)

epidermis

dermis

subcutaneous tissue

Plate 2-1. The Skin and Accessory Structures

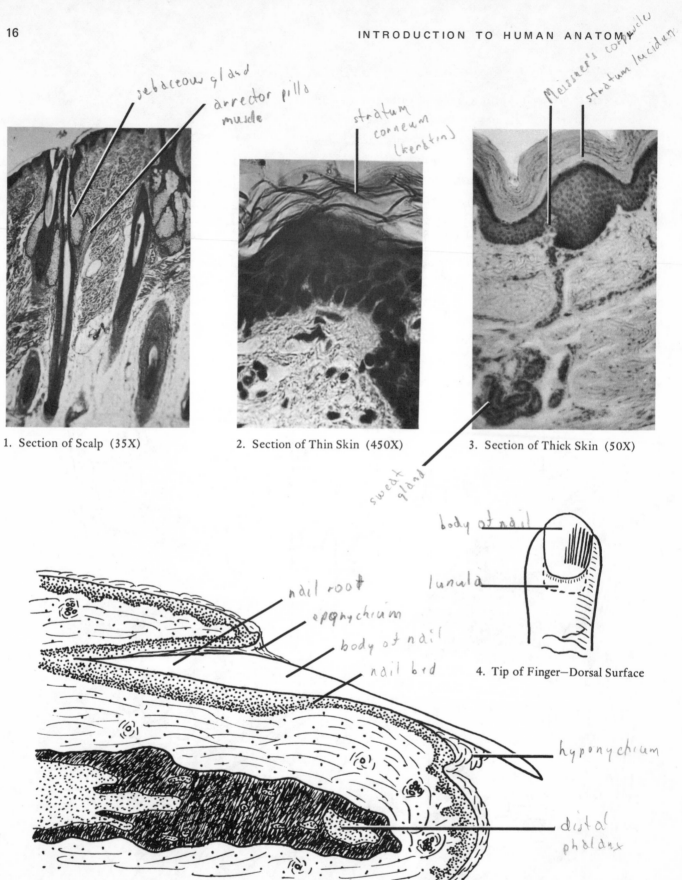

sebaceous gland

arrector pilli
muscle

stratum
corneum
(keratin)

Meissner's corpuscle

stratum lucidum

1. Section of Scalp (35X)

2. Section of Thin Skin (450X)

3. Section of Thick Skin (50X)

sweat
gland

body of nail

lunula

4. Tip of Finger—Dorsal Surface

nail root
eponychium
body of nail
nail bed

hyponychium

distal
phalanx

5. Longitudinal Section of Finger Tip Showing Nail (20X)

Plate 2-2. Accessory Organs of the Skin

GLOSSARY — Chapters 1 and 2

anatomy (à nat´o mi): G., ana, up; tome, cutting.

arrector (àr rek´tôr): L., arrigere, to raise.

corneum, cornea (kôr´ne um, -a): L., corneus, horny.

corium (kô´re um): G., chorion, leather, skin.

cutaneous (ku tā´ne us): L., cutis, skin.

epidermis (ep´i dēr´mis): G., epi, upon; derma, skin.

epithelium (ep i the´li um): G., epi, upon; thele, nipple.

eponychium (ep´o nik´i um): G., epi, upon; onyx, nail.

fascia (fash´e à): L., fascia, band, bundle.

granulosum (gran´u lō´sum): L., granum, grain.

integument (in teg´u ment): L., in, over; tegere, to cover.

lucidum (lū´sid um): L., lucidus, clear, full of light.

lunula (lū´nu là): L., dim. of luna, moon.

papilla, pl. ae (pà pil´à -e): L., papilla, nipple.

pilus, pl. pili (pī´lus, pē´lē): L., pilus, hair.

reticulum, pl. reticula (re tik´u lum, -a): L., reticulum, a little net.

sebaceous (se bā´shus): L., sebum, grease, tallow.

stratum, pl. a (strāy´tum): L., strat, a cover or spread.

3

SKELETAL SYSTEM AND ARTICULATIONS

GENERAL

The skeletal system, for our purposes, consists of the bony and cartilaginous framework of the body. The various skeletal components, the bones, are structurally and functionally related at the articulations, or joints as they are commonly called. These structures form the basis for movement, although they in themselves are passive. The active force is contributed by the skeletal muscles which in turn are activated by the nervous system. Therefore the skeleton, articulations, skeletal muscles, and nerves must be closely associated in our minds at all times.

The skeletal system—in addition to its contribution to movement—serves to give support to the soft tissues of the body and is involved in body form. It also is protective, housing securely the brain and spinal cord within the skull and vertebral column, respectively. The heart, lungs, and major blood vessels also receive protection within the rib cage. Some of the bones are important centers of blood cell formation.

The skeleton gives stability to the body. Each bone, when studied critically, shows a structure based upon sound mechanics and engineering principles (Plate 3-1). However, when we consider the skeleton as a whole, it may appear to be anything but stable, standing as it normally does on a small base (the feet) and its center of gravity being high. But, remembering that we are dealing with the living skeleton in a living organism, we realize that some stability may of necessity be sacrificed to versatility and freedom of movement. Furthermore, stability is a shifting thing in a moving organism. The base can easily be broadened by moving the feet apart and the center of gravity lowered by flexing the foot, the knees, and the thighs. The trunk can be shifted to keep its line of gravity over the base. Man in this position meets to a fair degree the requirements of stability: a broad base, a low center of gravity, and a line of gravity which falls well within the base.

Make a special effort to organize your work on the skeletal system. It will make it much easier to remember the terms that are used in this study. Reference to the word list at the end of this chapter will also help.

The skeleton, containing 206 bones, may be subdivided as follows (Plate 3-2):

Axial skeleton (80 bones)

Skull . . . . 29 bones
Vertebral column 26
Thorax
    Sternum 1
    Ribs 24
    Costal cartilages
Appendicular skeleton (126 bones)
Pectoral (shoulder) girdle 4
Bones of the forelimbs 60
Pelvic girdle 2
Bones of the hindlimbs 60

                                    206 bones

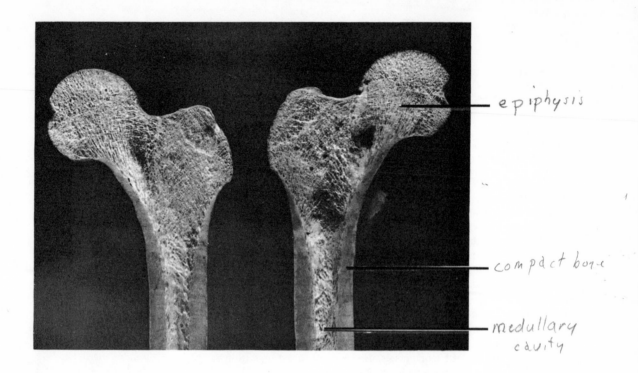

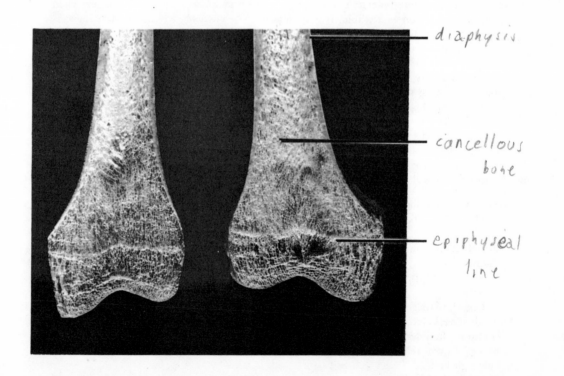

Plate 3-1. Photographs of the Proximal and Distal Ends of a Split Femur

Examine a split femur or other bones which have been sectioned to show the gross structure. Locate the following and Label them on Plate 3-1:

COMPACT BONE

CANCELLOUS BONE

EPIPHYSES

DIAPHYSIS

EPIPHYSEAL LINE

MEDULLARY OR MARROW CAVITY

What do we mean by PERIOSTEUM and ENDOSTEUM?

Examine a skull bone such as a frontal, and identify INNER and OUTER TABLES and the DIPLOË. Label these on Plate 3-3.

Bones have numerous irregularities on their surfaces: projections, depressions, holes. You will identify many of these as you study individual bones. It is difficult to give adequate definitions for some of them.

process	Any bony prominence or prolongation.
spine	A more or less sharp projection.
trochanter	A very large, usually blunt, process.
tubercle	Usually a small rounded eminence.
tuberosity	Usually a large rounded eminence.
condyle	A rounded process for articulation, usually covered with articular cartilage
epicondyle	A projection above a smooth articular eminence.
crest	A prominent ridge or border of bone.
hamulus	A projection shaped like a hook
head	A large rounded end of a bone.
facet	A small area; smooth, and usually covered with cartilage.
fossa	A depressed area; usually broad and shallow.
meatus	A short canal.
sinus	A cavity in a bone.
sulcus	A groove.
planum	A flat surface
foramen	A hole to allow passage of blood vessels or nerves.

Know

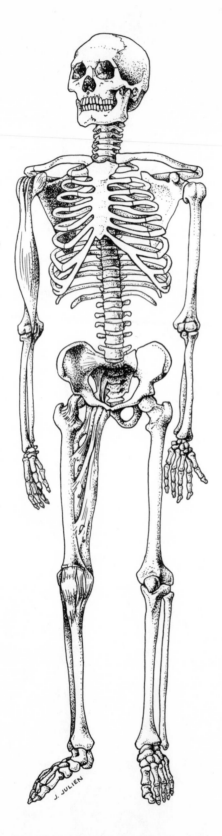

Plate 3-2. Skeletal System—Anterior View

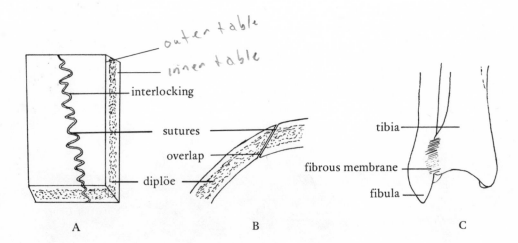

outer table
inner table
interlocking
sutures
overlap
diplöe
tibia
fibrous membrane
fibula

A   B   C

1. Types of Fibrous Articulation. A and B allow no movement; C, slight movement.

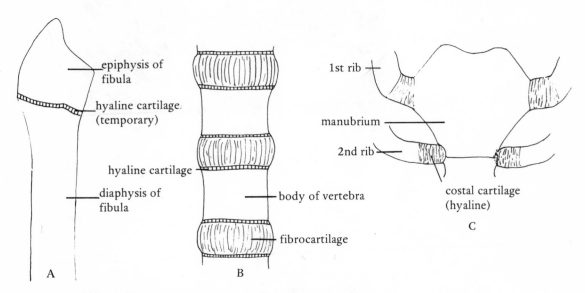

epiphysis of fibula
hyaline cartilage (temporary)
hyaline cartilage
diaphysis of fibula
body of vertebra
fibrocartilage

1st rib
manubrium
2nd rib
costal cartilage (hyaline)

A   B   C

2. Types of Cartilaginous Articulation. A, temporary; B and C, permanent.

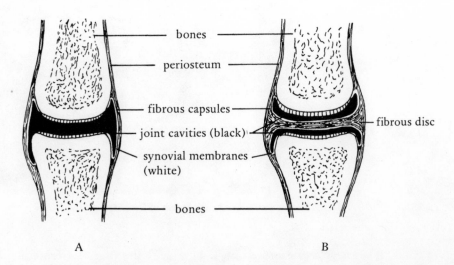

bones
periosteum
fibrous capsules
joint cavities (black)
synovial membranes (white)
bones
fibrous disc

A   B

3. Types of Synovial Articulation. A, with a single cavity; B, with two cavities and a fibrous disc.

Plate 3-3. Articulations

HISTOLOGY

Study slides of the following connective tissues:

A. Connective tissue proper

1. Loose (areolar) connective tissue. This tissue contains most of the cellular and intercellular elements that are found in other connective tissues. It is found under the skin and between organs, and is one of the most widely distributed of the body tissues.

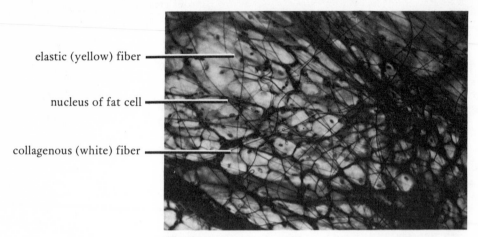

elastic (yellow) fiber

nucleus of fat cell

collagenous (white) fiber

Figure 3-1. Photomicrograph of Loose Connective Tissue

2. Dense (irregular) connective tissue (Figure 3-2). This tissue is similar to loose connective tissue in that it contains all three fiber types and a variety of cells. The white (collagenous) fibers are dominant and all components are irregularly arranged and closely packed. It is found in the corium of the skin and in the submucosa of the digestive tract.

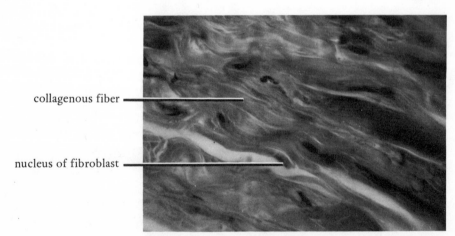

collagenous fiber

nucleus of fibroblast

Figure 3-2. Photomicrograph of Dense Connective Tissue

3. Regular connective tissues. In these tissues the fibers, especially the white fibers, are abundant and arranged in a fairly definite pattern.
    a. Tendons (white fibrous connective tissue) (Figure 3-3). These are composed of thick, closely packed bundles of white fibers which run parallel. Between the bundles of white fibers are rows of FIBROBLAST cells. LIGAMENTS are similar to

tendons but may show more irregularity in the arrangement of the white fibers. Some elastic fibers may be present. Examine a prepared slide.

b. Fibrous membranes. A large variety of structures fall into this category. Among them are the aponeuroses and deep fascia in which the white fibers are arranged in layers and tend to follow a parallel course.

The PERICHONDRIUM, PERIOSTEUM, SCLERA, CORNEA, DURA MATER and CAPSULES of certain organs show a less regular arrangement of fibers than the aponeuroses but are otherwise similar.

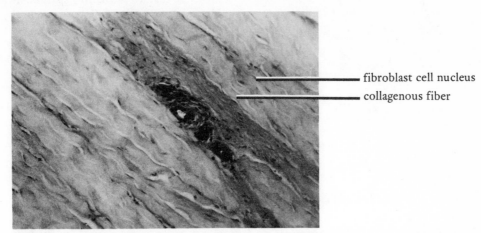

fibroblast cell nucleus
collagenous fiber

Figure 3-3. Photomicrograph of Tendon—White Fibrous
Connective Tissue

c. Lamellated. This tissue forms the relatively thin protective sheaths of some organs. It is well shown in the sheaths of Pacinian corpuscles (Plate 2-1, figure 1).

4. Special connective tissues
a. Mucous. This is an embryonic connective tissue found in the umbilical cord.
b. Elastic. Elastic connective tissue is sometimes considered among the regular connective tissues. It is composed of branching homogeneous fibers and fibroblasts and is found in some ligaments such as ligamentum nuchae and ligamenta flava. It is also found in the walls of arteries, the trachea, vocal cords, bronchi, and other organs. Examine a slide of this tissue (Figure 3-4).

collagenous fiber
(coiled)

elastic fibers

Figure 3-4. Photomicrograph of Elastic (Yellow)
Connective Tissue (80X)

c. Reticular. This tissue is found in lymph nodes, spleen, and liver. It is also associated with blood forming tissues. Its cells are called reticular and its fibers are fine,
branch, and form networks. Examine a slide of reticular tissue.

d. Adipose. When fat cells become so abundant that they crowd other tissue components, you have adipose tissue. The cells, in the living state, are heavily laden
with fat and the nucleus and cytoplasm are crowded toward the cell membrane. In
the prepared slides the fat is dissolved out, leaving an empty space, and the cells
look like "signet" rings. In some preparations the fat is allowed to remain in the cell
and can be stained black with osmic acid. In the narrow spaces between fat cells are
found fibroblasts, lymphoid, and mast cells. Collagenous, elastic, and reticular
fibers are also found.

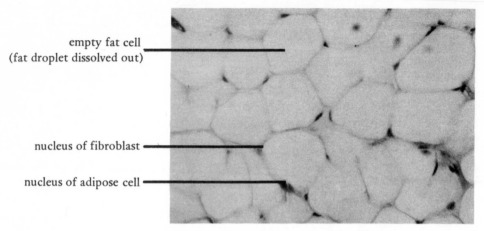

empty fat cell
(fat droplet dissolved out)

nucleus of fibroblast

nucleus of adipose cell

Figure 3-5. Photomicrograph of Adipose Tissue

e. Pigment tissue. This connective tissue consists of pigment cells (chromatophores)
in association with collagenous and elastic fibers. It is found in the choroid coat and
the iris of the eye.

B. Cartilage

This is the substance commonly known as gristle. It is firm, tough, and resilient and is
comprised of chondrocytes (cartilage cells) with an intercellular substance or MATRIX.
The cells occupy spaces in the matrix called LACUNAE. The thickened walls of the
lacunae constitute the CAPSULE. Cartilage is covered with a sheath of dense connective
tissue, the PERICHONDRIUM, except on bare surfaces in joint cavities.

1. Hyaline cartilage (Figure 3-6). Chondrocytes are enclosed in small spaces, the lacunae,
in a homogeneous matrix. While fibers do not show in the matrix of hyaline cartilage,
they are nevertheless there but are masked by the intercellular materials. Where is
it found?

The nuclei of the cells are prominent and the cytoplasm is clear.

2. Yellow or elastic cartilage. This is found in the external ear. Its fibers are elastic and
stained black on most microscope slides. Where else is it found?

Examine a slide (Figure 3-7).

3. White fibrocartilage. This is found in the intervertebral discs. White fibers dominate its
intercellar mass. Examine a slide (Figure 3-8).

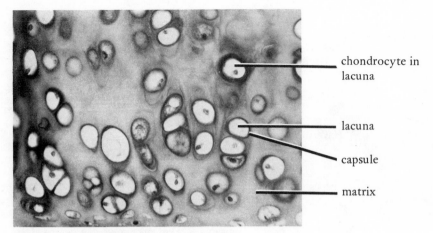

Figure 3-6. Photomicrograph of Hyaline Cartilage

chondrocyte in lacuna

lacuna

capsule

matrix

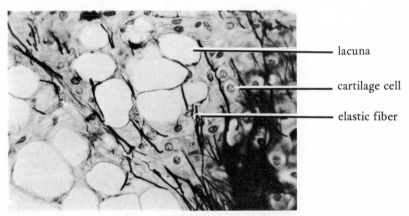

Figure 3-7. Photomicrograph of Yellow Elastic Cartilage (360X)

lacuna

cartilage cell

elastic fiber

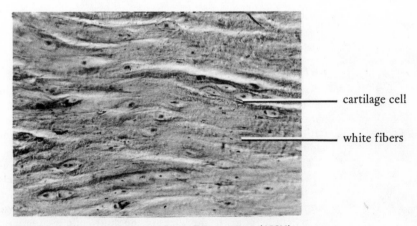

Figure 3-8. Photomicrograph of White Fibrocartilage (120X)

cartilage cell

white fibers

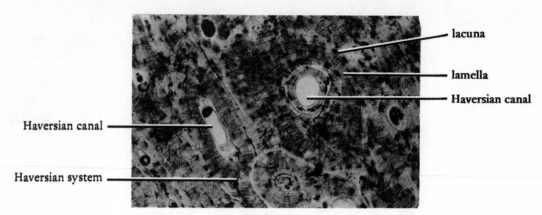

Figure 3-9. Photomicrograph of a Section of Ground Bone (80X)

C. Bone

Bone is composed of OSSEIN, a firm elastic material, impregnated with calcium salts. Living cells occur in spaces (LACUNAE) and are called OSTEOCYTES. The lacunae are interconnected by small canals (the CANALICULI) through which the processes of the osteocytes pass and interconnect. In compact bone these structures are arranged around a central canal called the HAVERSIAN CANAL, and the whole unit is an HAVERSIAN SYSTEM. Compact bone is made up of many of these Haversian systems. Figure 3-9 shows the above structures. What are the lamellae?

Describe Sharpey's fibers and their functions.

Distinguish between OSTEOCYTES, OSTEOBLASTS, and OSTEOCLASTS in terms of their functions.

ARTICULATIONS

As you proceed with the study of individual bones, be constantly alert to their place in the total skeleton. You should know the bones with which they articulate, and how they move one in relationship to another. In making these observations, try to classify each joint (articulation) according to the brief resumé below. You should refer to the textbook for additional information.

The bones and articulations come embryologically from a continuous mass of MESEN-CHYME which pushes out into the limb buds as well as in the areas of skeleton formation in the trunk region of the body. Condensations appear in the mesenchyme in the areas of bone formation and, other than in the vault of the skull, cartilage next appears to be replaced ultimately by bone. In the bones of the skull vault, membrane precedes bone formation. The intervening noncondensed portions of the mesenchyme give rise either to FIBROUS TISSUE or CARTILAGE, or hollow out to form a JOINT CAVITY partially lined with a SYNOVIAL MEMBRANE. These are the bases for the three general types of joints:

1. Fibrous joints.

2. Cartilaginous joints.

3. Synovial joints.

Obviously, these joints must be strengthened. This is accomplished by the continuation of the periosteum and perichondrium between the ends of the bones, to form fibrous capsules. These in turn are strengthened by ligaments and muscles which cross the joints.

1. Fibrous joints (Plate 3-3, figure 1)

In these joints there may be a minimum of fibrous tissue between the bones, as in the sutures of the skull (synarthrosis). Here no movement is allowed and the adjacent bones overlap (temporal and parietal bones), or form interlocking edges (frontal and parietal). These joints, in older individuals, tend to become completely bony (synostosis).

Other fibrous joints have more fiber, and hence allow some movement. The joint between the distal ends of the tibia and fibula allows slight movement. The fibrous membrane between the radius and ulna is extensive enough to allow rotation of the radius over the ulna (syndesmosis).

2. Cartilaginous joints (Plate 3-3, figure 2; Figure 3-10)

The cartilage in these joints may be HYALINE or FIBROCARTILAGE. The hyaline joints (synchondroses) we see between the ends (epiphyses) and shafts (diaphyses) of long bones, or between the bodies of sphenoid and occipital bones of infants. The cartilage of these joints is eliminated in the adult. It is permanent in the joints between ribs and sternum.

The FIBROCARTILAGINOUS JOINTS (SYMPHYSES) are found between the bodies of vertebrae and at the symphysis pubis. The ends of the bones are covered with an articular cartilage (hyaline) and between these a disc of fibrocartilage. The fibrocartilage is compressible, and hence allows slight movement.

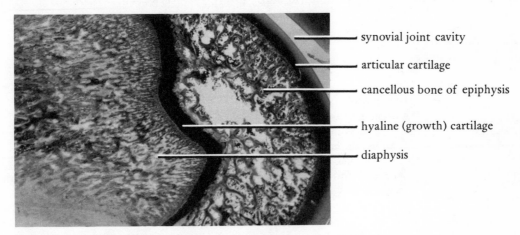

synovial joint cavity

articular cartilage

cancellous bone of epiphysis

hyaline (growth) cartilage

diaphysis

Figure 3-10. Photomicrograph of a Temporary Cartilaginous Articulation Between Diaphysis and Epiphysis of a Long Bone

3. Synovial joints (Plate 3-3, figure 3)

In general, these joints allow considerable freedom of movement. The amount of movement is determined by the shapes of the ends of the articulating bones, the arrangement of the supporting ligaments, the capsules, and the muscles. Most of the joints of the body are of this type.

Two general types of synovial joints are present in the body. The more common one has a SINGLE JOINT CAVITY and the other, TWO CAVITIES separated by an articular disc. The joint cavities are lubricated by a synovial fluid secreted by the synovial membrane which lines the inner surface of the fibrous capsule and which is reflected onto the side of the bone.

Examples of these are numerous. The HIP, ELBOW, and SHOULDER joints are good examples of the single-cavity type. The joint between the STERNUM and CLAVICLE is one with two cavities and an articular disc.

Movements in articulations. Certain terms are necessary to discuss intelligently the movements of the body. To learn these movements and to understand them now will save trouble later in our study of muscles.

FLEXION is a movement which results in the decrease in an angle between two parts. It takes place in the sagittal plane of the part. Examples are bending the elbow joint, the knee, and the foot. Since the foot, when in the standing position, is already in flexion, any further flexion is called DORSI-FLEXION. Dorsi-flexion also is used when the hand is over-extended.

EXTENSION increases the angle between two bones, as when the elbow joint or the knee are straightened. Extending the foot is sometimes referred to as plantar-flexion. Extension takes place in the sagittal plane.

ABDUCTION is the movement of a part, as an arm or leg, away from the mid-sagittal plane. Separating the fingers or toes is also abduction. It takes place in the frontal (coronal) plane.

ADDUCTION is the opposite of abduction, as when the limbs or fingers and toes are moved toward the midline of the body or of the hands or feet.

CIRCUMDUCTION is movement involving all of the above described movements, as when the arm is held to the side and made to describe a cone.

ROTATION is the movement made when a bone turns around an axis, either its own or that of another bone. The HUMERUS can rotate around its own axis at the shoulder joint; the ATLAS rotates on the DENS of the EPISTROPHEUS (axis). The RADIUS rotates around the ULNA, resulting in turning the palm of the hand down (PRONATION) or up (SUPINATION).

The Skull of a Bird is a poem in bone—its architecture is the 'frozen music' of morphology; in its mutely eloquent lines may be traced the rhythmic rhymes of the myriad amoebi-form animals which constructed the noble edifice when they sang together.

Elliott Coues

THE SKULL

A. General

The skull is divided into cranial and facial bones. The cranial bones are those that bound the cranial cavity; all others are facial bones.

Examine the skulls of the fetus, the child, and the adult, and study the following general features, labeling as many of the structures as possible on the appropriate diagrams (Plates 3-4 through 3-11).

1. Sutures—lines of union of the skull bones (Plates 3-4 to 3-11 inclusive)
   a. Sagittal—between parietal bones.
   b. Frontal (metopic)—present only in fetus and child; between two halves of frontal bone.
   c. Coronal—between frontal and parietal bones.
   d. Lambdoidal—between parietal and occipital bones.
   e. Squamous—between temporal and parietal bones.

2. What are Wormian or sutural bones?

3. Fontanels—membranous areas where ossification has not taken place (soft spots). Present in specimens of fetus and newborn (Plates 3-5, 3-6, and 3-11).
   a. Frontal—between antero-superior angles of the parietal bones and the superior angles of the two halves of the frontal.
   b. Occipital—between superior angle of the occipital and the posterior superior angles of the parietals.
   c. Sphenoid—between frontal, sphenoid, parietal, and squamous temporal.
   d. Mastoid—between occipital, parietal, and mastoid temporal.

4. Cavities and fossae
    a. Cranial cavity—houses brain.
    b. Middle ear cavity (temporal bone).
    c. Inner ear cavity (temporal bone).
    d. Orbital fossa—houses eyeball (bulb).
    e. Nasal cavity.
    f. Temporal fossa—medial to zygomatic arch.
5. Sinuses (air)—Study these in relationship to the bones in which they occur and from which they are named. How does air reach the sinuses?

    a. Frontal (Plate 3-4)
    b. Maxillary (Plate 3-4)
    c. Sphenoidal
    d. Ethmoidal air cells
    e. Mastoid air cells
6. Foramina—Notice the openings in the various bones of the skull which allow the passage of nerves and blood vessels. The largest is in the occipital bone and is known as the foramen magnum. Through it passes the spinal cord to merge with the brain. Study Plate 3-9.
7. Cranial bones (8)
    a. Single
        1) Frontal
        2) Ethmoid
        3) Occipital
        4) Sphenoid
    b. Paired
        1) Parietals
        2) Temporals
8. Facial bones (14)
    a. Single
        1) Mandible
        2) Vomer
    b. Paired
        1) Nasals
        2) Lacrimals
        3) Maxillae
        4) Zygomatics
        5) Palatines
        6) Inferior conchae

This gives a total of 22 bones in the human skull. However, if the ear ossicles of the temporal bone are counted separately and we include the hyoid bone, we then have 29. The ear ossicles are named the malleus, incus, and stapes, and will be studied with the temporal bone. The HYOID is a U-shaped bone located in the neck just above the larynx.

B. Surface anatomy
    Certain skeletal and other features are quite apparent on the surface of the body. Such structures are of value as landmarks.
    1. Zygomatic arch
        a. Extends from the attachment of the auricle (ear) forward to anterior edge of zygomatic bone. It is subcutaneous.
    2. Mastoid process
        a. The prominence felt below and in back of the ear. It is subcutaneous.

3. Hyoid bone
   a. It can be felt in the midline of the throat above the larynx. It is best to hold the head back when feeling for the hyoid. How is the hyoid bone held to the skull?

4. External occipital protuberance
   a. A prominence on the external surface of the occipital bone, above the foramen magnum.

C. The bones

No attempt will be made to describe the bones of the skull. Refer to your textbook or to some other elementary anatomy for descriptions and, using the materials available, locate the following:

1. Frontal bones (Plates 3-4, 3-5, 3-6, and 3-7)
   a. Orbital plates
   b. Superciliary ridges
   c. Squama (vertical-forehead)
   d. Frontal sinus
   e. Supra-orbital notch or foramen
   f. Zygomatic process
2. Parietal (Plates 3-7 and 3-11)
   a. Grooves for middle meningeal vessels
   b. Groove for superior sagittal sinus
   c. Name the sutures by which this bone articulates with neighboring bones.
3. Occipital (Plates 3-6, 3-8, 3-9 and 3-10)
   a. Foramen magnum
   b. Occipital condyles
   c. External occipital protuberance
   d. Sulci (grooves) for transverse, superior sagittal, and occipital venous sinuses.
   e. Hypoglossal canal
4. Temporal (Plates 3-6 through 3-10, 3-12)
   a. External acoustic meatus
   b. Squamous portion and grooves for middle meningeal vessel and for middle temporal artery
   c. Zygomatic process and mandibular fossa
   d. Mastoid portion and process
   e. Petrous portion and tympanic antrum
   f. Internal acoustic meatus
   g. Styloid process
   h. Auditory tube
   i. Tympanic cavity (middle ear cavity)
   j. Auditory ossicles—malleus, incus, stapes
   k. Mastoid cells
   l. Internal ear
      1) Semicircular canals
      2) Cochlea
   m. Jugular foramen
   n. Stylomastoid foramen
   o. Carotid canal
5. Sphenoid (Plates 3-8 through 3-10, 3-13)
   a. Sella turcica and hypophyseal fossa
   b. Anterior clinoid processes
   c. Posterior clinoid processes
   d. Sphenoidal air cells (sinus)
   e. Wings (greater and lesser)
   f. Pterygoid processes
   g. Optic foramen
   h. Optic groove

     i. Foramen rotundum
     j. Foramen ovale
     k. Foramen spinosum
     l. Pterygoid canal
     m. Superior orbital fissure
     n. Inferior orbital fissure
     o. Foramen lacerum
     Label Plate 3-13, figure 1.

6. Ethmoid
    a. Horizontal plate (cribriform) (Plate 3-8)
    b. Perpendicular plate (Plate 3-4)
    c. Lateral masses
       1) Superior conchae
       2) Middle conchae (Plate 3-4)
       3) Lamina orbitalis (Plate 3-7)
    d. Ethmoid air cells (sinus)
    e. Crista galli (Plate 3-8)

7. Inferior nasal conchae (Plate 3-4)

8. Vomer (Plate 3-4)
    a. Forms a part of nasal septum. What other bone contributes to the nasal septum?

9. Nasals (Plate 3-4)
    a. Form "bridge" of nose.

10. Lacrimals (Plate 3-7)
    a. Notice the sulcus which in the living subject houses the lacrimal sac.
    b. Lacrimal canal

11. Maxillae (Plates 3-4, 3-5, 3-7, and 3-9)
    a. Maxillary sinus
    b. Alveolar process—note teeth
    c. Palatine process
    d. Frontal process
    e. Incisive foramen
    f. Zygomatic process
    g. Infraorbital foramen

12. Zygomatics (Plates 3-4 and 3-7)
    a. Temporal process
    b. Frontal process
    c. Zygomaticofacial foramen

13. Palatines (Plates 3-9 and 3-10)
    a. Perpendicular plate
    b. Horizontal plate
    c. Sphenopalatine foramen
    d. Greater palatine foramen
    e. Lesser palatine foramen

14. Mandible (Plates 3-4 through 3-7)
    a. Body
    b. Rami
    c. Alveolar margin
    d. Condyloid process
    e. Coronoid process
    f. Mandibular foramen
    g. Mental foramen

15. Hyoid
    a. Body
    b. Greater horns
    c. Lesser horns

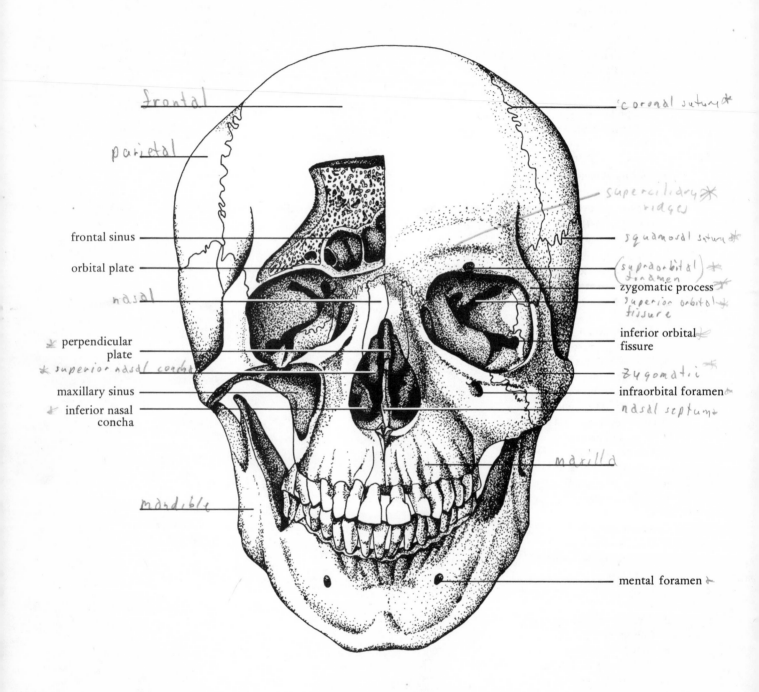

frontal

parietal

coronal suture *

superciliary * ridge

frontal sinus

squamosal suture *

orbital plate

(supraorbital) * foramen

nasal

zygomatic process *

superior orbital * fissure

perpendicular plate

inferior orbital fissure

* superior nasal concha

zygomatic *

maxillary sinus

infraorbital foramen

* inferior nasal concha

nasal septum *

maxilla

mandible

mental foramen *

Plate 3-4. Anterior View of the Skull

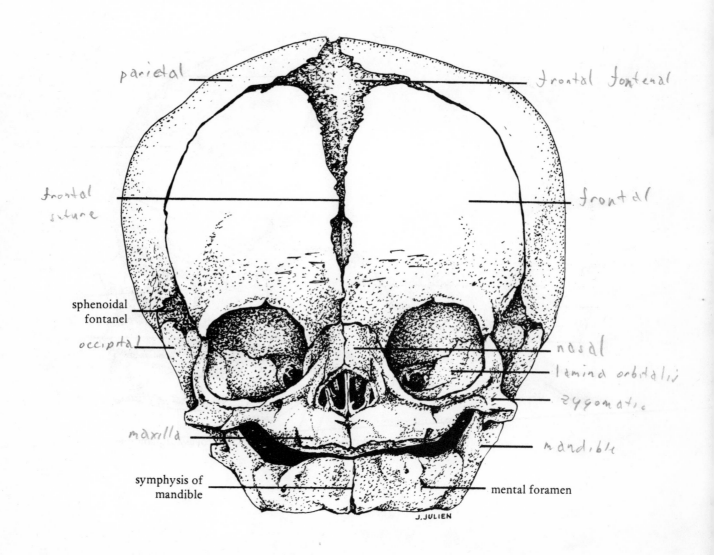

parietal

frontal fontenal

frontal suture

frontal

sphenoidal fontanel

occipital

nasal

lamina orbitalis

zygomatic

maxilla

mandible

symphysis of mandible

mental foramen

J. JULIEN

Plate 3-5. Skull of Newborn—Anterior View

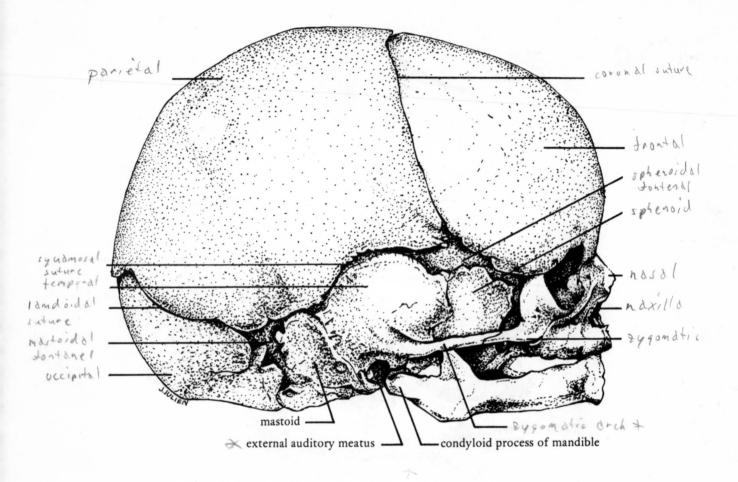

parietal

coronal suture

frontal

sphenoidal fontanel

sphenoid

squamosal suture

temporal

nasal

lambdoidal suture

maxilla

mastoidal fontanel

zygomatic

occipital

J. JULIEN

mastoid

zygomatic arch

external auditory meatus

condyloid process of mandible

Plate 3-6. Skull of Newborn—Lateral View

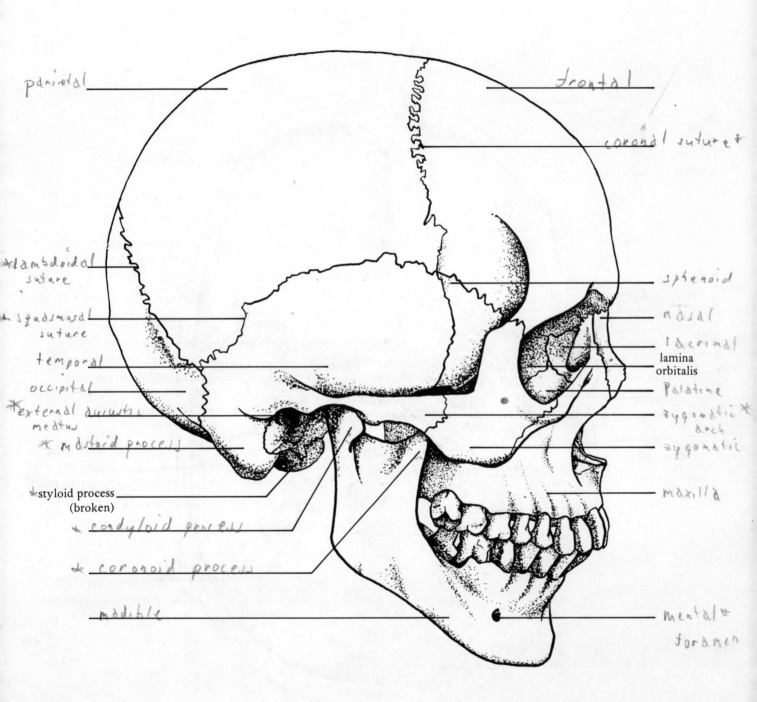

parietal

frontal

coronal suture*

lambdoidal suture

squamosal suture

temporal

occipital

external auditus medtus

mastoid process

styloid process (broken)

condyloid process

coronoid process

mandible

sphenoid

nasal

lacrimal

lamina orbitalis

Palatine

zygomatic arch *

zygomatic

maxilla

mental* foramen

Plate 3-7. Lateral View of the Skull

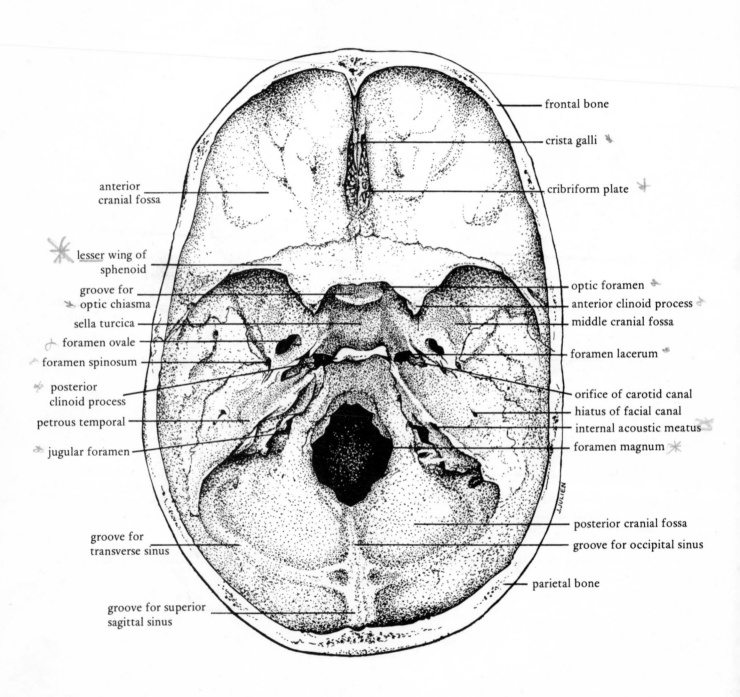

frontal bone

crista galli

cribriform plate

anterior
cranial fossa

optic foramen

lesser wing of
sphenoid

anterior clinoid process

groove for
optic chiasma

middle cranial fossa

sella turcica

foramen lacerum

foramen ovale

foramen spinosum

orifice of carotid canal

posterior
clinoid process

hiatus of facial canal

internal acoustic meatus

petrous temporal

foramen magnum

jugular foramen

posterior cranial fossa

groove for occipital sinus

groove for
transverse sinus

parietal bone

groove for superior
sagittal sinus

Plate 3-8. Floor of Cranial Cavity

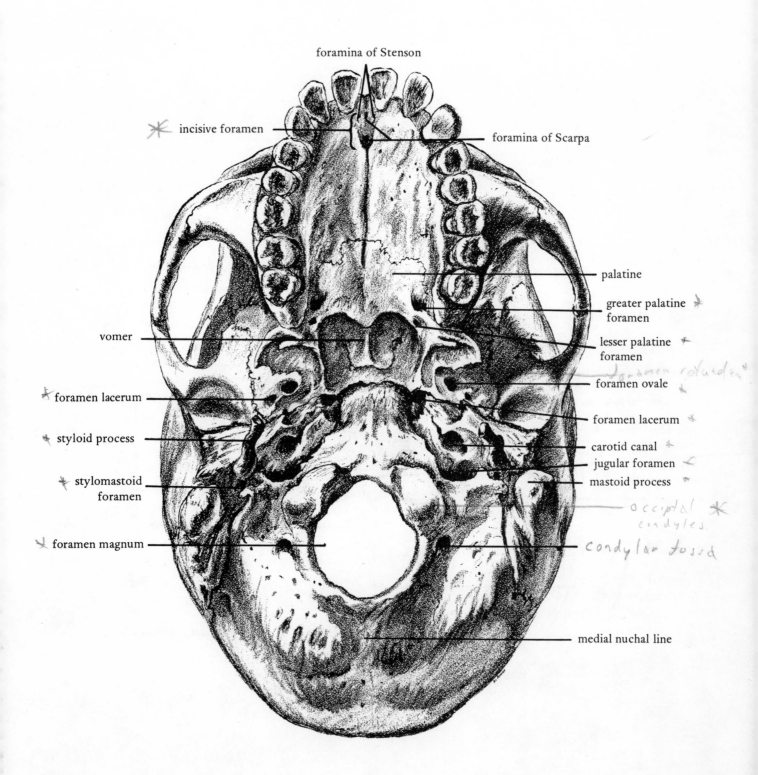

foramina of Stenson

✳ incisive foramen

foramina of Scarpa

palatine

greater palatine ✳
foramen

vomer

lesser palatine ✳
foramen

foramen rotundum✳

✳ foramen lacerum

foramen ovale ✳

foramen lacerum ✳

✳ styloid process

carotid canal ✳

jugular foramen ✳

✳ stylomastoid
foramen

mastoid process ✳

occipital ✳
condyles.

✳ foramen magnum

condylar fossa

medial nuchal line

Plate 3-9. Base of the Skull

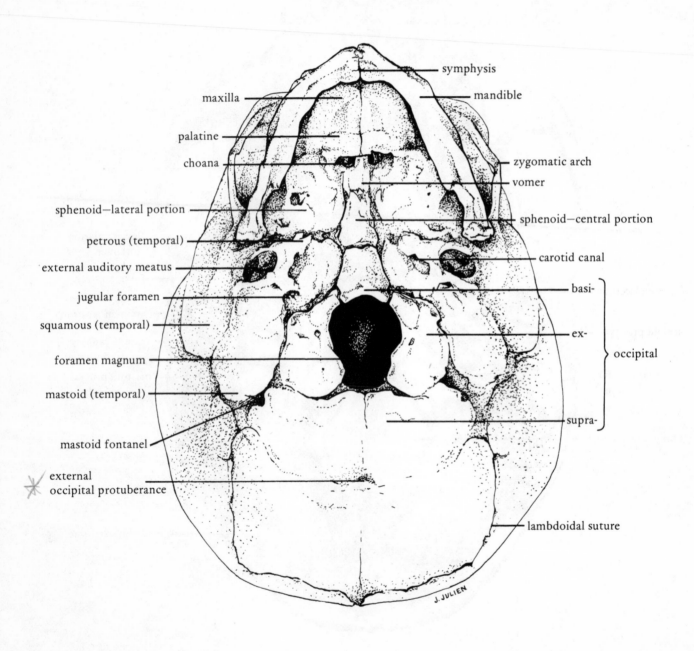

maxilla

palatine

choana

sphenoid—lateral portion

petrous (temporal)

external auditory meatus

jugular foramen

squamous (temporal)

foramen magnum

mastoid (temporal)

mastoid fontanel

external
occipital protuberance

symphysis

mandible

zygomatic arch

vomer

sphenoid—central portion

carotid canal

basi-

ex-   occipital

supra-

lambdoidal suture

J. JULIEN

Plate 3-10. Skull of Newborn—Base

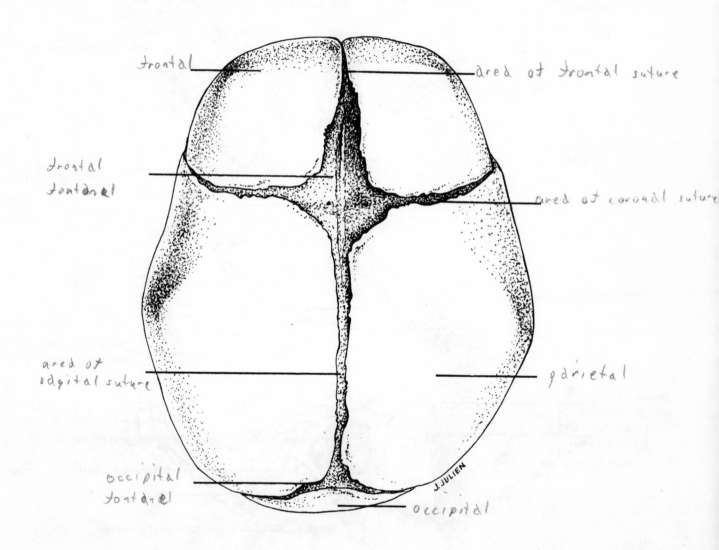

frontal

area of frontal suture

frontal fontanel

area of coronal suture

area of sdgital suture

parietal

occipital fontanel

occipital

J.JULIEN

Plate 3-11. Skull of Newborn—Superior View

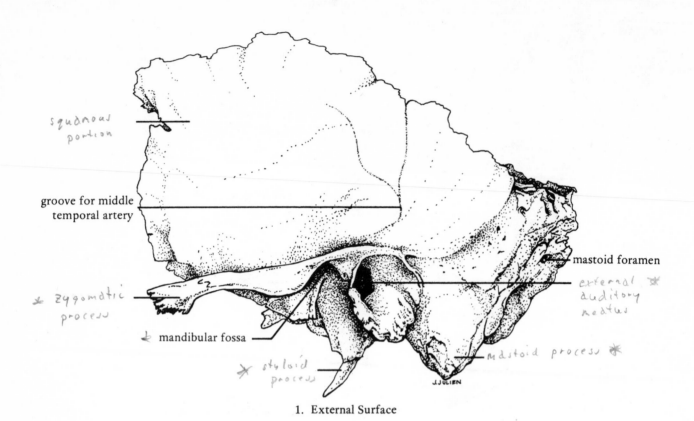

squamous portion

groove for middle temporal artery

zygomatic process

mandibular fossa

styloid process

mastoid foramen

external auditory meatus

mastoid process

J. JULIEN

1. External Surface

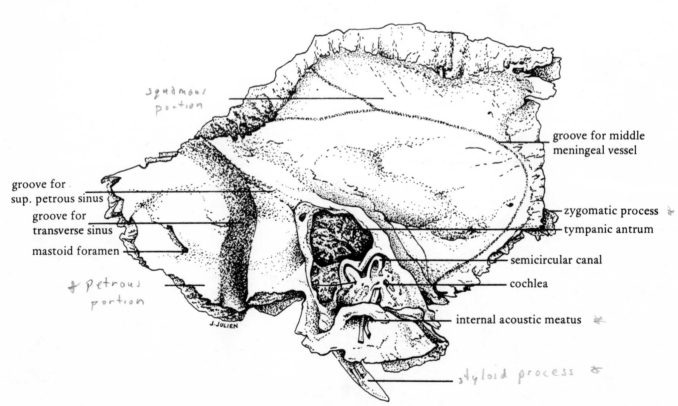

squamous portion

groove for sup. petrous sinus

groove for transverse sinus

mastoid foramen

Petrous portion

J. JULIEN

groove for middle meningeal vessel

zygomatic process

tympanic antrum

semicircular canal

cochlea

internal acoustic meatus

styloid process

2. Internal Surface; roof of petrous bone opened
   to show ear structure

Plate 3-12. Left Temporal Bone

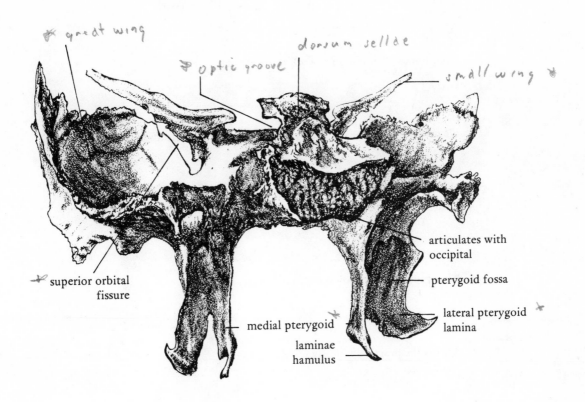

great wing

optic groove

dorsum sellae

small wing

articulates with
occipital

pterygoid fossa

superior orbital
fissure

lateral pterygoid
lamina

medial pterygoid
laminae

hamulus

1. Posterolateral View

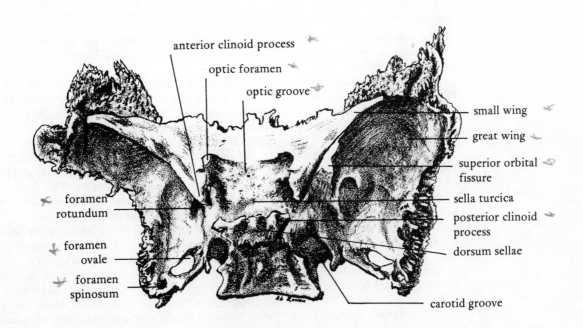

anterior clinoid process

optic foramen

optic groove

small wing

great wing

superior orbital
fissure

sella turcica

foramen
rotundum

posterior clinoid
process

foramen
ovale

dorsum sellae

foramen
spinosum

carotid groove

2. Superior View

Plate 3-13. The Sphenoid Bone

QUESTIONS

1. Name the bones which form the hard palate.

2. What bones form the framework of the orbit?

3. What bones form the vertical plate dividing the nose into two nasal passageways?

4. What are the foramina for in the cribriform plate of the ethmoid?

5. What types of articulation are found in the skull?

6. What is the practical importance of fontanels?

VERTEBRAL COLUMN

A. General

The vertebral column is composed of 24 vertebrae, the sacrum, and the coccyx. The 24 vertebrae are placed in three groups, the upper 7 being cervical, the next 12 thoracic, and the last 5 lumbar.

A vertebra is generally composed of a BODY, PEDICLES, LAMINAE, SPINOUS PROCESS, TRANSVERSE PROCESSES, and VARIOUS ARTICULAR PROCESSES. The pedicles and laminae form a NEURAL ARCH which, together with the body, enclose a VERTEBRAL FORAMEN. The vertebral foramen houses the NERVE CORD.

Label the diagrams of vertebrae (Plates 3-14 through 3-16).

Adjacent vertebrae articulate through the medium of WHITE FIBRO-CARTILAGINOUS PADS situated between their bodies. These are known as INTER-VERTEBRAL DISKS. They are bound together by strong ligaments. The disks are compressible and flexion, extension, abduction and adduction are possible at these cartilaginous joints. Rotation also takes place in the cervical and thoracic regions.

The sacrum is a single bone, but one that originates as five vertebral units which gradually fuse. Their lines of fusion can be seen on close examination. The sacrum serves as a strong point for the articulation of the pelvic girdle—the SACROILIAC JOINT.

The coccyx consists of from 3 to 5 reduced vertebrae—the remnants of a tail skeleton.

When viewed from the front or back, the vertebral column forms a straight line. If it swings to one side or the other, the condition is known as SCOLIOSIS, which may be caused by poor posture or disease. When viewed from the side, a normal vertebral column shows four curves: CERVICAL, THORACIC, LUMBAR, and SACRAL. Label these on Plate 3-14, figure 2.

Of these curves the thoracic and sacral are said to be PRIMARY; the lumbar and cervical, SECONDARY. An abnormal posterior convexity in the thoracic region is known as KYPHOSIS; an abnormal posterior concavity in the lumbar region, as LORDOSIS.

Study the articulated skeletons of the adult and the fetus; note as many of the above features as possible.

B. Cervical vertebrae (7)

A cervical vertebra may be recognized by one or more of the following characteristics:

1. The transverse processes are wide and contain a canal (foramen transversarium) for the passage of the vertebral artery (Plate 3-14, figure 3, and Plate 3-15).

2. The spinous process may be bifid and the bodies small.

3. There are no articulating fossae on the transverse processes.

4. Three cervical vertebrae have special structural features. The first is known as the ATLAS; it is a ring-like bone. The body is very much reduced and the vertebral foramen divided by a transverse ligament into anterior and posterior compartments. The anterior compartment contains the dens of the axis and the posterior one, the spinal cord. There are large concave surfaces on the superior aspect for the articulation with the skull. Label Plate 3-15, figure 1.

5. The second vertebra is the AXIS or EPISTROPHEUS, and is characterized by a prominent process called the DENS, projecting from its superior surface. The dens fits into the anterior compartment of the vertebral foramen of the atlas, and serves as a pivot for the rotation of the atlas. Thus we are able to turn our heads. Label Plate 3-15, figure 2.

6. The seventh cervical vertebra is called VERTEBRA PROMINENS because of its large spinous process. It serves as an important landmark in the neck.
Identify these structures on a disarticulated vertebral column.

C. Thoracic vertebrae (12)

The thoracic vertebrae are best recognized by their articulating facets or demifacets for the ribs. These facets or demifacets are located on the bodies and on the ends of the transverse processes.

Locate these articulating facets, and see if you can discover other means of recognizing thoracic vertebrae. Label Plate 3-14, figure 1.

D. Lumbar vertebrae (5)

The lumbar vertebrae have heavy bodies, wide spinous processes, and they lack facets for rib articulation. Label Plate 3-16, figure 1.

E. Sacrum (5)

Locate the spinous processes, intervertebral foramina, transverse processes, and notice the auricular surface for articulation with the os coxae of the pelvic girdle. Label Plate 3-16, figure 2.

F. Coccyx (3 to 5)

The most rudimentary part of the vertebral column. It is triangular, and its base is attached to the sacrum. Label on Plate 3-16, figure 2.

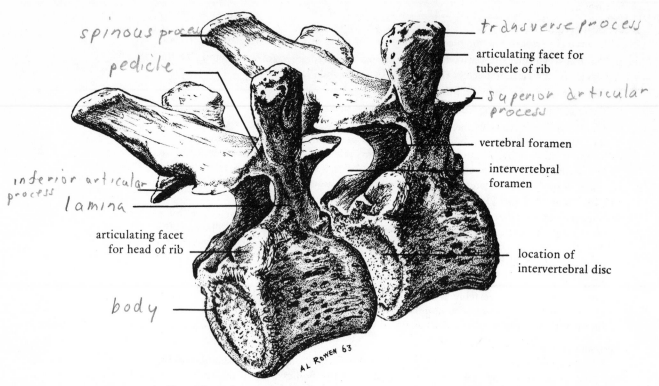

spinous process

pedicle

transverse process

articulating facet for
tubercle of rib

superior articular
process

vertebral foramen

intervertebral
foramen

inferior articular
process

lamina

articulating facet
for head of rib

location of
intervertebral disc

body

AL ROWEN 63

1. Two Thoracic Vertebrae—view from below and the right side

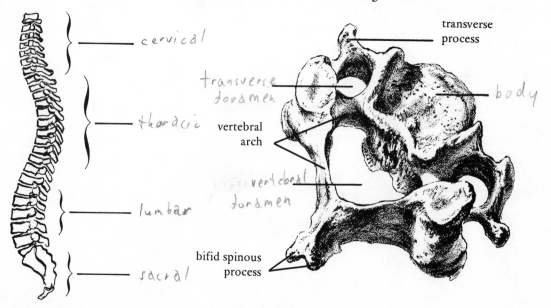

cervical

transverse
process

transverse
foramen

body

vertebral
arch

thoracic

lumbar

intervertebral
foramen

sacral

bifid spinous
process

2. Normal Curvatures of Vertebral
Column—lateral view

3. A Cervical Vertebra

Plate 3-14. The Vertebral Column

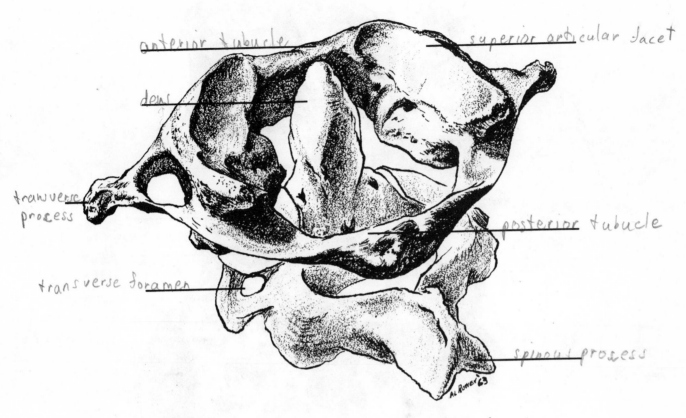

anterior tubucle

superior articular facet

dens

transverse process

posterior tubucle

transverse foramen

spinous process

AL Rowex 63

1. The First (Atlas) and Second (Axis) Cervical Vertebrae

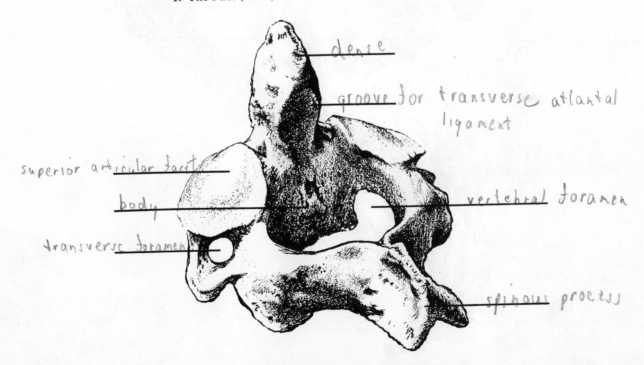

dense

groove for transverse atlantal ligament

superior articular facet

body

vertebral foramen

transverse foramen

spinous process

2. The Second (Axis) Cervical Vertebra

Plate 3-15. Specialized Cervical Vertebrae

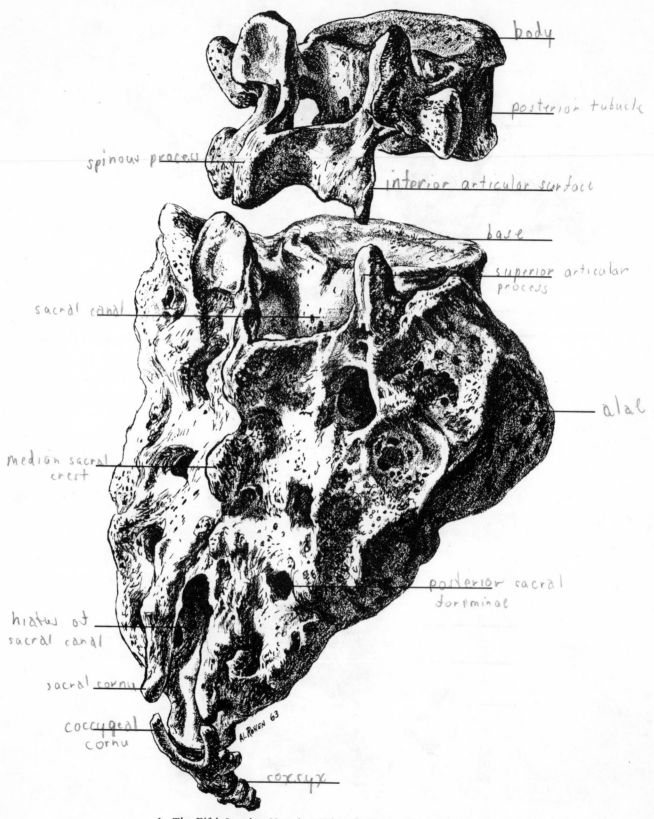

body

posterior tubercle

spinous process

inferior articular surface

base

superior articular process

sacral canal

alae

median sacral crest

posterior sacral foramina

hiatus of sacral canal

sacral cornu

coccygeal cornu

coccyx

AL ROWEN 63

1. The Fifth Lumbar Vertebra (Above)—Posterolateral View

2. The Sacrum and Coccyx (Below)—Posterolateral View

Plate 3-16. Lumbar Vertebra, Sacrum and Coccyx

QUESTIONS

1. Describe some of the movements of the normal vertebral column.

2. What are some of the causes of abnormal curvatures of the vertebral column?

BONES OF THE THORAX, AND COSTAL CARTILAGES

The bones of the thorax consist of the 12 pairs of ribs and the sternum. Study both the adult and fetal skeletons to note differences in shape of the thorax. Study also the ribs of a disarticulated skeleton to compare them in size, shape, and mode of articulation to the thoracic vertebrae. Note the costal cartilages which lie between the anterior ends of the ribs and the sternum.

A. Ribs

You should be able to recognize the following structures or features of a rib. Label Plate 3-17, figure 1.

1. The angle—the point of sharpest curvature of the rib.
2. The head—for articulation with body of the vertebra.
3. The tubercle—for articulation with the transverse process of the vertebrae.
4. The neck—between the head and tubercle.
5. True ribs—the first 7 pairs.
6. False ribs—the last 5 pairs.
7. Floating ribs—the last 2 pairs (included as false ribs).

B. Sternum

Identify and label the following on Plate 3-17, figure 2.

1. Manubrium—the superior portion of the sternum which articulates with the clavicles.
2. Body (gladiolus)—the middle portion.
3. Xiphoid process—usually cartilaginous.
4. Articulating facets—for the costal cartilages.
5. How does the STERNUM of the adult differ from that of the fetus?

6. Sternal angle—found at the junction of the manubrium and the body, and serving as an important location point for structures within the thorax. It marks the point of articulation of the second costal cartilage.
7. Jugular or presternal notch—on the superior border of the manubrium.

C. Costal cartilages

The first 7 pairs of ribs have costal cartilages which articulate with the sternum. The costal cartilages of the 8th, 9th, and 10th pairs articulate with the 7th cartilage. The 11th and 12th pairs are floating ribs.

The costal cartilages give flexibility to the thorax which is important in breathing.

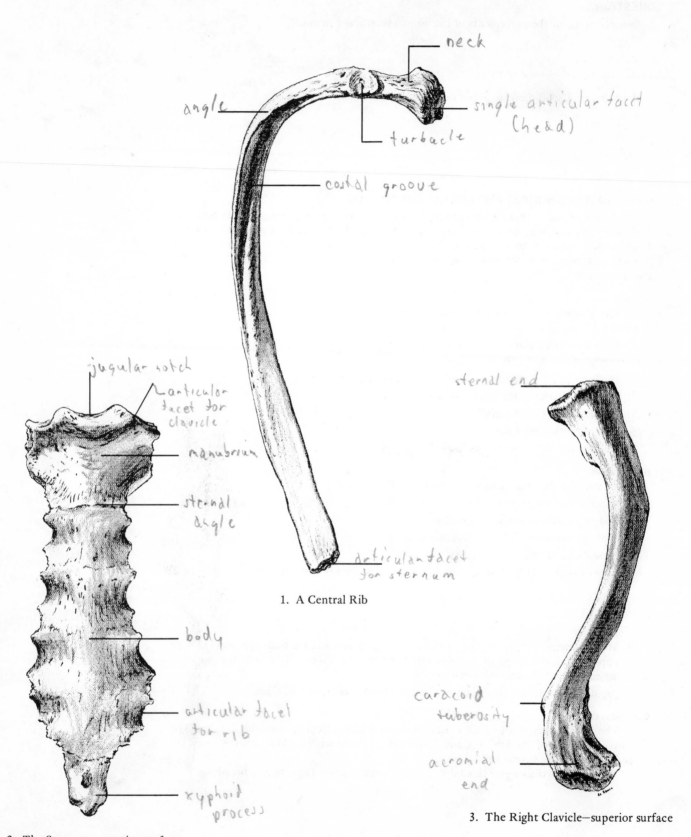

neck

angle

single articular facet (head)

turbacle

costal groove

jugular notch

articular facet for clavicle

manubrium

sternal angle

body

articular facet for rib

xyphoid process

articular facet for sternum

sternal end

caracoid tuberosity

acromial end

1. A Central Rib

2. The Sternum—anterior surface

3. The Right Clavicle—superior surface

Plate 3-17. Ribs and Sternum

PECTORAL (SHOULDER) GIRDLE (Plates 3-17 through 3-19)

This girdle serves as the supporting structure for the forelimb. It consists of 2 pairs of bones, the clavicles anteriorly, and the scapulae posteriorly. The clavicles, through their connections with the manubrium, make the only direct articulation between this girdle and the axial skeleton. Label Plate 3-17, figure 3, and Plate 3-18, figures 1 and 2.

A. Clavicles
1. Sternal (inner) end.
2. Acromial (outer) end.
3. Anterior border.
4. Coracoid tuberosity (conoid tubercle).

B. Scapulae
1. Body.
2. Spine.
3. Acromion process.
4. Superior, medial (vertebral) and lateral (axillary) borders.
5. Glenoid fossa.
6. Coracoid process.
7. Supraspinous fossa.
8. Infraspinous fossa.
9. Subscapular fossa.

FORELIMB

Study the various joints of the upper extremity, noting the types of movement possible. Reference should be made to the articulated skeleton.

A. Humerus
It articulates at glenoid cavity of scapula. Label Plates 3-19 and 3-20.
1. Head.
2. Anatomical neck.
3. Greater and lesser tubercle.
4. Intertubercular groove.
5. Surgical neck.
6. Shaft.
7. Deltoid tuberosity.
8. Medial and lateral epicondyles.
9. Capitulum.
10. Trochlea.
11. Coronoid fossa.
12. Olecranon fossa.

B. Ulna (Plates 3-19 and 3-20)
It articulates with the humerus, forming a hinge-joint, and lies on the medial side of the forearm. Label on Plates 3-19 and 3-20.
1. Olecranon.
2. Coronoid process.
3. Trochlear (semilunar) notch.
4. Radial notch.
5. Styloid process.

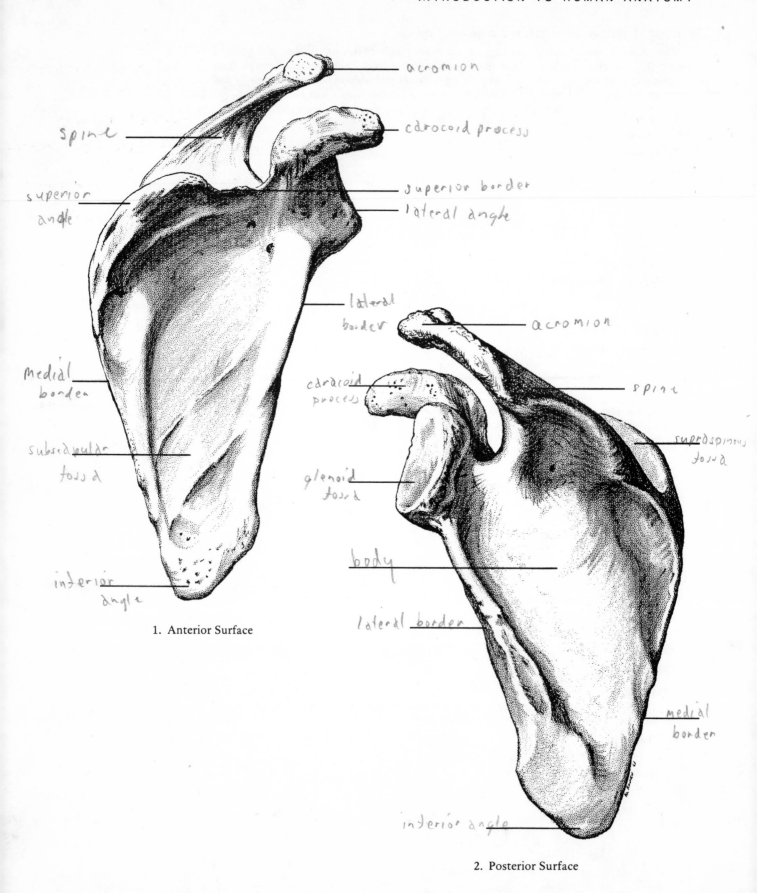

acromion

cdrocoid process

spine

superior border

lateral angle

superior angle

lateral border

medial border

acromion

cdrocoid process

spine

subscapular fossa

glenoid fossa

supraspinous fossa

body

inferior angle

lateral border

medial border

inferior angle

1. Anterior Surface

2. Posterior Surface

Plate 3-18. The Left Scapula

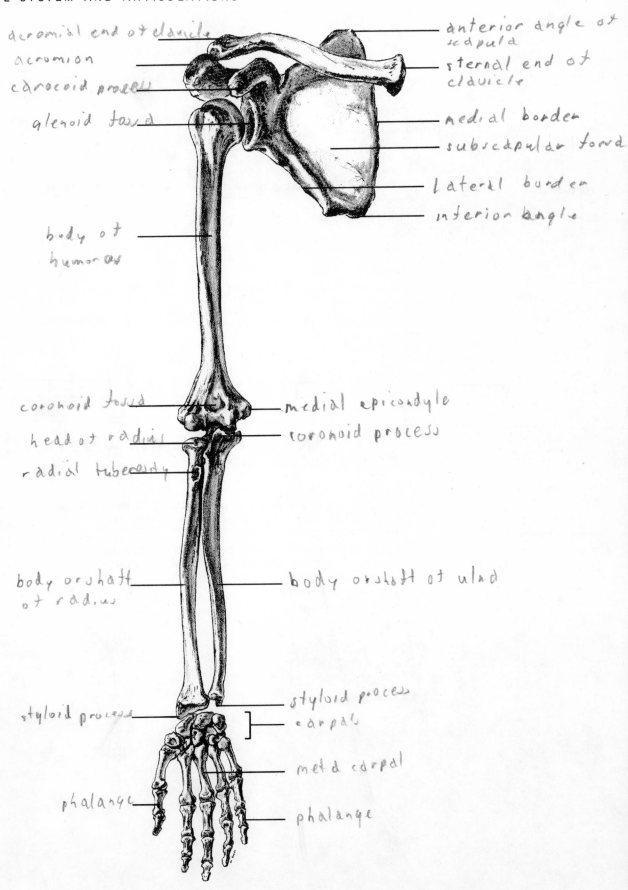

acromial end of clavicle

acromion

coracoid process

glenoid fossa

anterior angle of scapula

sternal end of clavicle

medial border

subscapular fossa

lateral border

inferior angle

body of humerus

coronoid fossa

head of radius

radial tuberosity

medial epicondyle

coronoid process

body or shaft of radius

body or shaft of ulna

styloid process

styloid process

carpals

metacarpal

phalange

phalange

Plate 3-19. Skeleton of Right Arm and Shoulder—Anterior View

C. Radius

    The radius is located on the lateral or thumb side of the forearm. The head is flat on top and round for articulation with the humerus and ulna. The lower end is large and articulates with the carpus. Label on Plates 3-19 and 3-20.

    1. Head.

    2. Tuberosity.

    3. Ulnar notch.

    4. Styloid process.

D. Carpus (wrist) (Plate 3-21)

    There are 8 carpal bones arranged in two rows. Those in the proximal row, from lateral to medial side, are:

    1. Scaphoid.

    2. Lunate.

    3. Triangular.

    4. Pisiform.

Those in the distal row, from lateral to medial side, are:

    5. Trapezium.

    6. Trapezoid.

    7. Capitate.

    8. Hamate.

E. Metacarpus (Plate 3-21)

    This region consists of 5 bones numbered from the thumb side medially, and they form the framework of the palm of the hand.

F. Digits

    There are 5 digits. Number one is the thumb and consists of two phalanges. The other digits have three phalanges each. Label the diagram of the hand on Plate 3-21.

PELVIC (HIP) GIRDLE

    The pelvic girdle is composed of 2 OS COXAE (INNOMINATE). Each of these consists embryologically of an upper expanded portion (ILIUM), a lower posterior element (ISCHIUM), and a lower anterior element (PUBIS). In the adult these three parts are completely fused. Each part contributes to the ACETABULUM.

    The os coxae articulate anteriorly to form the SYMPHYSIS PUBIS. Posteriorly, they articulate with the sacrum to form the SACROILIAC JOINTS. Together with the sacrum and coccyx, they form the pelvis.

    What are the following:

1. True pelvis.

2. False pelvis.

3. Arcuate line.

How do male and female pelves differ?

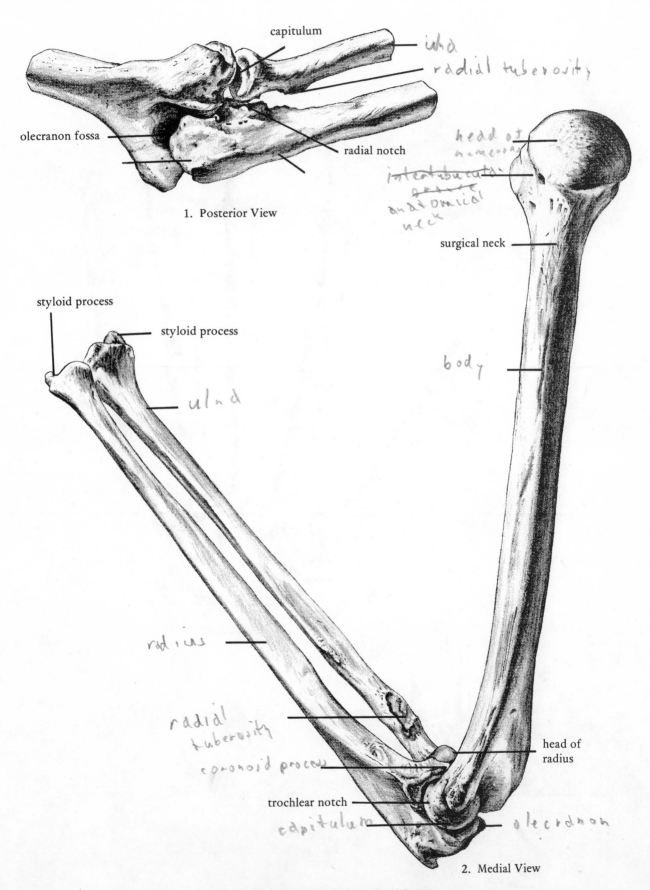

capitulum

ulna

radial tuberosity

olecranon fossa

radial notch

head of humerus

intertubercula

anatomical neck

surgical neck

1. Posterior View

styloid process

styloid process

ulna

body

radius

radial tuberosity

coronoid process

head of radius

trochlear notch

capitulum

olecranon

2. Medial View

Plate 3-20. Bones of the Right Arm and Forearm

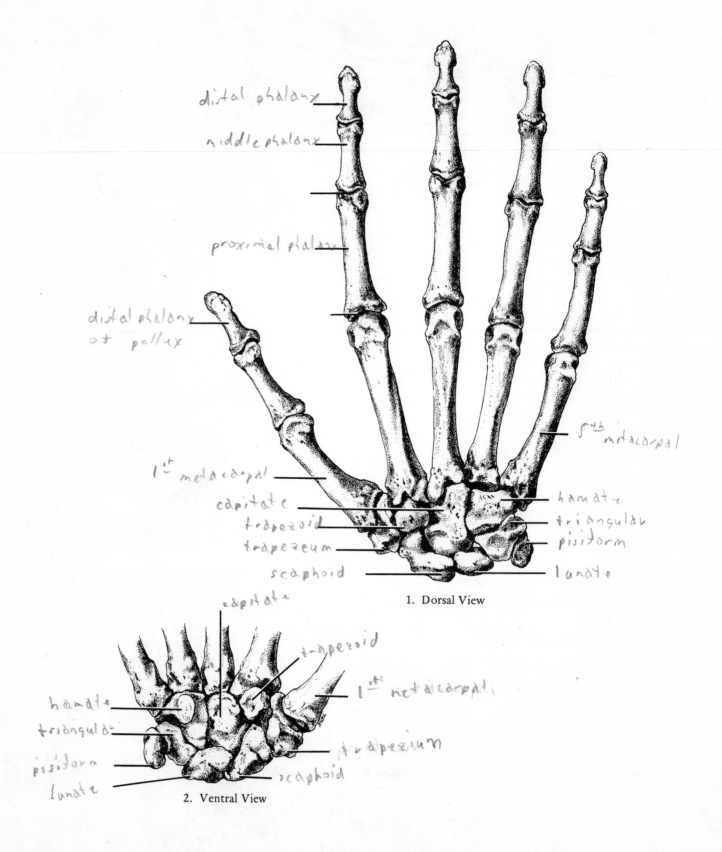

distal phalanx

middle phalanx

proximal phalanx

distal phalanx of pollux

1st metacarpal

capitate

trapezoid

trapezeum

scaphoid

5th metacarpal

hamate

triangular

pisiform

lunate

1. Dorsal View

capitate

trapezoid

1st metacarpal

hamate

triangular

pisiform

lunate

trapezium

scaphoid

2. Ventral View

Plate 3-21. Skeleton of the Right Hand

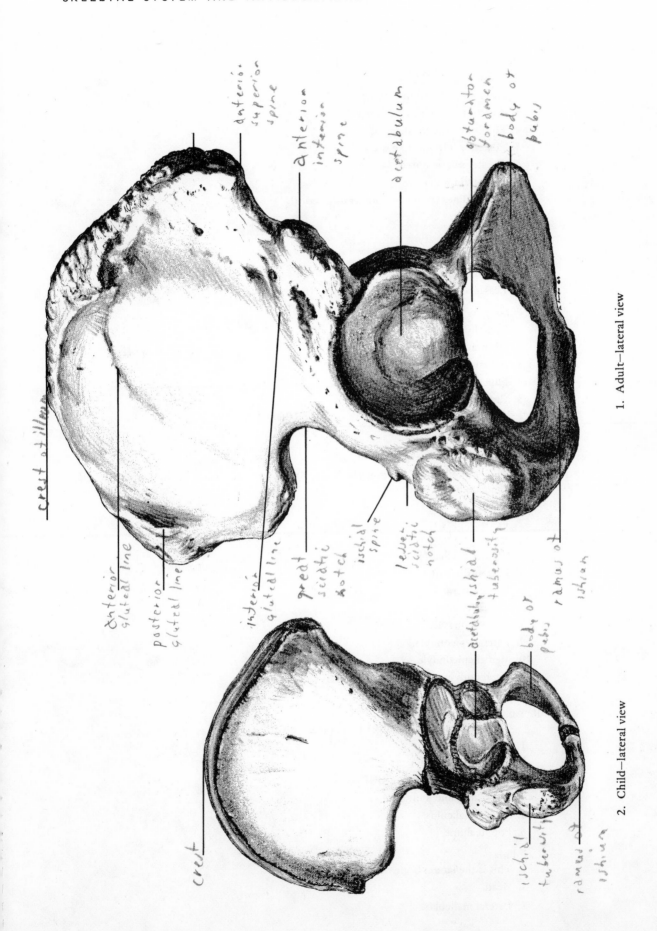

crest of ilium

anterior superior spine

anterior inferior spine

acetabulum

obturator foramen

body of pubis

anterior gluteal line

posterior gluteal line

inferior gluteal line

great sciatic notch

ischial spine

lesser sciatic notch

acetabulum

ischial tuberosity

body of pubis

ramus of ischium

1. Adult—lateral view

crest

ischial tuberosity

ramus of ischium

2. Child—lateral view

Plate 3-22. Right Hip Bone (Os Coxae) of Adult and Child

Study the articulations of the pelvis.

A. Ilium
1. Crest.
2. Anterior superior iliac spine.
3. Anterior inferior iliac spine.
4. Posterior superior iliac spine.
5. Posterior inferior iliac spine.
6. Greater sciatic notch.
7. Acetabulum.
8. Gluteal lines (posterior, anterior, inferior).

B. Ischium
1. Ischial tuberosity.
2. Obturator foramen.
3. Acetabulum.
4. Lesser sciatic notch.

C. Pubis
1. Symphysis.
2. Obturator foramen.
3. Acetabulum.
4. Superior and inferior rami.
5. Crest of pubis.
Label the os coxae of the child and adult on Plate 3-22.

HINDLIMB (Plate 3-23)

A. Femur
This is the longest bone in the body. Study its articulation in the acetabulum of the innominate bone.
1. Head.
2. Fovea capitis.
3. Neck.
4. Greater trochanter.
5. Lesser trochanter.
6. Linea aspera.
7. Lateral condyle.
8. Medial condyle.
9. Lateral epicondyle.
10. Medial epicondyle.
11. Intercondylar notch.
Label.

B. Tibia (shin bone)
This is the medial and larger bone of the lower leg.
1. Head.
2. Tuberosity.
3. Condyles, lateral and medial.
4. Intercondyloid eminence.
5. Medial malleolus.
6. Popliteal line.

C. Fibula
This is the lateral bone of the lower leg.
1. Head.
2. Lateral malleolus.

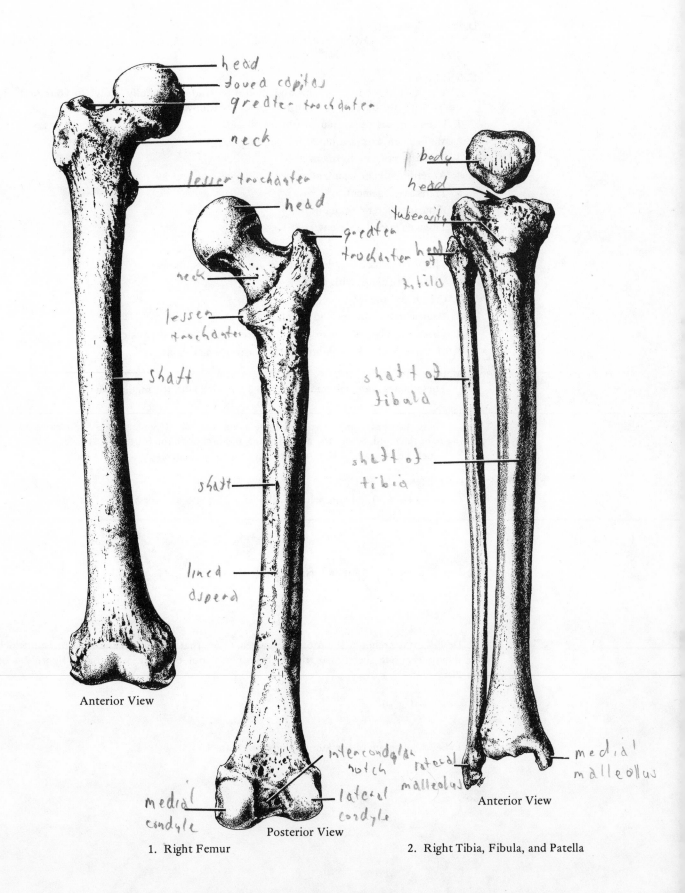

head
foued capites
greater trochanter
neck
lesser trochanter
head
greater trochanter
neck
lesser trochanter
shaft
shaft
linea aspera

body
head
tuberosity
head of tibia
shaft of fibula
shaft of tibia

medial condyle

intercondylar notch
lateral condyle

lateral malleolus
medial malleolus

Anterior View

Posterior View

Anterior View

1. Right Femur

2. Right Tibia, Fibula, and Patella

Plate 3-23. Bones of the Hindlimb (Thigh and Leg)

D. Patella (kneecap)

This is a SESAMOID BONE lying in front of the knee joint. Label the above on Plate 3-23.

E. The knee

The knee is a complex joint and should be studied carefully. Refer to your text and other books for detailed description. Label the following on Plate 3-24.

1. Lateral meniscus (semilunar fibrocartilage).

2. Medial meniscus (semilunar fibrocartilage).

3. Posterior cruciate ligament.

4. Anterior cruciate ligament.

5. Transverse ligament.

6. Fibular collateral ligament.

7. Tibial collateral ligament.

F. Tarsus

This is composed of 7 bones. They are named as follows:

1. Talus—articulates with tibia.

2. Calcaneus—the large heel bone.

3. Navicular—at anterior end of talus.

4. Cuboid—on lateral side of foot attached to anterior end of calcaneus.

5,6,7 Cuneiforms—3 small bones anterior to the navicular.

G. Metatarsus

These bones are numbered from 1 to 5, starting with the medial side.

H. Digits

These are 5 in number and have the same number of phalanges as the corresponding digits in the hand. Study the articulations and arches of the foot.

Label the diagram of the foot on Plate 3-25, figure 1.

QUESTIONS

1. Compare the pectoral and pelvic girdles as to strength and versatility of action.

2. Describe the knee joint and its action.

3. Describe the arches of the foot, naming the bones that form them and the function which they serve. See sketches of the arches of the foot on plate 3-25. Label figure 2-4 of Plate 3-25.

4. Label the diagram of the human skeleton (Plate 3-2).

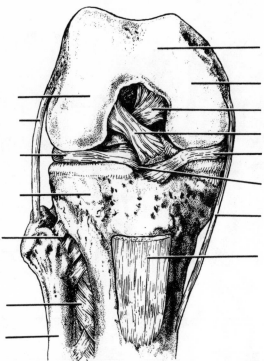

1. Anterior View

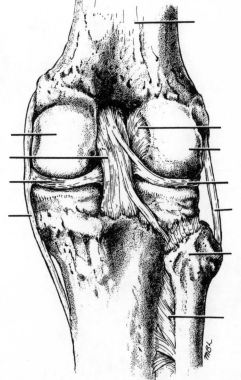

3. Posterior View

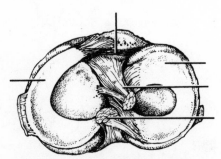

2. Menisci and Cruciate Ligaments—
   Superior View

Plate 3-24. Right Knee Joint

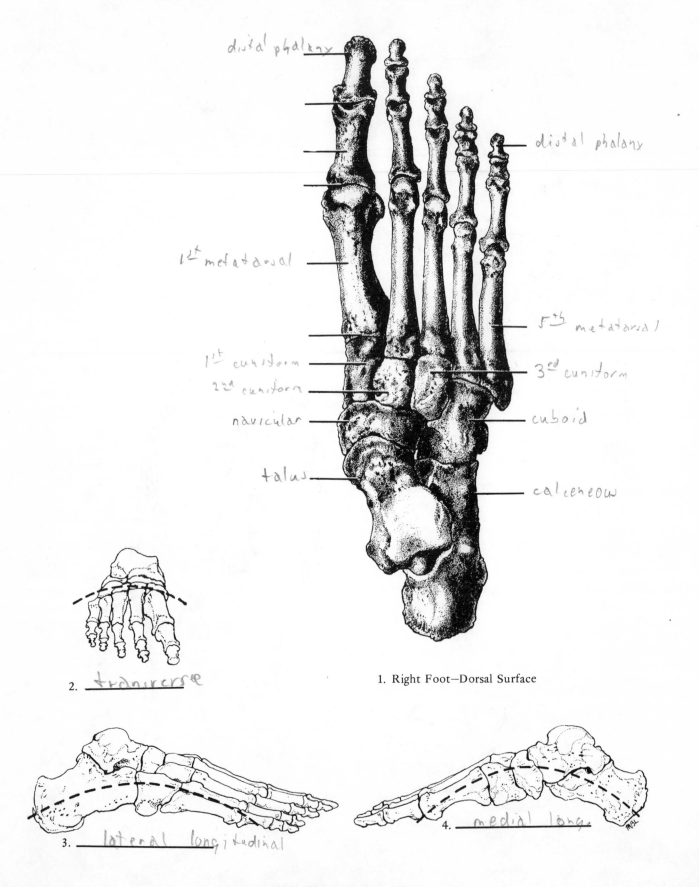

distal phalanx

distal phalanx

1ˢᵗ metatarsal

5ᵗʰ metatarsal

1ˢᵗ cuniform

3ʳᵈ cuniform

2ⁿᵈ cuniform

navicular

cuboid

talus

calcaneou

2. ___transverse___

1. Right Foot—Dorsal Surface

3. ___lateral longitudinal___

4. ___medial long.___

Plate 3-25. The Arches of the Foot

GLOSSARY — Chapter 3

acetabulum (as´e tab´u lum): L., acetum, vinegar, —a little saucer for vinegar.

acoustic (á kōōs´tik): G., akoustikos, pertaining to hearing.

acromion, acromial (á krō mi on, –ál): G., akros, top; omos, shoulder.

adipose (ad´i pōs): L., adeps, adipis, fat.

alveolar (al vē´ō lér): L., alveolus, a little cavity.

amphiarthroid, amphiarthrosis (am´fi är throid, thrō´sis): G., amphi, both; arthrosis, articulation.

areolar (á rē´ō lér): L., areola, dim. of area, space.

atlas (at´lás): G., tlao, to bear. (Atlas, a titan).

axis (ak´sis): L., axis, axle, axis.

bifid (bī fid): L., bi, two; findere, to cleave.

calcaneus (kal kā´nē us): L., calx, heel.

canaliculus, pl. li (kan´á lik´u lus, –lī): L., canalis, channel.

capitate (kap´i tāt): L., capitatus, from caput, head.

capitulum (ká pit´u´lum): L., caput, a small head.

carpus, pl. carpi (kär´pus, –pi): G., karpos, wrist.

cartilage (kär´ti lij): L., cartilago, cartilage.

cervical (sēr´vi kál): L., cervix, neck.

clavicle (klav´i k'l): L., clavicula, dim. of clavis, key.

coccyx, coccygeal (kŏk´six, –sij´e al): L., coccyx, cuckoo.

cochlea (kok´le á): L., cochlea, snail.

collagen, collagenous (kol´lá jen, kol lá´jen us): G., kolla, glue; genes, born.

concha, pl. –chae (kôngk´á, –ē): L., concha, shell.

condyle (kon´dīl): L., condylus, knuckle.

coracoid (kôr´á koid): G., korakoeides, like a crow's beak.

coronal (n.: kôr´o nál, n'l, adj.: ko ro´nál, n'l): L., coronarius, crown, wreath.

coronoid (kôr´o noid): G., korone, crow.

costal (kôs´tál): L., costa, rib.

coxa, ae (kôk´sá; –sē): L., hip, angle.

cribriform (krib´ri fôrm): L., cribrum, sieve.

cruciate (krōō´shi at): L., from crux, crucis, cross.

cuneiform (kū nē´i fôrm; also kū´nē i form): L., cuneus, wedge.

dens (denz): L., dens, dentis, tooth

diaphysis, pl. diaphyses (dī af´i sis, –sēz): G., dia, between; physis, growth.

diploë (dip´lō e): G., diploos, double.

endosteum, pl. endostea (en dos´te um, –á): G., end, within; osteon, a bone.

epicondyle (ep´i kon´dil): G., epi, upon; condylus, knuckle.

epiphysis, pl. epiphyses (e pif´i sis, –sēz): G., epi, on; physis, growth.

epistropheus (ep´i strō´fe us): G., epi, upon; strepho, turn.

ethmoid, ethmoidal (eth´moid, –ál): G., ethmoe, sieve.

femur (fē mēr): L., femur, thigh.

fontanelle (fon´tá nel´): F., fontanelle, a little fountain.

foramen, pl. foramina (fo ra´men, fo ram´i ná): L., foramen, an opening.

fossa (fôs´á): L., fossa, a pit, cavity.

frontal (frun´tål): L., frons, brow, forehead.

gladiolus (glad i o´lus, or glá di´o lus): L., gladiolus, a small sword.

glenoid (glē´noid): G., glene, a socket.

hamate (hā´māt): L., hamulus, a little hook.

haversian (hȧ vēr´zhȧn): Havers, a 17th century physician.

hyaline (hī´ȧ lin): G., hyalos, glass.

hyoid (hī´oid): G., hyoideus, u-shaped (upsilon).

ilium (il´e um): L., ilium, flank.

incus (in´kus): L., incus, anvil.

infraspinous (in´frȧ spī´nus): L., infra, below; spina, thorn.

intervertebral (in´tēr´vēr´te brȧl): L., inter, between; vertebra, joint.

ischium (is´ki um): G., ischion, hip.

kyphosis (kī fō´sis): G., kyphos, humpbacked.

lacrimal (lak´ri mȧl): L., lacrima, tear.

lacuna, pl. ae (lȧ kū´nȧ, -ne): L., lacuna, pit, lake, ditch.

lambdoidal (lam doi´dȧl): G., lambda, the letter for "lambda," (Λ, λ, l), eidos, shape.

lamella, pl. lae (lȧ mel´á, -lē): L., dim. of lamina, plate, leaf, layer.

lamina (lam´i nȧ): L., lamina, a thin plate.

linea (lē´nā ȧ): L., linea, line.

lordosis (lôr do´sis): G., lordos, bent so as to be convex in front.

lumbar (lum´bēr): L., lumbus, loin.

lunate (lū´nat): L., lunatus, from luna, moon.

magnum (mag´num): L., magnus, great.

malleolus (ma lē´o lus): L., malleolus, little hammer.

malleus (mal´ē us): L., malleus, hammer.

mandible, mandibular (man´di bl, man dib´ū lȧr): L., mandibula, jaw.

manubrium (ma nū´bri um): L., manubrium, handle.

mastoid (mas´toid): G., mastos, breast.

matrix, pl. matrices (mā´triks, mat´ri sēz): L., matrix (mater), womb, groundwork, mold.

maxilla, maxillary (mak sil´ȧ, -ery): L., maxilla, jawbone.

meatus (me ā´tus): L., meatus, passage.

medullary, medulla (med´u ler i, me dul´ȧ): L., medulla, pith, marrow.

meninx, pl. meninges (mē´ningks, mē nin´jēz): G., meninx, membrane.

meniscus (me nis´kus): G., meniskos dim. of mene, the moon.

metacarpus (met´ȧ kär´pus): G., meta, after, next; karpos, wrist.

metatarsus (met´ȧ tär´sus): G., meta, after; tarsos, a flat surface.

multangular (mul tang´gu lēr): L., multus, many; angular, angles.

navicular (nȧ vik´u lēr): L., navicula, dim. of navis, a ship.

obturator (ob tu rā´tēr): L., obturo, to close, shut.

occipital (ok sip´i tȧl): L., occiput, back of the head.

olecranon (o lec´rȧ non): G., olene, ulna; kranion, skull.

ossein (os´e in): L., osseus, bony.

ossicle (os´i k'l): L., ossiculum, dim. of os, a bone.

palatine (pal´ȧ tīn): L., palatum, palate.

parietal (pȧ rī´e tal): L., paries, wall.

patella (på tel´å): L., patella, a small pan or dish.

pectineal (pek´tin´e ål): L., pecten, comb.

pectoral, pectoralis (pek´to rål, –rā lis): L., pectus, breast.

pedicle (ped´i k'l): L., pediculus, foot stalk, little foot, dim. of pes, foot.

perichondrium, pl. –dria (per´i kôn´dri um, –dre a): G., peri, around; chondros, cartilage.

periosteum, pl. –tia (per´i os´te um, –ti a): G., peri, around; osteon, bone.

petrous (pet´rus, pe´trus): L., petrosus, rocky.

phalanx, pl. phalanges (fa´langks or fal, –lan gēz): G., phalanx, battle line.

pisiform (pī´si fôrm): L., pisum, peak; forma, shape.

prominens (prom´i nens): L., prominen, projecting.

pterygoid (ter´i goid, p'ter´): G., pteron, wing.

pubis (pū´bis): L., pubes, hair.

radial (rā´di ål): L., radius, ray.

sacrum (sā´krum): L., sacer, sacred.

sagittal (saj´i tål): L., sagitta, an arrow.

scoliosis (skō li ō´sis): G., skolios, crooked.

sella (sel´å): L., sella, saddle, seat.

semilunar (sem i lū´nẽr): L., semi, half; luna, moon.

sinus (sī´nus): L., sinus, cavity or hollow space.

skeleton (skel´e tun): G., skello, make dry.

sphenoid, sphenoidal (sfē´noid, –noi d'l): G., sphen, wedge; eidos, likeness.

squamous (skwā´mus): L., squama, scale.

stapes (stā´pēz): L., stapes, stirrup.

sternum (stẽr´num): G., sternon, breastbone.

styloid (stī´loid): G., stylos, pillar; eidos, likeness.

subscapular (sub skap´u lẽr): L., sub, under; skaupla, shoulder, blade.

superciliary (sū´pẽr sil´i ẽr i): L., super, above, over; cilium, eyebrow.

supraspinous (sū´prå spī´nus): L., supra, above; spina, thorn.

suture (sū´tur): L., suo, to sew.

tarsus (tä´sus): G., tarsos, a flat surface.

temporal (tem´po ral): L., tempora, the temples.

thoracic (tho ras´ik): L., thorax, thorax.

trochanter (trō kan´tẽr): G., trochos, wheel.

trochlea (trok´lē å): L., trochlea, pulley.

tubercle (tū´bẽr k'l): L., tuberculum, dim. of tuber, a hump or knob.

tuberosity (tū bẽr os´i ti): L., tuber, a hump, knob.

turcica (tẽr´sik å): L., turkish.

vertebra, –ae (vẽr´ti brå, –brē): L., vertebra, a joint.

vomer (vō´mẽr): L., vomer, plowshare.

xiphoid (zif´oid): G., xiphos, sword; eidos, form or shape.

zygomatic (zī´go mat´ik): G., zygoma, yoke, bar.

4

MUSCULAR SYSTEM

MUSCLE TISSUES

Three kinds of muscle tissue are to be found in the human body: SMOOTH or NONSTRIATED, CARDIAC or HEART, and SKELETAL or STRIATED MUSCLE. The first two types are under the control of the involuntary nervous system, and the third is controlled by the voluntary nervous system.

The SMOOTH or NONSTRIATED MUSCLE is found in many of the internal organs such as the organs of digestion, the walls of blood vessels, the uterus, urinary bladder and ureters. It is usually found in layers, and is composed of cells that are spindle-shaped and have single, centrally located nuclei. There are no striations on these cells or fibers (Figure 4-1).

The CARDIAC or HEART MUSCLE makes up the major portion of the heart wall. Its fibers or cells have cross striations. The nuclei are centrally located, and the fibers branch and interconnect to give a continuity not found in the other muscle tissues. Each fiber has a number of cross stripes or lines known as INTERCALATED DISKS (Figure 4-2).

The STRIATED or SKELETAL MUSCLE tissue is characterized by long fusiform fibers, each containing numerous oval nuclei peripherally placed. The fibers have cross striations which are more conspicuous than those in cardiac muscle. Numerous MYOFIBRILS or SARCOSTYLES extend longitudinally through the fibers (Figure 4-3).

Although we consider only the skeletal muscle tissues as composing the "muscular system," it is advantageous to study all three types of tissue at one time for purposes of comparison. Smooth and cardiac muscles will be considered again when we study those systems in which they occur (Figures 4-1 through 4-3).

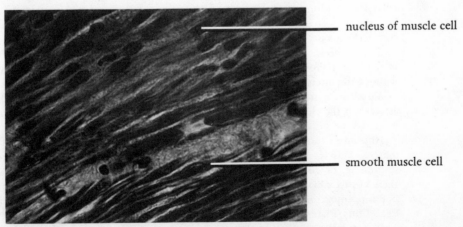

nucleus of muscle cell

smooth muscle cell

Figure 4-1. Photomicrograph of Smooth Muscle (450X)

67

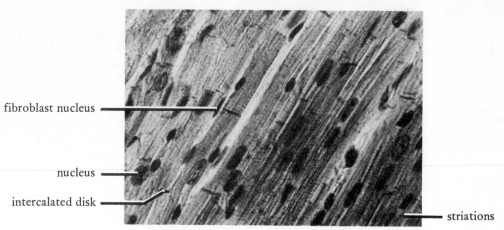

fibroblast nucleus

nucleus

intercalated disk

striations

Figure 4-2. Photomicrograph of Cardiac Muscle (450X)

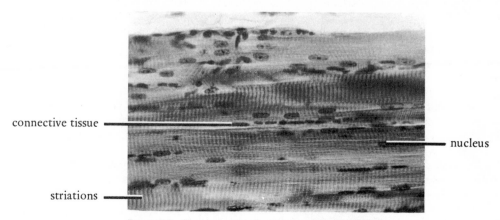

connective tissue

nucleus

striations

Figure 4-3. Photomicrograph of Skeletal Muscle (360X)

GENERAL

A skeletal muscle is composed of many fibers or cells held together by connective tissue and usually attached to the skeleton by means of tendons. The tendon of the muscle attached to the bone which is moved by the contraction is called the TENDON OF INSERTION. The tendon attached to the less movable structure is the TENDON OF ORIGIN. Tendons are composed of white fibrous (collagenous) connective tissue and attach into the periosteum of the bones. The connective tissue binding the muscle fibers is areolar connective tissue.

Some muscles such as those of the abdomen are broad and flat and terminate anteriorly in tendinous sheets called APONEUROSES. Others may attach directly to the periosteum without the interposition of tendons.

Muscles are arranged in superficial and deep layers. Study the superficial muscles of man as seen on the chart provided in the laboratory. Also keep this in mind as you dissect the cat or study the cadaver (Plate 4-1).

Any given movement of the body is caused, usually, by the action of more than one muscle. Muscles work in groups, not singly. Also, because muscles are capable only of shortening, or contracting, they must be arranged in antagonistic groups. Thus on the arm there are FLEXOR muscles to bend the forearm, and EXTENSOR muscles to carry out the opposite movement. Keep these facts in mind as you study the charts and do your dissections (Plates 4-1, 4-5, and 4-7).

It is not the purpose of this course to teach all the muscles of the human body. Only a few representative muscles from each region will be learned—enough, it is hoped, to give the student a good understanding of how this system operates. The muscles to be learned on the

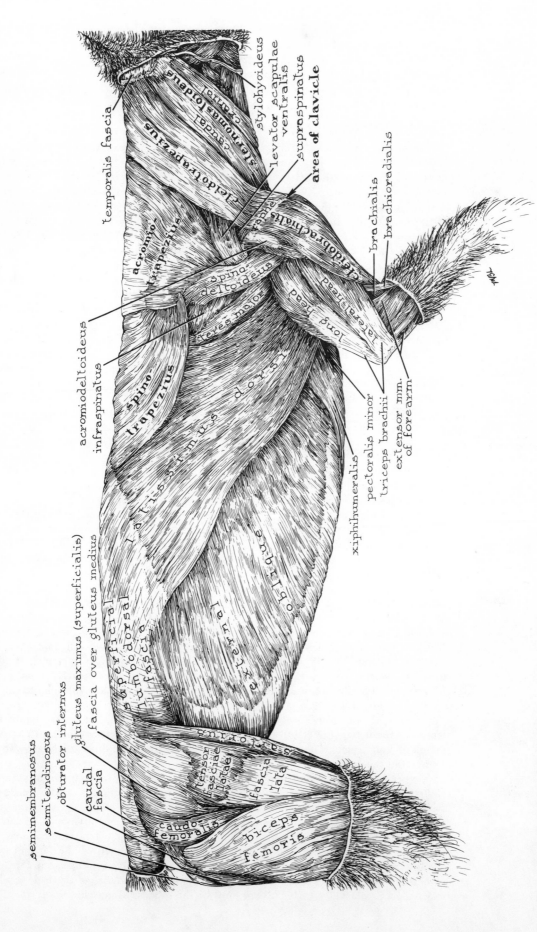

temporalis fascia

cleidomastoideus

cleidomastoideus

sternomastoideus

stylohyoideus

levator scapulae ventralis

supraspinatus

area of clavicle

brachialis

brachioradialis

acromiotrapezius

cleidobrachialis

acromiodeltoideus

infraspinatus

spino-trapezius

spino-deltoideus

teres major

lateral

long

lateral head

l a t i s s i m u s   d o r s i

xiphihumeralis

pectoralis minor

triceps brachii

extensor mm. of forearm

semimembranosus

semitendinosus

obturator internus

gluteus maximus (superficialis)

fascia over gluteus medius

caudal fascia

s u p e r f i c i a l   l u m b o d o r s a l   f a s c i a

external

oblique

s a r t o r i u s

tensor fasciae latae

fascia lata

caudofemoralis

b i c e p s   f e m o r i s

From Crouch, *Text-Atlas of Cat Anatomy*, courtesy of Lea & Febiger

Plate 4-1. Superficial Muscles of the Cat—Lateral View

cadaver are given in the table below. These muscles have been dissected and can easily be identified. The counterparts of these muscles on the cat should be dissected by the student. Your human anatomy textbook will serve as an adequate guide for the study of the cadaver. Also, sketching some of the muscles on the diagrams (Plates 4-10 through 4-13) and labeling those on Plates 4-13 and 4-14 will help you to understand their functions. Do your muscle dissection on the right side, leaving the left side for blood vessels and nerves.

EXTERNAL FEATURES OF THE CAT

Before skinning the cat for muscle study, note the following external structures.

The body is divided into head, neck, trunk (thorax and abdomen), and tail. The forelegs consist of the arm or BRACHIUM, the forearm or ANTEBRACHIUM, the CARPUS or wrist, METACARPUS or palm, and the five claw-tipped DIGITS. The hindlimbs consist of the THIGH, LEG (shank), TARSUS or ankle, METATARSUS or foot with its four claw-tipped DIGITS. Note that the claws are retractable. They should be cut to avoid damage to you during dissection. The first or great toe is lost on the hindfoot of the cat. The feet are provided with thick PADS (tori); those on the front feet have three parts; on the hind feet four parts. Each toe also has a pad terminally (Plates 4-6 and 4-8).

On the head one should notice the TACTILE WHISKERS or VIBRISSAE around the mouth, the EXTERNAL NARES of the NOSE, the AURICLE or PINNA of the EXTERNAL EAR (Plate 4-3) and the EYES with LIDS and NICTITATING MEMBRANE. The latter may be seen in the medial corner of the eye.

Note the NIPPLES of the mammary glands along the ventrolateral sides of the abdomen and count them. They are present in both male and female but less prominent in the male.

Examine the ANAL OPENING beneath the tail and determine the sex of the animal by examining the area ventral and anterior to the ANUS. The VULVA of the female consists of a slightly elevated area with the UROGENITAL APERTURE opening from it. In the male the SCROTUM containing the TESTES is seen just anterior to the anus and the UROGENITAL APERTURE can be seen at the end of the PENIS.

DISSECTION OF SOME MUSCLES OF THE CAT

In preparing the cat for muscle dissection, the skin must be removed. Recall, as you remove the skin, its microscopic structure which you studied earlier in the course. Also review the various derivatives of the skin such as hair, nails, and glands.

Make a shallow longitudinal incision in the MIDDORSAL LINE of the SACRO-LUMBAR REGION. After penetrating the skin, use the fingers or a blunt instrument to loosen the skin by probing peripherally from the edges of the incision. In loosening the skin in this manner, it may be necessary to lengthen the incision. The loose connective tissue which binds the skin to the underlying structures is called the SUPERFICIAL FASCIA.

As you pull the skin from the lateral surfaces of the body, you should notice the white cords that extend between it and the muscles at regular intervals along the body. These are the cutaneous nerves. Following the course of these nerves, you may also see the cutaneous arteries. It may be necessary to cut the skin laterally in the midregion of the body to facilitate its removal. Working forward on the ventral side, you will note fibers of the CUTANEOUS MAXIMUS MUSCLE which comes off with the skin. Where these continue into the deeper muscles they should be cut free. Cutaneous muscles allow a jerking movement of the skin. They are similar to the facial muscles which enable man to express his emotions in his face.

The skin about the head and neck is often thick and tough, and it may be difficult to remove. Special care and effort are required, and you should notice the PLATYSMA (skin) muscle in this region. The skin should pull over the forelimbs quite easily and can be cut loose about the digits.

Next remove the skin on the posterior part of the body by separating it around the tail and cutting the tail off at about the fourth caudal vertebra. Incisions should be made around the anus and genital organs that leave these organs covered. Finally, slip the skin off from the hind limbs and cut it from around the digits. If your specimen is a male, be careful not to remove the spermatic cords which lie between the legs. These will be studied later.

Having skinned the cat, the next step is to remove as much of the fat and fascia as possible from the surface of the muscles. As you do this, watch for changes in the direction of muscle fibers as this will enable you to locate muscle boundaries. If this is done with care and patience, you will be able to see most of the superficial muscles. Study the diagrams

(Plates 4-1 through 4-4), which will enable you to identify most of these muscles and to compare them with those of man.

Having identified the superficial muscles try to determine, at least in a general way, what their functions are. If you have a cat's skeleton to examine, it will help you in determining these functions. Freeing the muscles from the underlying ones and putting tension on them will help to determine their origins and insertions as well as their actions. You will be led to the conclusion that many of these muscles have their origins on the axial skeleton, and their insertions on the appendicular skeleton. These are EXTRINSIC muscles and move the limbs in relationship to the trunk. A few are INTRINSIC to the head and trunk, and move one part of the trunk in relationship to another or in relationship to the head. The remaining ones are intrinsic to the limbs and cause movements within the limbs themselves. While these generalizations may be obvious, it is highly important to keep them in mind as you study all muscles and arrange them in functional groups.

A. Some extrinsic muscles of the shoulder and forelimb

1. These muscles originate on the axial skeleton and insert on the appendage. They serve two main functions: (a) to hold the shoulder girdle in place, and (b) to move the appendage as a whole.

   You should dissect the following muscles on the cat and learn their counterparts on the human body. See Table I, on page 75, for some of the differences between the muscles of cat and man.

   a. clavotrapezius

   b. acromiotrapezius

   c. spinotrapezius

   d. latissimus dorsi

   e. rhomboideus major

   f. rhomboideus minor

   g. pectoralis major

   h. pectoralis minor

   i. serratus anterior (ventralis)

   j. levator scapulae

   k. cleidomastoideus

   The CLAVOTRAPEZIUS, ACROMIOTRAPEZIUS, SPINOTRAPEZIUS, and LATISSIMUS DORSI have already been studied. They should be transected at their origins to expose the underlying muscles—the RHOMBOIDEUS MAJOR and MINOR which have their origins on the spines of the vertebrae and their insertions on the vertebral border of the scapula. They are retractors of the scapula and also move it forward. Note also in the cat the long, slender muscle running from the scapula to the occipital bone, the rhomboideus capitis (Plate 4-2).

   Place a probe under the rhomboideus muscles and transect them to expose the SERRATUS ANTERIOR (VENTRALIS) and LEVATOR SCAPULAE (Plate 4-4). The former arises by a number of serrations from the first nine or ten ribs and inserts on the vertebral border of the scapula, and serves to depress the scapula and rotate it backward. The latter arises from the last four or five cervical vertebrae, inserts on the superior angle of the scapula and elevates the scapula and rotates it forward. These two muscles are in part antagonistic in their actions, but they serve together to suspend the trunk.

   Turn now to the ventral side of the cat and examine and dissect the pectoralis group of muscles. Careful cleaning away of any remaining fascia will reveal the edges of the various muscles of this group. Plate 4-3 shows the relationship of these muscles. On the cat's left side the pectoantebrachialis has been cut and reflected to show the pectoralis major.

   A thin band of muscle about one-half inch wide and with parallel fibers extends laterad from the cranial end of the sternum to insert on the fascia at the proximal end of the forearm. This is the pectoantebrachialis muscle. It lies over the pectoralis muscles which should now be dissected.

   Cut the right pectoantebrachialis near its origin and pull the ends back to reveal the pectoralis major. It originates on the sternum and median raphe of the thorax and

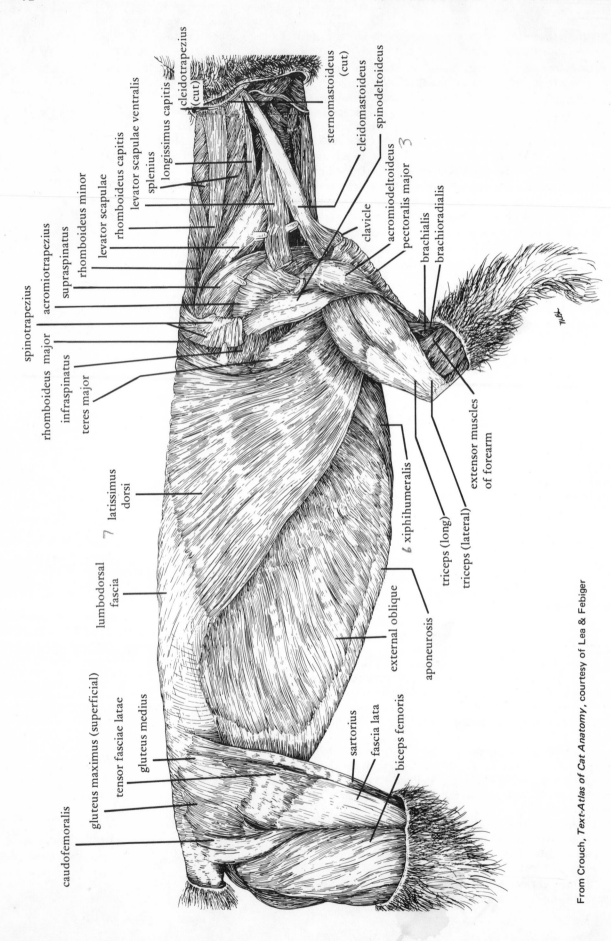

cleidotrapezius (cut)
cleidomastoideus
sternomastoideus (cut)
longissimus capitis
levator scapulae ventralis
splenius
rhomboideus capitis
rhomboideus minor
levator scapulae
supraspinatus
acromiotrapezius
spinotrapezius
rhomboideus major
infraspinatus
teres major

spinodeltoideus
pectoralis major
acromiodeltoideus
clavicle
brachialis
brachioradialis

latissimus dorsi

extensor muscles of forearm

lumbodorsal fascia

xiphihumeralis
triceps (long)
triceps (lateral)

external oblique
aponeurosis

caudofemoralis
gluteus maximus (superficial)
tensor fasciae latae
gluteus medius

sartorius
fascia lata
biceps femoris

From Crouch, *Text-Atlas of Cat Anatomy*, courtesy of Lea & Febiger

Plate 4-2. Superficial Muscles of the Cat—Lateral View
Trapezius and Sternomastoid Muscles Removed

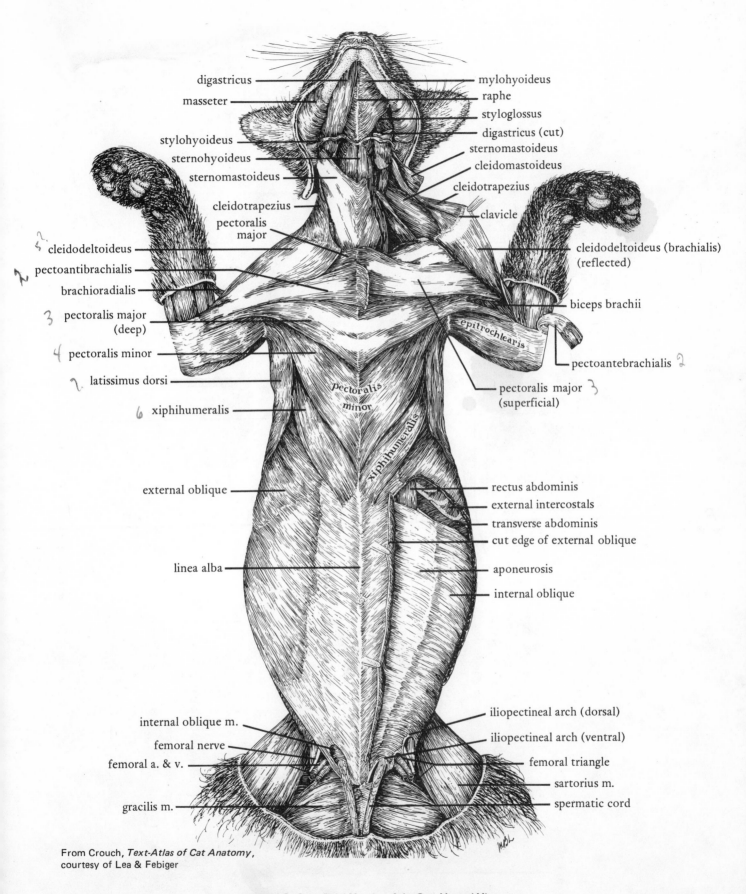

digastricus

masseter

stylohyoideus

sternohyoideus

sternomastoideus

cleidotrapezius

pectoralis
major

cleidodeltoideus

pectoantibrachialis

brachioradialis

pectoralis major
(deep)

pectoralis minor

latissimus dorsi

xiphihumeralis

external oblique

linea alba

internal oblique m.

femoral nerve

femoral a. & v.

gracilis m.

mylohyoideus

raphe

styloglossus

digastricus (cut)

sternomastoideus

cleidomastoideus

cleidotrapezius

clavicle

cleidodeltoideus (brachialis)
(reflected)

biceps brachii

epitrochlearis

pectoantebrachialis

pectoralis major
(superficial)

pectoralis

minor

xiphihumeralis

rectus abdominis

external intercostals

transverse abdominis

cut edge of external oblique

aponeurosis

internal oblique

iliopectineal arch (dorsal)

iliopectineal arch (ventral)

femoral triangle

sartorius m.

spermatic cord

From Crouch, *Text-Atlas of Cat Anatomy*,
courtesy of Lea & Febiger

Plate 4-3. Superficial Muscles of the Cat—Ventral View

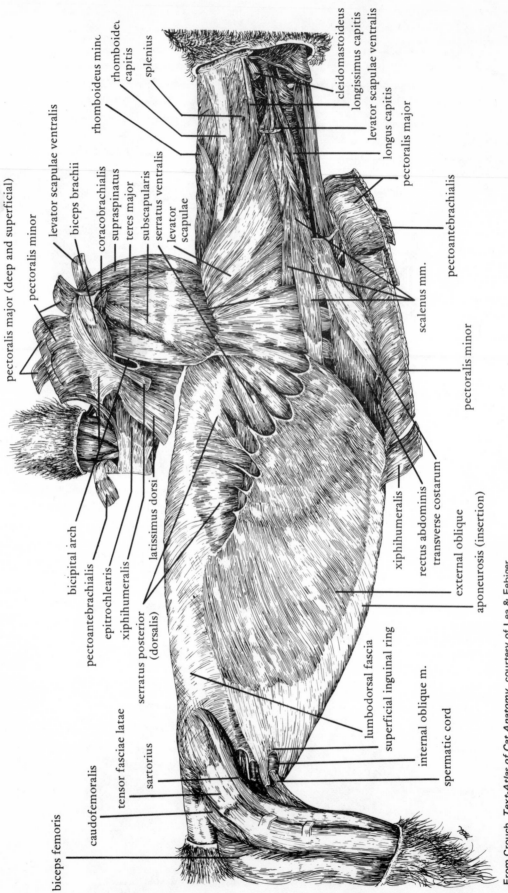

pectoralis major (deep and superficial)

pectoralis minor

levator scapulae ventralis

biceps brachii

coracobrachialis

supraspinatus

teres major

subscapularis

serratus ventralis

levator scapulae

rhomboideus minor

rhomboideus capitis

splenius

cleidomastoideus

longissimus capitis

levator scapulae ventralis

longus capitis

pectoralis major

pectoralis minor

scalenus mm.

pectoantebrachialis

bicipital arch

pectoantebrachialis

epitrochlearis

xiphihumeralis

serratus posterior (dorsalis)

latissimus dorsi

biceps femoris

caudofemoralis

tensor fasciae latae

sartorius

lumbodorsal fascia

superficial inguinal ring

internal oblique m.

spermatic cord

xiphihumeralis

rectus abdominis

transverse costarum

external oblique

aponeurosis (insertion)

Plate 4-4. Superficial and Deep Muscles of the Cat—Lateral View

From Crouch, *Text-Atlas of Cat Anatomy*, courtesy of Lea & Febiger

inserts on the humerus. Its cranial fibers lie in front of the pectoantebrachialis, while caudad its fibers form a shallow V-shape and lie over the deeper V-shape of the pectoralis minor. The pectoralis minor also originates on the sternum and inserts on the humerus. An effort should be made to separate these muscles. You will notice that each consists of two or more parts. Posterior to the pectoralis minor is the remaining muscle of the group, the xiphihumeralis which, as its name suggests, originates on the xiphoid process and inserts on the humerus. It is narrow, very thin, and does not occur in man.

TABLE I. Some Differences in Superficial Muscles—Cat and Man

Cat	Man
clavotrapezius acromiotrapezius spinotrapezius	trapezius
rhomboideus capitis	(absent)
clavodeltoideus acromiodeltoideus spinodeltoideus	deltoideus
sternomastoideus cleidomastoideus	sternocleidomastoideus
pectoralis major	completely covers pectoralis minor, inserts higher
pectoralis minor	inserts on scapula, rather than on humerus
pectoantebrachialis	(absent)
xiphihumeralis	(absent)
levator scapulae ventralis	(absent)
epitrochlearis	(absent)
biceps femoris gracilis } very broad muscles	much narrower, relatively
caudofemoralis	(absent)
gluteus maximus— smaller than gluteus medius	larger than gluteus medius

In the neck region craniad of the pectoralis muscles locate the STERNO-MASTOIDEUS muscles which originate on the manubrium of the sternum and insert in the mastoid region of the skull. Notice that these muscles meet in the mid-ventral neck region and then diverge, each passing deep to the external jugular, the large vein on the side of the neck. Remove the right sternomastoideus and note dorsal to it and originating on the clavicle a narrower muscle, the CLEIDOMASTOIDEUS (Plate 4-3). It inserts also on the mastoid region of the skull. Its origin lies lateral to the external jugular vein. What is the action of the sterno and cleidomastoideus muscles? What is their counterpart in man?

You may now transect (cut across) the muscles of the pectoralis group about one inch from their origins on the sternum, being careful not to cut the underlying structures. Carefully lift the lateral ends of these muscles, removing the fat and fascia underneath them, and draw them toward their insertions on the humerus. Examine their insertions closely to note their relationship (Plates 4-4 through 4-6). Notice too the arteries, veins, and nerves in the axillary region now exposed. These should be damaged no more than necessary in examining muscles in the area.

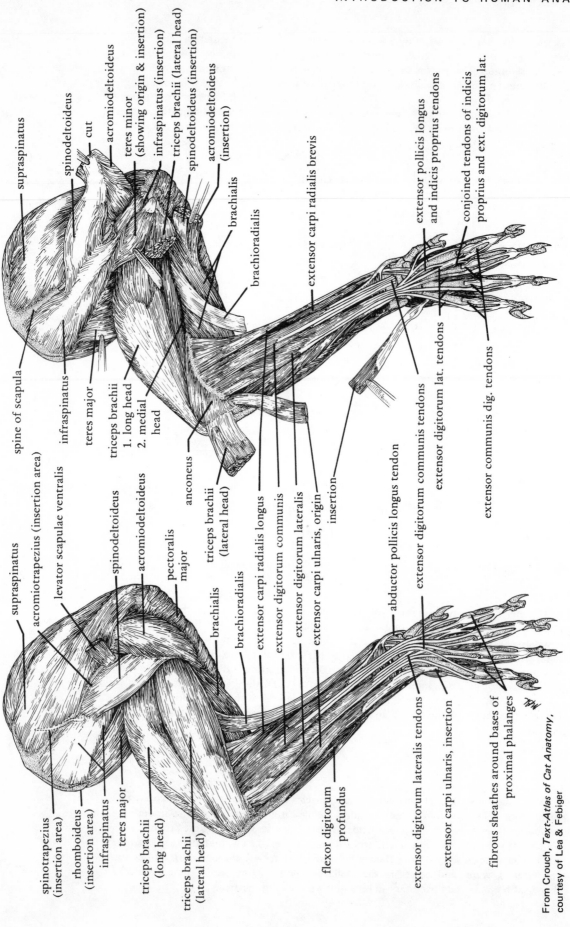

Plate 4-5. Superficial and Deep Muscles of the Scapula and Forelimb of the Cat—Lateral View

From Crouch, *Text-Atlas of Cat Anatomy*, courtesy of Lea & Febiger

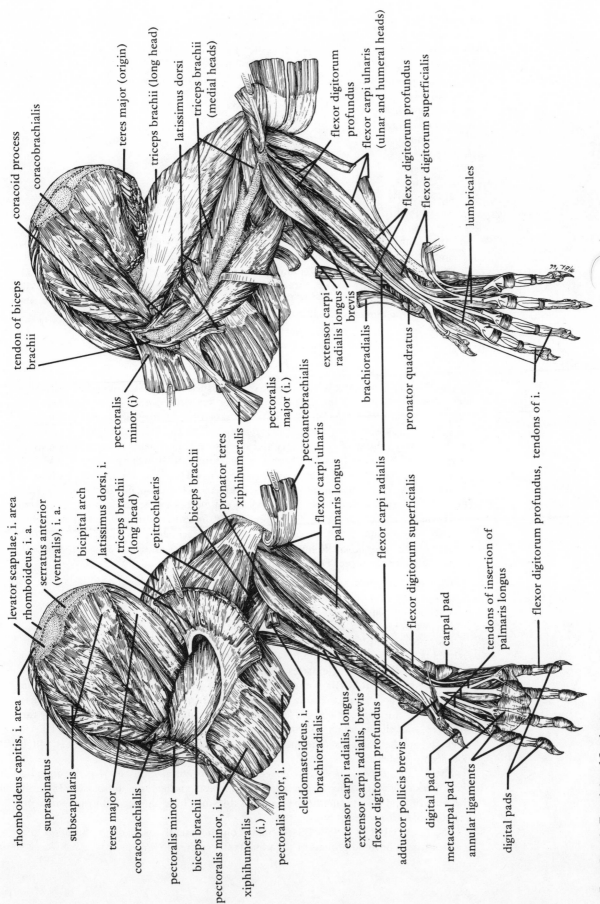

Plate 4-6. Superficial and Deep Muscles of the Scapula and Forelimb of the Cat—Medial View

rhomboideus capitis, i. area

levator scapulae, i. area

rhomboideus, i. a.

serratus anterior (ventralis), i. a.

supraspinatus

subscapularis

teres major

coracobrachialis

pectoralis minor

biceps brachii

pectoralis minor, i.

xiphihumeralis (i.)

pectoralis major, i.

cleidomastoideus, i.

brachioradialis

extensor carpi radialis, longus

extensor carpi radialis, brevis

flexor digitorum profundus

adductor pollicis brevis

digital pad

metacarpal pad

annular ligaments

digital pads

bicipital arch

latissimus dorsi, i.

triceps brachii (long head)

epitrochlearis

biceps brachii

pronator teres

xiphihumeralis

flexor carpi ulnaris

palmaris longus

flexor digitorum superficialis

flexor carpi radialis

flexor digitorum superficialis

carpal pad

tendons of insertion of palmaris longus

flexor digitorum profundus, tendons of i.

pectoantebrachialis

pectoralis major (i.)

pectoralis minor (i)

tendon of biceps brachii

coracoid process

coracobrachialis

teres major (origin)

triceps brachii (long head)

latissimus dorsi

triceps brachii (medial heads)

extensor carpi radialis longus brevis

brachioradialis

pronator quadratus

flexor digitorum profundus

flexor carpi ulnaris (ulnar and humeral heads)

flexor digitorum profundus

flexor digitorum superficialis

lumbricales

From Crouch, *Text-Atlas of Cat Anatomy,* courtesy of Lea & Febiger

B. Some intrinsic muscles of the shoulder and forelimb

These muscles are located entirely within the appendage. They may be divided into three groups: (a) operating over the shoulder joint, (b) operating over the elbow joint, and (c) operating over the joints of the wrist and hand.

1. Muscles operating principally over the shoulder joint (Plates 4-2, 4-4, 4-5, and 4-6)
   a. clavodeltoideus (clavobrachialis)
   b. acromiodeltoideus
   c. spinodeltoideus
   d. supraspinatus
   e. infraspinatus
   f. teres major
   g. teres minor
   h. subscapularis
   i. coracobrachialis

The first three muscles have already been identified and, as indicated in Table II, are the counterpart of the DELTOIDEUS of man. You should notice that the clavotrapezius which inserts on the clavicle and the clavodeltoideus which has its origin there are almost one continuous muscle sometimes called the brachiocephalicus (Plate 4-1). The acromiodeltoideus has its origin from the acromion of the scapula and inserts on the humerus; the spinodeltoideus has its origin on the spine of the scapula, its insertion on the humerus. What is their action?

By transecting the deltoids the SUPRA and INFRASPINATUS muscles are easily located in the fossae of the scapula which are similarly named. They insert on the humerus. The TERES MAJOR lies along the axillary border of the scapula and inserts on the humerus which it flexes and rotates medially. The TERES MINOR originates on the axillary border of the scapula and inserts on the humerus in such a position as to rotate the humerus laterally. It shares this function with the INFRASPINATUS. Note that the teres major and minor lie on opposite sides of the origin of the long head of the triceps—the teres minor to the lateral side and the teres major to the medial side (Plate 4-5, figure 2). The SUBSCAPULARIS muscle lies in the subscapular fossa and inserts on the lesser tuberosity of the humerus. It draws the humerus mediad and helps to hold the shoulder joint in place. The coracobrachialis runs from the coracoid process of the scapula to the humerus. It is a very slender muscle and can be seen best when you study the biceps brachii (Plate 4-6).

2. Muscles operating principally around the elbow joint (Plates 4-5 and 4-6)
   a. triceps brachii
   b. brachialis anticus
   c. biceps brachii

The medial aspect of the arm in the cat is covered by a broad extension of the latissimus dorsi known as the EPITROCHLEARIS. It should be cut and reflected in order to see the underlying muscles (Plate 4-6).

The TRICEPS BRACHII is the big extensor of the forearm. It has its insertion on the olecranon process of the ulna. Its LONG HEAD, lying on the back of the arm, has its origin on the inferior glenoid margin of the scapula, and hence crosses both the shoulder and elbow joints. Its broad LATERAL HEAD and the MEDIAL HEAD originate on the humerus. The medial head consists of several slips in the cat which you need not identify.

The BICEPS BRACHII, largely covered by the pectoralis muscles, has its origin on the superior glenoid border of the scapula and inserts on the radial tuberosity. It flexes the forearm and also supinates the hand. It does not have the second origin—that on the coracoid process—as it has in man.

The BRACHIALIS ANTICUS originates on the lateral aspect of the humerus and inserts on the coronoid process of the ulna. It flexes the forearm.

3. Muscles operating over the joints of the wrist and hand. These muscles will not be dissected or identified in this course. Some are illustrated, however, on Plates 4-5 and 4-6.

    a. Flexors of the wrist and fingers are on the anterior (volar) surface of the forearm. The superficial muscles of this group arise from the medial epicondyle of the humerus; the deep muscles, from the radius and ulna.

    b. Extensors of the wrist and fingers are on the posterior (dorsal) surface of the forearm. The superficial muscles of this group arise from or near the lateral epicondyle of the humerus except for the extensor carpi ulnaris which arises from the ulna. The deep muscles, other than the supinator, arise from the radius and ulna.

    c. Other muscles lie entirely within the hand.

C. Muscles of the head

The most numerous of the muscles of the head are those involved in facial expression. They are superficial muscles and will not be studied, although you should note them on the diagrams in your textbook.

The muscles that do concern us are those involved in mastication. Most of these, however, should be left for identification when we study the mouth and salivary glands.

1. Principal muscles of mastication

    a. masseter
    b. temporal
    c. pterygoideus lateralis
    d. pterygoideus medialis
    e. digastricus

The MASSETER and TEMPORAL muscles may be located on yourselves. If you close your jaws firmly and at the same time press hard on your cheek just in front of the angle of the jaw, you will feel the contraction of the MASSETER. It originates on the zygomatic arch and inserts on the coronoid process and lateral fossa of the mandible. Now press just back of the posterior margin of the orbit and set the jaws firmly and you will feel the contraction of the temporalis muscle. It has its origin in the temporal fossa and its insertion on the coronoid process of the mandible.

The DIGASTRICUS is a depressor of the mandible. Its insertion is on the lower border of the mandible and its origin on the mastoid and jugular processes of the temporal bone. It does not have the two well defined bellies that it has in man.

D. Muscles of the thorax

These are the muscles that are intrinsic to the thorax; i.e., have both their origins and insertions in this region. They are concerned primarily with the bellows action of the thorax as it is involved in breathing. Take note of these breathing movements on yourselves.

1. Principal muscles of breathing

    a. diaphragm
    b. external intercostals
    c. internal intercostals

The DIAPHRAGM will be seen later when you open the body cavities. It lies between the thoracic cavities and the peritoneal cavity and its contraction increases the size of the thorax.

The INTERCOSTAL muscles are easily seen in the intercostal spaces. The EXTERNAL INTERCOSTALS have their fibers running in a ventrocaudad direction and their contractions aid in inspiration of air. The INTERNAL INTERCOSTALS are seen by carefully dissecting away the fibers of the external intercostals. Their fibers run at about a 70° angle to those of the externals. The serve in expiration of air.

Other thoracic muscles are apparent, but we shall not study them.

E. Muscles of the abdominal wall

These muscles serve to support and compress the abdominal wall. In so doing they aid in expiration of air by forcing the diaphragm up. Also because they overlap to the thoracic region, they exert downward pull on the ribs and sternum and again aid in expiration. They are also tensed in coughing and sneezing, and aid in defecation and in parturition.

1. Four muscles must be dissected in this area (Plates 4-3, 4-4 and 5-4)
   a. external oblique
   b. internal oblique
   c. transversus abdominis
   d. rectus abdominis

   The EXTERNAL OBLIQUE is the most extensive of this group. It originates dorsally from the dorsolumbar aponeurosis, cranially to the rib cage at the digitations of the serratus anterior. It inserts with its counterpart of the other side at the LINEA ALBA (midventral line) by an aponeurosis. These and other aponeuroses serve to sheathe the RECTUS ABDOMINIS muscles which run longitudinally either side of the linea alba. The rectus abdominis attaches at the sternum and the first and second costal cartilages. It runs to the ISCHIOPUBIC SYMPHYSIS.

   Carefully cut through the external oblique, longitudinally. The INTERNAL OBLIQUE will be found underneath it and can be recognized by the fact that its fibers run in the opposite direction. It is not as extensive as the external oblique. Finally, cut through the INTERNAL OBLIQUE to reveal underneath it the TRANSVERSUS ABDOMINIS which lies just external to the subserous fascia and the PERITONEUM which line the body cavity.

   Examine the INGUINAL region, where the external oblique meets the leg. In man the edge of the external oblique in this area forms a strong thickened band, the INGUINAL LIGAMENT. This is not so apparent in the cat (Plates 4-3 and 4-4). This area is relatively weak, and the intestine sometimes is forced through into the INGUINAL CANAL in the male. This is called INGUINAL HERNIA, and you should read more about this problem in your textbook.

F. Muscles of the pelvic girdle and thigh

   The muscles of this region should be compared with those of the shoulder girdle and limb. Recall that the pelvic girdle is quite firmly articulated to the sacrum and that the acetabulum is a deeper socket than the glenoid fossa of the scapula. Hence movements, in general, are more limited in this area than in the shoulder.

   We may consider these muscles in two main groups: (a) those which originate on the pelvic girdle and insert on the femur and hence work across the hip joint, and (b) those which originate entirely or in part on the pelvic girdle and cross both the hip and knee joints to insert on the lower leg.

1. Muscles working across hip joint only (Plates 4-2 and 4-7)
   a. gluteus maximus
   b. gluteus medius
   c. caudofemoralis
   d. adductor femoris
   e. psoas major
   f. iliacus

2. Muscles working across both the hip and knee joints
   a. sartorius
   b. tensor fasciae latae
   c. biceps femoris
   d. gracilis
   e. semitendinosus
   f. semimembranosus
   g. quadriceps femoris—composed of
        vastus lateralis   ⎫
        vastus medialis   ⎬   do not cross hip joint
        vastus intermedius ⎭
        rectus femoris

   Review the superficial muscles of the hip and thigh regions referring to Plates 4-1 and 4-8. Notice particularly the aponeurotic sheath on the craniolateral aspect of the thigh which covers tightly the underlying muscle. This is the tendinous insertion of the TENSOR FASCIAE LATAE muscle. Its aponeurosis of origin covers the GLUTEUS MEDIUS muscle. Just back of the gluteus medius is the much smaller GLUTEUS

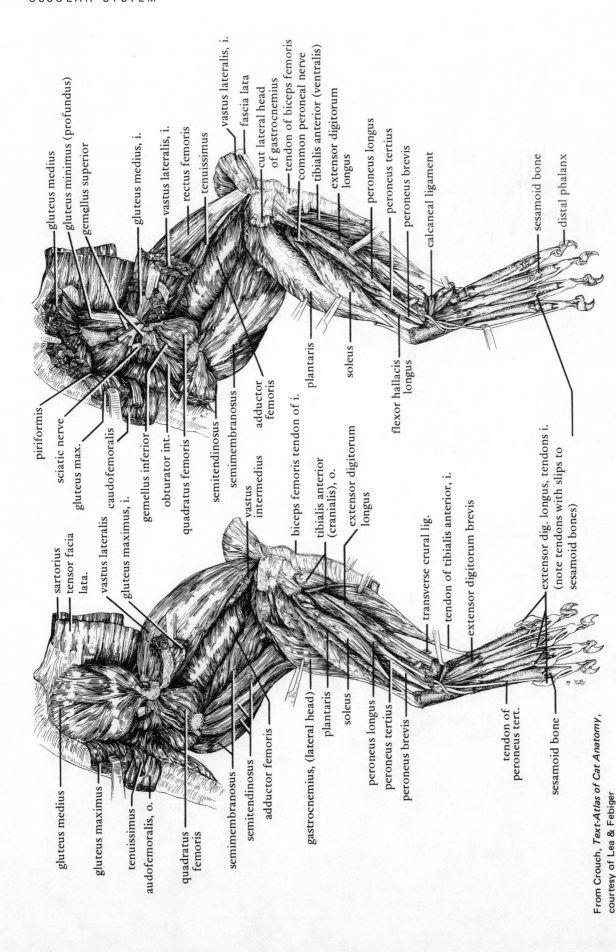

Plate 4-7. Deep Muscles of the Right Hindlimb of the Cat—Lateral View

gluteus medius
gluteus minimus (profundus)
gemellus superior
gluteus medius, i.
vastus lateralis, i.
rectus femoris
tenuissimus
vastus lateralis, i.
fascia lata
cut lateral head of gastrocnemius
tendon of biceps femoris
common peroneal nerve
tibialis anterior (ventralis)
extensor digitorum longus
peroneus longus
peroneus tertius
peroneus brevis
calcaneal ligament
sesamoid bone
distal phalanx

piriformis
sciatic nerve
gluteus max.
caudofemoralis
gemellus inferior
obturator int.
quadratus femoris
semitendinosus
semimembranosus
adductor femoris
vastus intermedius
biceps femoris tendon of i.
plantaris
soleus
flexor hallacis longus

sartorius
tensor facia lata.
vastus lateralis
gluteus maximus, i.
tibialis anterior (cranialis), o.
extensor digitorum longus
transverse crural lig.
tendon of tibialis anterior, i.
extensor digitorum brevis
extensor dig. longus, tendons i. (note tendons with slips to sesamoid bones)

gluteus medius
gluteus maximus
tenuissimus
audofemoralis, o.
quadratus femoris
semimembranosus
semitendinosus
adductor femoris
gastrocnemius, (lateral head)
plantaris
soleus
peroneus longus
peroneus tertius
peroneus brevis
tendon of peroneus tert.
sesamoid bone

From Crouch, *Text-Atlas of Cat Anatomy,*
courtesy of Lea & Febiger

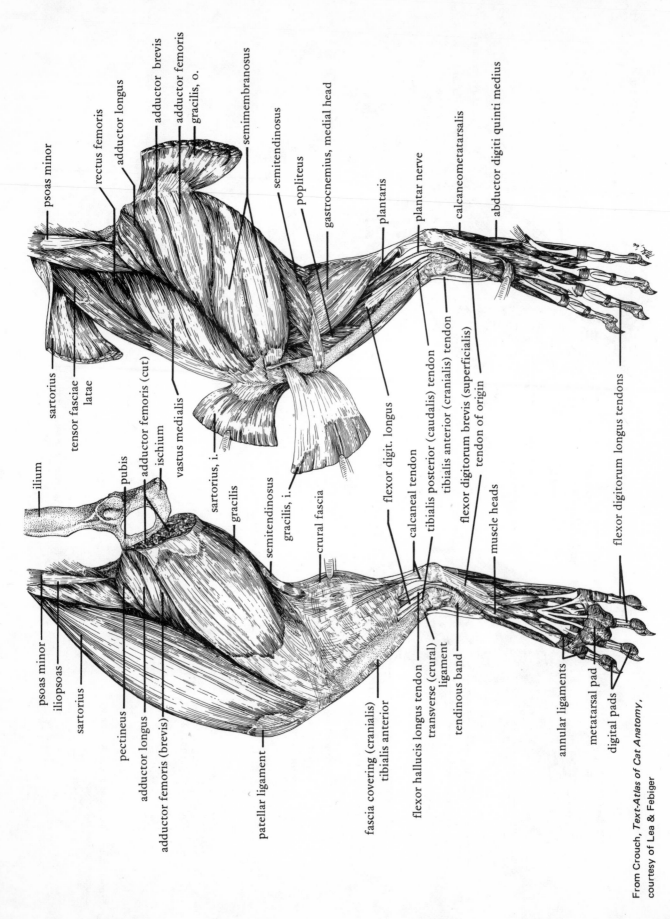

Plate 4-8. Superficial Muscles of the Right Hindlimb of the Cat—Medial View

From Crouch, *Text-Atlas of Cat Anatomy*, courtesy of Lea & Febiger

psoas minor
rectus femoris
adductor longus
adductor brevis
adductor femoris
gracilis, o.
semimembranosus
semitendinosus
popliteus
gastrocnemius, medial head
plantaris
plantar nerve
calcaneometatarsalis
abductor digiti quinti medius

sartorius
tensor fasciae latae
adductor femoris (cut)
ischium
vastus medialis
sartorius, i.
gracilis, i.
crural fascia
flexor digit. longus
calcaneal tendon
tibialis posterior (caudalis) tendon
tibialis anterior (cranialis) tendon
flexor digitorum brevis (superficialis)
tendon of origin
muscle heads
flexor digitorum longus tendons

ilium
pubis
adductor femoris (brevis)

psoas minor
iliopsoas
sartorius
pectineus
adductor longus
patellar ligament
gracilis
semitendinosus
fascia covering (cranialis)
tibialis anterior
flexor hallucis longus tendon
transverse (crural) ligament
tendinous band
annular ligaments
metatarsal pad
digital pads

MAXIMUS and still farther back is the caudofemoralis, a small muscle which inserts with the broad BICEPS FEMORIS. The latter inserts by an aponeurosis on the tibia, and is an extensor of the thigh and flexor of the lower leg. Just in front of the tensor fasciae latae is the strap-like SARTORIUS muscle and, medial to it, the GRACILIS.

The sartorius and gracilis may now be transected and reflected to expose the ADDUCTOR FEMORIS, a thick mass of muscle inserting on the femur. Care must be taken to distinguish between the adductor femoris and the SEMIMEMBRANOSUS and SEMITENDINOSUS which lie behind it (Plates 4-7 and 4-8). The two latter muscles are the "hamstrings" and insert to the tibia. Other adductor muscles are present in this area, but are not so clearly defined as in man. The FEMORAL ARTERY and VEIN may be seen just medial to the sartorius muscle.

Return now to the BICEPS FEMORIS and CAUDOFEMORALIS and separate them carefully from the underlying structures and then transect them at their midpoints, being careful not to destroy the SCIATIC nerve which passes beneath the biceps femoris (Plates 4-1 and 4-7).

Next, carefully cut through the muscular portion of the TENSOR FASCIAE LATAE and peel back its insertion to expose the large VASTUS LATERALIS and VASTUS MEDIALIS components of the QUADRICEPS FEMORIS. The vastus lateralis and medialis meet on the cranial aspect of the thigh and when they are separated at this point the strong round RECTUS FEMORIS will be exposed. Transection of the rectus femoris will in turn reveal the fourth member of the quadriceps group which lies directly on the cranial aspect of the femur, the VASTUS INTERMEDIUS. The quadriceps muscles serve as powerful extensors of the lower leg having their common insertion on or near the PATELLA. The rectus femoris alone of this group originates on the pelvis and hence flexes the thigh as well as extending the lower leg. Study Plates 4-1 and 4-7 through 4-9.

The PSOAS MAJOR and ILIACUS may be seen later in our course when we study the pelvic viscera.

G. Muscles of the lower leg (shank) and foot

We did no dissection of the muscles of the forearm and hand. If we had, we would note the similarity to those of the shank and foot which we are now ready to study. Those of the shank and foot are fewer and simpler than those of the forearm and hand, but they illustrate many of the same facts of muscle mechanics. Keep these facts in mind as you do your dissection.

It is especially important to trace out to their attachments the tendons of insertion of these muscles to see how they are related to the complex skeletal structure of the foot. Note the CRURAL LIGAMENTS which hold the tendons to the underlying skeleton. Some of these must be cut to follow the tendons to their insertions. Study Plates 4-7 through 4-9.

1. Crosses knee joint to tibia (Plate 4-9)
   a. popliteus
2. Cross ankle joint to foot (Plates 4-7 through 4-9)
   a. gastrocnemius (also crosses knee joint)
   b. soleus
   c. plantaris
   d. tibialis anterior
   e. extensor digitorum longus (also crosses knee joint)
   f. peroneus longus
   g. peroneus brevis
   h. peroneus tertius
   i. flexor digitorum longus
   j. flexor hallucis longus
   k. tibialis posterior

The most obvious muscle of the shank is the gastrocnemius. It arises by lateral and medial heads from the femur, and inserts by way of the TENDON OF ACHILLES onto the calcaneus. Separation of the heads of the gastrocnemius will reveal the PLANTARIS muscle which lies between them. Also, in relationship to the lateral head of the gastrocnemius, will be found the SOLEUS muscle. Its insertion tendon, together with that of the gastrocnemius, forms a sheath enclosing the slender tendon of the plantaris. These muscles are collectively known as the "calf muscles."

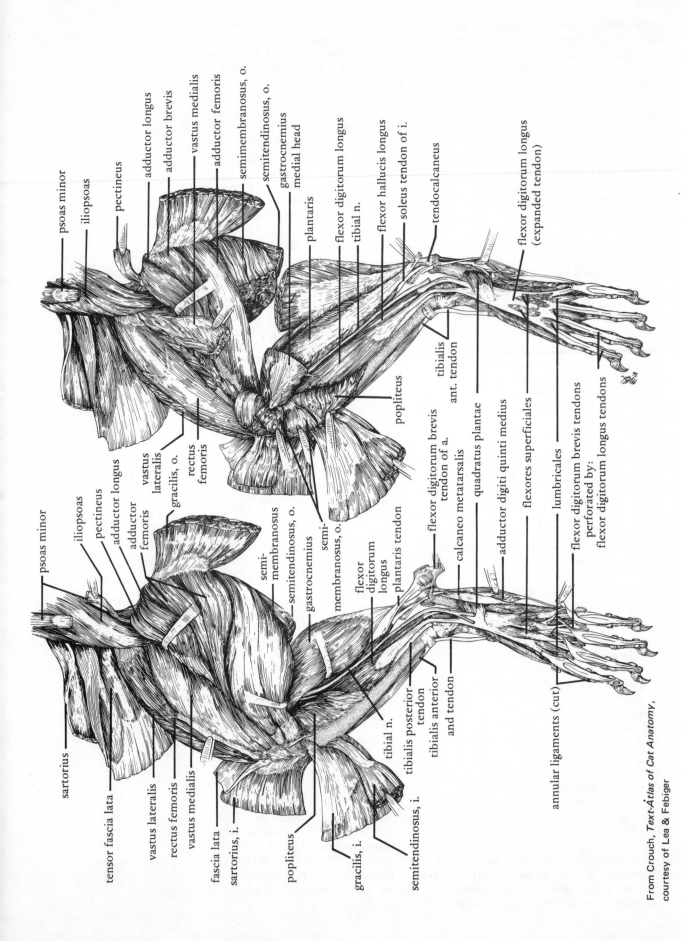

Plate 4-9. Deep Muscles of the Right Hindlimb of the Cat—Medial View

From Crouch, *Text-Atlas of Cat Anatomy*, courtesy of Lea & Febiger

The prominent muscle on the lateral side of the tibia is the TIBIALIS ANTERIOR. It embraces closely the EXTENSOR DIGITORUM LONGUS. Separate these two muscles and find the origin of the tibialis anterior on the upper aspect of the tibia and that of the extensor digitorum longus on the lateral epicondyle of the femur. Trace their tendons of insertion to the foot. What function do they serve?

Another prominent, although slender, muscle on the lateral side of the leg is the PERONEUS LONGUS extending from the proximal end of the fibula to a narrow tendon which passes around the lateral aspect of the lateral malleolus to meet the bases of the metatarsals on their superior surfaces. It is a plantar-flexor of the foot. Lying directly under the peroneus longus is the PERONEUS TERTIUS. It extends along about two-thirds the length of the fibula and inserts into an extensor tendon of the fifth toe. The remaining muscle of this group, the PERONEUS BREVIS, lies beneath the other two and sends its tendon of insertion around the back of the lateral malleolus to the foot. It is an extensor of the foot.

The TIBIALIS POSTERIOR lies back of the tibia with its origin in part on the fibula. It inserts on the navicular and middle cuneiform tarsals and serves to extend the foot.

Finally, locate the FLEXOR DIGITORUM LONGUS and the FLEXOR HALLUCIS LONGUS which are combined in the cat. They lie against the ventral surface of the tibia and fibula and have a common tendon which diverges to the digits.

Additional muscles intrinsic to the foot will not be considered.

H. Muscles of the vertebral column

While we attempt no dissection of these muscles, the lumbodorsal fascia of the back should be removed to show the thick muscle mass enclosed in a tough glistening fascia. It is called the EPAXIAL muscle mass and is separated from the muscles in the abdominal region, the hypaxial muscles, by a deep furrow. In the lumbar region, the epaxial mass can be divided into a median portion, the MULTIFIDUS SPINAE, and much thicker lateral portions, the SACROSPINALIS. The sacrospinalis divides into other longitudinal parts anteriorly. This is a complex system of muscles which extends the vertebral column. Anteriorly, splenius capitis, semispinalis capitis, and longissimus capitis muscles move the head in relationship to the vertebral column (Plate 4-2). Other muscles—many of them small—are also involved.

MUSCLES OF MAN (Plates 4-10 through 4-15)

While the preceding directions pertain to the cat, our chief concern is with learning some muscles of the human body. Fortunately, cat and human muscles are much the same so that we can gain our desired knowledge by dissecting the cat, by studying demonstrations on the cadaver, and by studying our text and other books.

Plates 4-10 through 4-13 may be used for drawing the human muscles in relationship to the skeleton as indicated earlier in these directions. By this means origins and insertions and actions can be visualized and more easily remembered. To emphasize function you may use red for flexors, blue for extensors, orange for abductors, and green for adductors. If a given muscle has more than one of these functions, you may stripe it with the appropriate colors.

The muscles of man may be labeled on Plates 4-14 and 4-15.

The following table lists some of the more obvious muscles of man with their origins, insertions, and actions. The student, using the tools mentioned above—dissection of cat, demonstrations on cadaver, books and charts—should learn these muscles.

QUESTIONS

1. What is the inguinal canal?

2. What are prime movers, antagonistics, synergists, and fixators?
   Give examples.

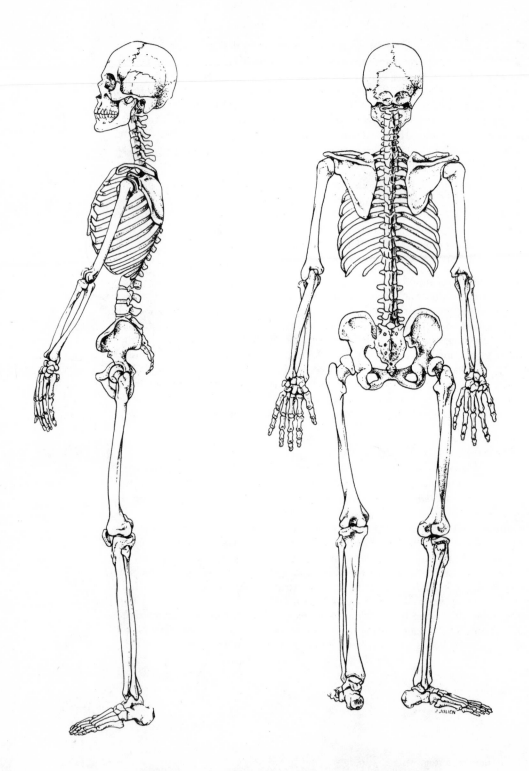

Plate 4-10. Lateral and Posterior View of Human Skeleton

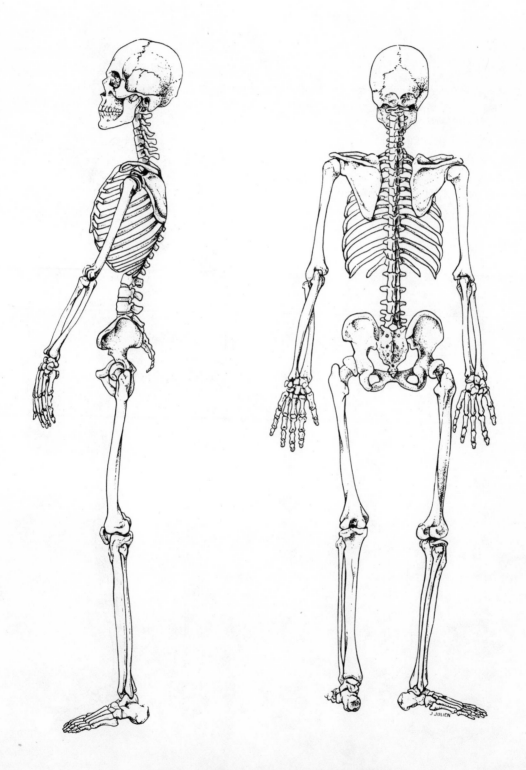

Plate 4-11. Lateral and Posterior View of Human Skeleton

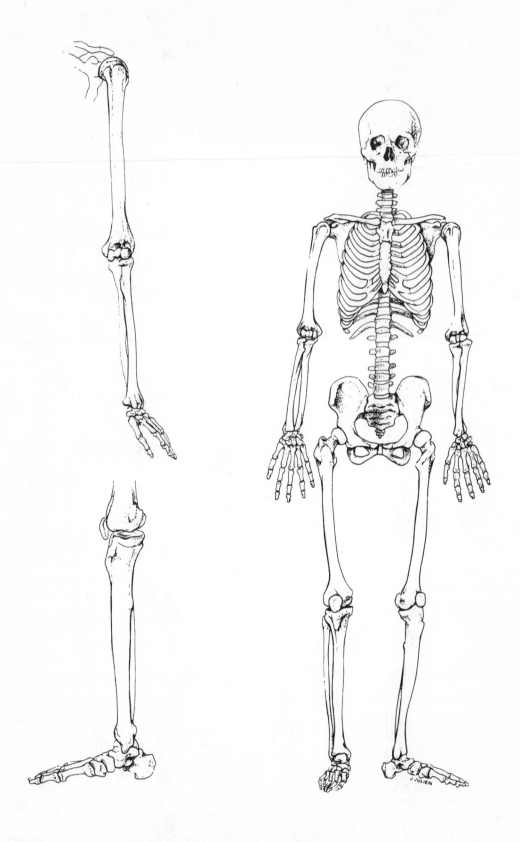

**Plate 4-12. Upperlimb Skeleton, Anterior View; Leg Skeleton,
Medial View; Human Skeleton, Anterior View**

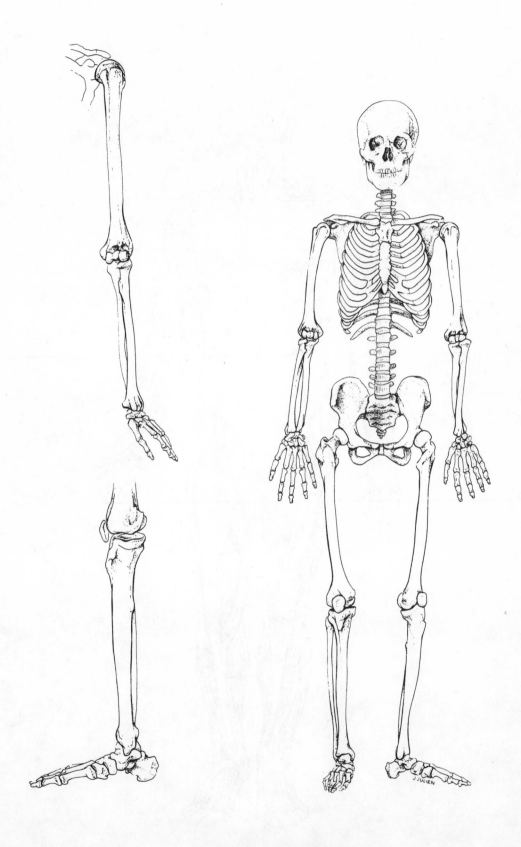

**Plate 4-13. Upperlimb Skeleton, Anterior View; Leg Skeleton,
Medial View; Human Skeleton, Anterior View**

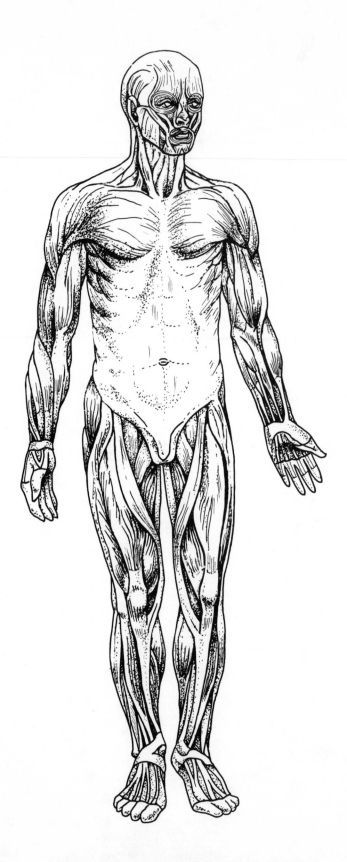

Plate 4-14. Superficial Muscles of Man—Anterior View

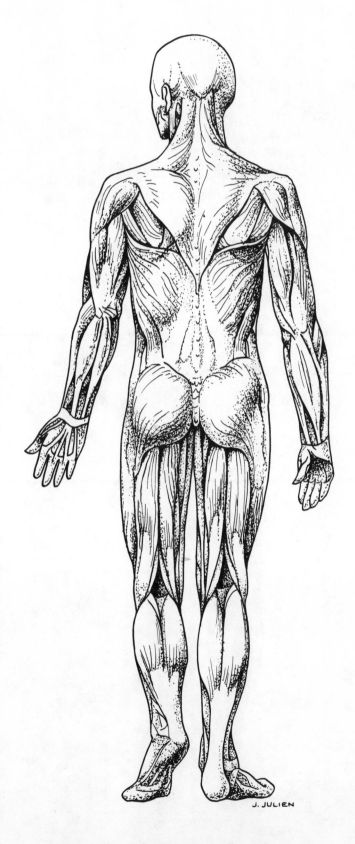

Plate 4-15. Superficial Muscles of Man—Posterior View

TABLE II. Some Muscles of Man

	Name of Muscle	Origin	Insertion	Action
1.	Masseter	Maxilla—its zygomatic process and adjacent areas	Ramus of mandible	Elevates mandible to close mouth
2.	Temporal	Temporal fossa	Coronoid process of mandible	Elevates and draws mandible backward—closes mouth
3.	Pterygoideus externus	Great wing of sphenoid and pterygoid plate	Condyle of mandible	Moves jaw forward and sideways, helps open mouth
4.	Pterygoideus internus	Palatine, maxilla, and pterygoid plate	Ramus of mandible	Elevates mandible and closes mouth
5.	Trapezius	From occipital bone to ligamentum nuchae to spine of vertebra prominens to spinous processes of twelve thoracic vertebrae	Clavicle, acromion and spine of scapula	Varied, depending on condition of neighboring parts. Raises shoulder, draws head back, retracts scapula, braces back the shoulder
6.	Latissimus dorsi	Lower thoracic vertebrae, lumbar and sacral vertebrae, iliac crest; lower ribs	Intertubercular groove of humerus	Lower fibers depress scapula. Depress humerus, draws humerus backward and rotates it inward
7.	Rhomboideus major	Spinous processes of first four or five thoracic vertebrae	Vertebral border of scapula	Move inferior angle of scapula backward and upward, slight rotation
8.	Rhomboideus minor	Ligamentum nuchae, spinous processes of last cervical and first thoracic vertebrae	Vertebral border of scapula	
9.	Levator scapulae	First four cervical vertebrae	Vertebral border of scapula	Lifts the angle of the scapula
10.	Pectoralis major	Clavicle, sternum, cartilages of true ribs, and external oblique	Crest of greater tubercle of humerus	Adducts arm, inward rotation
11.	Pectoralis minor	Third, fourth, and fifth ribs	Coracoid process of scapula	Rotates scapula downward, depresses shoulder
12.	Serratus anterior	Upper nine ribs	Vertebral border of scapula	Abduction of scapula
13.	Sternocleidomastoideus	Sternum and clavicle	Mastoid of temporal	Together they flex head on chest; separately they draw head toward shoulder of same side
14.	Deltoideus	Clavicle, acromion process, and spine of scapula	Deltoid tuberosity of humerus	Abduction of humerus
15.	Supraspinatus	Supraspinous fossa of scapula	Greater tubercle of humerus	Abduction of humerus
16.	Infraspinatus	Infraspinous fossa of scapula	Greater tubercle of humerus	Outward rotation of humerus
17.	Teres major	Lower part of axillary border of scapula	Crest of lesser tubercle of humerus	Adduction and rotation of arm
18.	Teres minor	Axillary border of scapula	Greater tubercle of humerus	Outward rotation of humerus
19.	Subscapularis	Subscapular fossa of scapula	Lesser tubercle of humerus	Inward rotation of arm
20.	Coracobrachialis	Coracoid process of scapula	Middle of medial surface of humerus	Flexion and adduction of humerus

		Origin	Insertion	Function
21.	Triceps brachii	Long head from infraglenoid tuberosity of scapula, medial and lateral heads from body of humerus	Olecranon of ulna	Extension of forearm
22.	Brachialis anticus	Lower half of anterior surface of humerus	Coronoid process of ulna	Flexion of forearm
23.	Biceps brachii	Long head from supraglenoid margin of scapula, short head from coracoid process of scapula	Tuberosity of radius	Flexion of forearm, supination of hand
24.	Diaphragm	Lower rim of thorax	A central tendon	Increases vertical diameter of thorax
25.	External intercostals	Lower border of a rib	Upper border of rib below	Elevation of ribs, increase anteroposterior diameters of the thorax
26.	Internal intercostals	Inner surface of a rib	Upper border of rib below	Lower the ribs, decrease the diameters of the thorax
27.	External oblique	Lower eight ribs	Anterior half of iliac crest and by broad aponeurosis to linea alba	Compresses abdominal viscera
28.	Internal oblique	Inguinal ligament, crest of ilium and lumbodorsal fascia	Lower six ribs, linea alba, and crest of pubis	Compresses abdominal viscera
29.	Transversus abdominis	Inguinal ligament, crest of ilium, lumbodorsal fascia, costal cartilages of lower six ribs	Linea alba and crest of pubis	Compresses abdominal viscera
30.	Rectus abdominis	Crest of pubis	Xiphoid process of sternum, costal cartilages of fifth, sixth, and seventh ribs	Compresses abdominal viscera; Flexes trunk
31.	Gluteus maximus	Iliac crest, sacrum, side of coccyx, aponeurosis of sacrospinalis	Gluteal ridge of femur and fascia lata	Extension of femur, outward rotation
32.	Gluteus medius	Outer surface of ilium	Greater trochanter of femur	Abduction of femur, inward rotation
33.	Adductor magnus	Ischium	Linea aspera of femur }	Adducts femur }
34.	Adductor longus	Pubis		
35.	Adductor brevis	Pubis		
36.	Psoas major	Lumbar vertebrae	Lesser trochanter of femur	Flexion of femur
37.	Iliacus	Iliac fossa	Lesser trochanter	Flexion of femur
38.	Sartorius	Anterior superior spine of ilium	Proximal end of tibia, medial side	Flexion of leg on thigh, and thigh on pelvis
39.	Tensor fasciae latae	Anterior crest and spine of ilium	On thigh in fascia latae	Tightening of the fascia lata, abduction and inward rotation of thigh

TABLE II. Some Muscles of Man (Continued)

	Name of Muscle	Origin	Insertion	Action
40.	Biceps femoris	Tuberosity of ischium, linea aspera of femur	Head of fibula and lateral condyle of tibia	Flexion of leg on thigh and extension of thigh
41.	Gracilis	Inferior ramus of pubis	Inner surface of tibia just below head	Adduction of thigh, flexion of leg upon thigh
42.	Semitendinosus	Tuberosity of ischium	Medial surface of body of tibia	Flexion of the leg upon the thigh, extension of thigh
43.	Semimembranosus	Tuberosity of ischium	Medial condyle of tibia	
44.	Quadriceps femoris			
	a. Rectus femoris	Anterior inferior iliac spine and brim of acetabulum	Common tendon to tuberosity of tibia	Extension of leg upon thigh, rectus femoris also flexes the thigh
	b. Vastus lateralis	Linea aspera		
	c. Vastus medialis	Linea aspera		
	d. Vastus intermedius	Anterior surface of the femur		
45.	Gastrocnemius	Medial and lateral condyles of femur	Calcaneus	Gastrocnemius flexes tibia upon femur, together with the soleus it extends the foot (plantar flexion)
46.	Soleus	Head of fibula and medial border of tibia		
47.	Tibialis anterior	Lateral condyle and upper two-thirds of shaft of tibia	Base of first metatarsal and under surface of first cuneiform	Flexes and inverts the foot
48.	Extensor digitorum longus	Lateral condyle of tibia and anterior surface of fibula	Second and third phalanges of four lesser toes	Extension of toes and flexion of foot upon leg
49.	Peroneus longus	Head and lateral surface of body of fibula	Lateral side of first metatarsal and first cuneiform	Extension (plantar flexion) and eversion of foot, helps maintain transverse arch
50.	Flexor digitorum longus	Posterior surface of tibia	By four tendons into last phalanges of four outer toes	Flexion of phalanges and extension of foot
51.	Flexor hallucis longus	Distal two-thirds of posterior of fibula surface	Base of phalanx of great toe	Flexion of great toe and extension of foot
52.	Tibialis posterior	Shaft of tibia and fibula and interosseus membrane	Under surface of navicular, calcaneus, three cuneiforms, cuboid, second, third, and fourth metatarsals	Extends the foot at the ankle joint

GLOSSARY — Chapter 4

abdominal (ab dom ′ i nȧl): L., abdomen, belly.

abductor (ab duk ′ tĕr): L., ab, away; ducere, to lead.

adductor (ad duk ′ tĕr): L., ad, to; ducere, to lead.

aponeurosis (ȧp ′ o nu rō ′ sis): G., apo, from; neuron, tendon.

cleido (klī ′ dō): G., kleis, key.

digastricus (dī gas ′ trik us): G., di, two; gaster, belly.

epaxial (ep aks ′ i ȧl): G., epi, upon; L. axis.

extrinsic (ek strin ′ sik): L., extrinsecus, on the outside.

gluteus (glo͞o te ′ us): G., gloutos, rump.

gracilis (grȧ sil ′ is): L., gracilis, slender.

hallux (hal ′ uks): L., hallux, great toe.

hernia (hûr ′ ni ȧ): L., hernia, a rupture.

hypaxial (hī pak ′ si al): G., hypo, below; axis, axis.

inguinal (ing ′ gui nȧl): L., inguen, groin.

intercalate (in tûr ′ kȧ lāt): L., intercalo, to put between.

intrinsic (in trin ′ sik): L., intrinsicus, inward.

masseter (ma se ′ tĕr): G., maseter, a chew.

peroneus (per on ′ nē us): G., perone, pin of a brooch, referring to the fibula.

plantaris (plan ta ′ ris): L., planta, sole of foot.

psoas (sō ′ ȧs, psō ′ –): G., psoa, a muscle of the loin.

pterygoid (ter ′ i goid, pter ′): G., pteron, wing.

sarcostyle (sär ′ kô stil): G., sarx, flesh; stylos, pillar.

sartorius (sär tō ′ ri us): L., sartor, tailor.

symphysis (sim ′ fi sis): G., symphysis, a growing together.

5

COELOM AND VISCERA

Having completed the dissection of the muscles, we will study next the CELOM or BODY CAVITY and its subdivisions. Also, we will identify the more obvious internal organs or VISCERA, leaving a detailed study until later (Plate 5-1).

Make an incision to the right side of the LINEA ALBA, starting in the lower abdominal region and extending it forward to the ribs. Use scissors and be careful not to damage the internal organs. Now extend the incision into the thorax about one-half inch from the sternum, cutting through the muscles and costal cartilages. Be particularly careful as you approach the first rib not to cut into the large vessels which lie close underneath. Now bring the incision over to the mid-line of the neck and with a blunt instrument separate the neck muscles to expose the trachea and larynx. On either side of the trachea pick away the fascia and other supporting tissues and locate the COMMON CAROTID ARTERY, INTERNAL JUGULAR VEIN, and VAGOSYMPATHETIC NERVE enclosed in a common sheath. Lying along the trachea just below the larynx will be seen the elongated lobes of the THYROID GLAND. Embedded in the dorsomedial side of the thyroid gland you may be able to locate the PARATHYROIDS. These glands belong to the ENDOCRINE SYSTEM.

A. Thoracic cavities

Returning to the incision made through the thoracic wall, spread it open to note the membranous partition which attaches to the midventral line. This is a double membrane, called the MEDIASTINAL SEPTUM or PLEURA; it separates the two PLEURAL (LUNG) CAVITIES from each other and is reflected onto them as their lining. The PARIETAL PLEURA dorsally is reflected onto the lung as its VISCERAL PLEURA. At this point it forms the PULMONARY LIGAMENT. On the side that has been cut free from the sternum, press the lung mediad and at the same time push the body wall laterally and dorsally to expose the inner surfaces of the ribs. Nick the ribs with a scalpel at the level of their dorsal curvature and they will then break easily and allow a wider opening of the cavity. A transverse cut through the body wall just back of the DIAPHRAGM, which separates the THORACIC from the PERITONEAL cavities, will facilitate matters. The diaphragm also may be cut free from body walls.

Again examine the MEDIASTINAL SEPTUM and notice that it divides to pass around each side of the PERICARDIUM which encloses the heart. Dorsal and anterior to the heart these membranes enclose other organs such as the aorta, venae cavae, trachea, esophagus, and thymus gland. This area, containing these and other structures, is called the MEDIASTINUM or MEDIASTINAL SPACE. Having identified these structures and cavities, cut the mediastinal septum free from the sternum and open that side of the thorax in the same manner as you did the other.

This region is now ready for more detailed study in connection with the appropriate body systems. To review—you have opened the THORACIC CAVITY and found it to be separated from the peritoneal cavity by the DIAPHRAGM. The thoracic cavity itself is divided into the two PLEURAL CAVITIES, one around each lung, a PERICARDIAL CAVITY around the heart, and a space, the MEDIASTINUM, between the double wall of the MEDIASTINAL SEPTUM.

B. Peritoneal cavity

The peritoneal (abdominopelvic) cavity, like thoracic cavities, is lined with a serous membrane, but it is known as the PARIETAL PERITONEUM rather than the parietal pleura or parietal pericardium. It is reflected over the various organs as the VISCERAL PERITONEUM. The organs therefore are outside of the peritoneal cavity. The organs are supported by MESENTERIES, LIGAMENTS, and OMENTA which are double layers of the peritoneum. MESENTERIES suspend various organs of the digestive canal, LIGA-MENTS suspend organs other than those of the digestive tube, and OMENTA connect various digestive organs with other organs. Blood vessels, lymphatics, and nerves run between the two layers of the MESENTERIES, LIGAMENTS, and OMENTA to supply the organs.

Only a few of the more obvious mesenteries, ligaments and omenta will be described. The GREATER OMENTUM hangs as an apron over the internal organs, and may contain a large amount of stored fat. Actually, it is a much overgrown fold drawn out into a sac which attaches to the GREATER CURVATURE of the STOMACH and encloses part of the PANCREAS and the SPLEEN in its descending portion. The space inside the greater omentum is called the LESSER PERITONEAL CAVITY or OMENTAL BURSA, and may be reached by a small opening, the EPIPLOIC FORAMEN (foramen of Winslow) dorsal to the stomach on the right side. A LESSER OMENTUM extends from the LESSER CURVATURE of the stomach and DUODENUM to the liver. The COMMON BILE DUCT, HEPATIC ARTERY, and HEPATIC PORTAL VEIN run in this omentum.

The liver is attached to the diaphragm by a CORONARY LIGAMENT, and to the ventral body wall and diaphragm by the FALCIFORM LIGAMENT.

Farther back in the body cavity the URINARY BLADDER is attached to the linea alba of the ventral body wall by the MEDIAN UMBILICAL (SUSPENSORY) LIGA-MENT. The LATERAL LIGAMENTS of the bladder can be seen on either side of the urinary bladder along with the URETERS and "wads" of fat. By pulling the urinary bladder caudad the URETERS from the kidneys can be seen entering it. If the cat is a male a small duct can be seen on each side looping around the ureter and turning caudad to enter the outlet of the bladder, the URETHRA. These ducts are the sperm ducts, DUCTUS DEFERENS.

Now push the digestive tract to one side and notice the two "swellings" on the dorsal body wall. These are the KIDNEYS. They are covered over by the parietal peritoneum as are the ADRENAL GLANDS which are small endocrine glands embedded in the fat above and mediad to the kidneys. Organs lying back of the parietal peritoneum are said to be RETROPERITONEAL. Notice also that the SMALL INTESTINE is supported by a mesen-tery to the dorsal body wall, the MESENTERY PROPER. The MESOCOLON and MESO-RECTUM mesenteries support the large intestine.

If your cat should be a female the Y-shaped UTERUS consisting of BODY and HORNS is easily seen cephalad of the urinary bladder. A small OVARY can be seen at the upper extremity of each horn of the uterus just caudad of the kidneys. An OVARIAN LIGAMENT supports the ovary and BROAD and ROUND LIGAMENTS support the uterus. A SUSPENSORY LIGAMENT extends forward from the ovary.

The peritoneal cavity of man is often divided into two parts, the ABDOMINAL and PELVIC regions. There is no barrier between these two portions as they flow one into the other. The abdominal portion contains the liver, stomach, small and large intestines, spleen and pancreas. The pelvic contains the sigmoid colon, rectum, urinary bladder and, in the female, the ovaries, uterine tubes and uterus. In the male, the prostate gland, seminal vesicles, and part of the ductus deferens are in the pelvic region.

The body cavities are closed spaces except in the females where the peritoneal cavity opens to the outside through the organs of the reproductive system.

Label Plates 5-2 through 5-4.

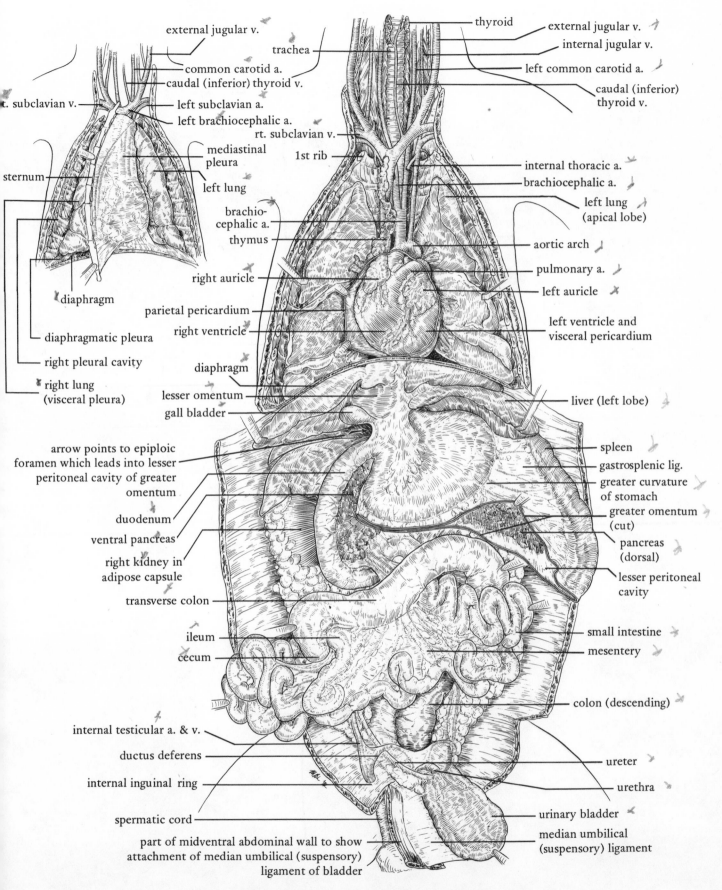

external jugular v.

trachea

common carotid a.

caudal (inferior) thyroid v.

r. subclavian v.

left subclavian a.

left brachiocephalic a.

rt. subclavian v.

mediastinal pleura

sternum

left lung

brachio-cephalic a.

thymus

right auricle

parietal pericardium

right ventricle

diaphragm

diaphragmatic pleura

right pleural cavity

right lung (visceral pleura)

1st rib

thyroid

external jugular v.

internal jugular v.

left common carotid a.

caudal (inferior) thyroid v.

internal thoracic a.

brachiocephalic a.

left lung (apical lobe)

aortic arch

pulmonary a.

left auricle

left ventricle and visceral pericardium

lesser omentum

gall bladder

arrow points to epiploic foramen which leads into lesser peritoneal cavity of greater omentum

duodenum

ventral pancreas

right kidney in adipose capsule

transverse colon

ileum

cecum

liver (left lobe)

spleen

gastrosplenic lig.

greater curvature of stomach

greater omentum (cut)

pancreas (dorsal)

lesser peritoneal cavity

small intestine

mesentery

colon (descending)

internal testicular a. & v.

ductus deferens

internal inguinal ring

spermatic cord

part of midventral abdominal wall to show attachment of median umbilical (suspensory) ligament of bladder

ureter

urethra

urinary bladder

median umbilical (suspensory) ligament

Plate 5-1. Celom and Viscera of the Cat—Anterior View

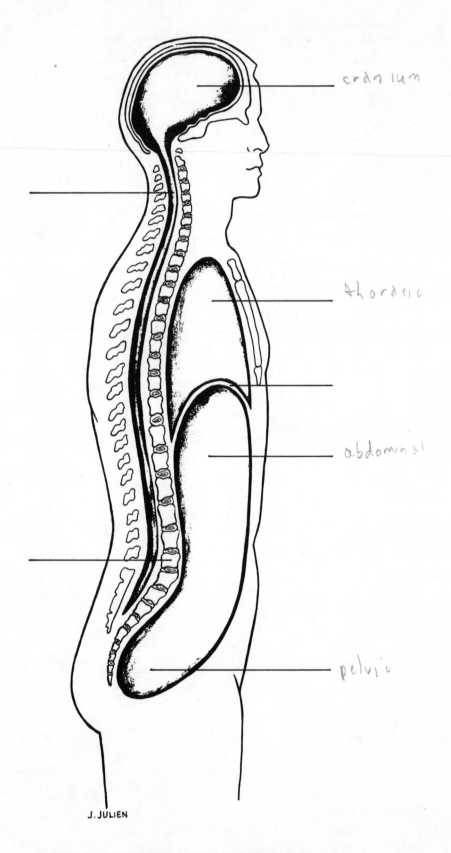

cranium

thoracic

abdominal

pelvic

J. JULIEN

Plate 5-2. Anterior and Posterior Cavities of the Human Body

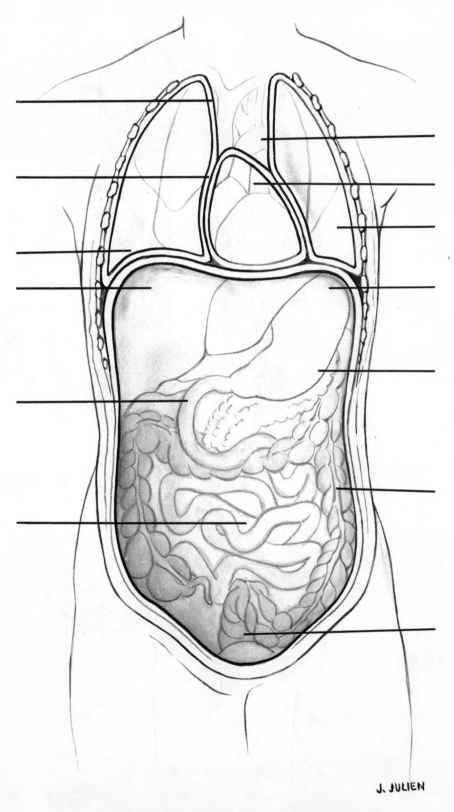

Plate 5-3. Anterior (Ventral) Cavities of the Human Body

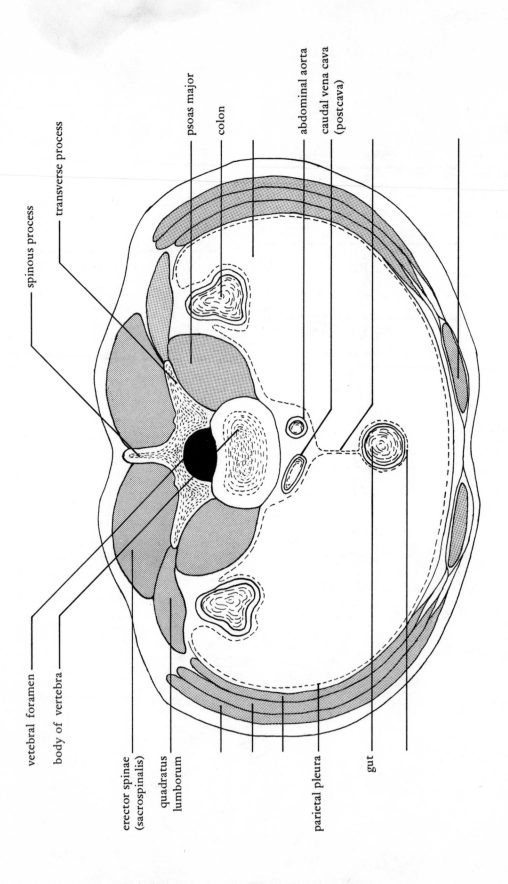

Plate 5-4. Diagrammatic Cross Section of the Human Body Through the Lower Abdomen

spinous process

transverse process

psoas major

colon

abdominal aorta

caudal vena cava (postcava)

vetebral foramen

body of vertebra

erector spinae (sacrospinalis)

quadratus lumborum

parietal pleura

gut

GLOSSARY — Chapter 5

adrenal (à drē´nàl): L., ad, upon; renes, kidneys.

bursa (bûr´sà): L., bursa, a purse.

carotid (kà ro´tid): G., karos, stupor.

celom (sē´lom): G., koilos, hollow.

colon (ko´lon): G., kolon, member.

coronary (kor´o ner´i): L., corona, crown, wreath.

deferens (def´ēr enz): L., defero, carry away.

diaphragm (dī´à fram): G., dia, between; phragnynai, to enclose.

duodenum (dū´o dē´num): L., duodeni, twelve.

endocrine (en´do krin): G., endo, within; krinein, to separate.

epiploic (ep´i plō´ik): G., epiploon, omentum.

falciform (fal´si fôrm): L., falx, sickle.

linea alba (lin´ē à al´bà): L., linea, line; albus, white.

mediastinum (mē´di as ti´num): L., mediastinus, being in the middle.

mesentery (mes´en ter´i): G., mesos, middle; enteron, gut.

omentum (o men´tum): L., omentum, fat skin.

ovary (o´và ri): L., ovum, egg.

pancreas (pan´kre as): G., pas, all; kreas, flesh, meat.

parathyroid (par´à thī´roid): G., para, rear; thyreos, shield; eidos, form.

pericardium (per´i kär´di um); G., peri, around; kardia, heart.

pleura (ploor´à): G., pleura, rib, side.

rectum (rek´tum): L., rectus, straight.

retroperitoneal (ret´ro per´i tō ne´àl): L., retro, back; G., peri, around; teino, stretch.

spleen (splēn): G., splen, spleen.

thyroid (thī´roid): G., thyreos, shield; eidos, form.

umbilical (um bil´i kàl): L., umbilicus, navel.

ureter (u rē´tēr): G., oureter, ureter.

urethra (u rē´thrà): G., from ouron, urine.

uterus (u´tēr us): L., uterus, womb.

vagus (vā´gus): L., vagus, wandering.

viscera (vis´ēr à): L., viscus, internal organ.

6

CIRCULATORY SYSTEM

GENERAL

A. Structure

The circulatory system is composed of two important subdivisions, the BLOOD-VASCULAR and the LYMPH-VASCULAR. The former consists of the HEART, ARTERIES, ARTERIOLES, CAPILLARIES, VENULES, VEINS, and the BLOOD which is confined normally within these structures. They form therefore a CLOSED SYSTEM of circulation. It is also a DOUBLE SYSTEM. The blood which has circulated from the heart through the aorta, its branches, and the capillaries is returned to the heart by the large veins. It is then sent out again through a pulmonary artery to the lungs and once again returned to the heart. The former circuit is called the SYSTEMIC, the latter the PULMONARY. The lymph-vascular system is formed of LYMPH CAPILLARIES which gather TISSUE FLUID from the body and of LYMPHATIC VESSELS which have in their course LYMPH NODES. The lymphatic vessels ultimately connect with large veins above the heart, thus emptying their LYMPH into the blood.

B. Function

The functions of the circulatory system all center about transportation. Food and oxygen are carried by it to the tissues. Carbon dioxide and other waste products of metabolism are carried from the tissues to the proper organs of excretion. Hormones are distributed through the body, temperature is regulated, and many of the body's defenses against disease are centered in this system. The anatomy of this system can be best understood if we keep the above functions in mind.

PROCEDURE

A beginning course does not provide sufficient time to permit a complete dissection of the circulatory system. Your efforts should therefore be directed toward learning:

1. The general plan of the system.
2. The structure of the major organs.
3. The names and locations of major blood vessels.

The following procedure is recommended.

A. General plan of blood-vascular system
1. The use of chart showing double circulation.

B. The heart
1. Demonstration by instructor of human heart and its relationships as seen in the cadaver.
2. Examination of a model and of a chart of the human heart.
3. Dissection and study of the heart of a cat.

C. Locating and naming the larger blood vessels in man and their dissection in the cat.

D. Microscopic examination of cardiac muscle, an artery, a vein, and blood.

E. Lymphatic system. Demonstration and examination of charts and microscope slides. A cat with the lymphatics injected is helpful.

BLOOD-VASCULAR SYSTEM

A. The heart

1. Position
   a. Study the position of the heart in the cadaver, and notice its relationship to the ribs and sternum, the diaphragm, the mediastinum, and the lungs.
   b. Study the cat's heart in the same way.
   c. What are the apex, base, and diaphragmatic surfaces of the heart?

   d. Note the major vessels entering and leaving the heart; the superior and inferior venae cavae on the right side, the aorta and pulmonary arteries at the base of the heart, the pulmonary veins dorsally or posteriorly. Label Plate 6-3.

2. Pericardium. The heart is enclosed in a double-walled sac, the pericardium. Open this sac by cutting along the midventral line. The inner wall of this sac adheres to the heart and is known as the EPICARDIUM or VISCERAL PERICARDIUM. The visceral pericardium is continuous at the base of the heart with the PARIETAL PERI-CARDIUM or outer wall of the sac. The parietal pericardium is reinforced with connective tissue making it a tough coat, but its inner surface is smooth. It attaches to the diaphragm inferiorly. Between these two layers there is a potential space, the PERICARDIAL CAVITY.

   The opposing surfaces of the visceral and parietal pericardia are lubricated by a small amount of serum. Make a diagram to show the relationships just described. Label.

3. Myocardium (Plate 6-1). The myocardium is the muscular portion of the heart. The chambers of the heart should be opened now to NOTE THE VARIATION IN THE THICKNESS OF THE MYOCARDIUM. This operation may be carried out leaving the heart in place in the animal, or the heart may be removed. If you remove the heart, carefully cut it free from the attached vessels and other structures.

   Open the right atrium first by making an incision through its wall between its main vessels, the superior and inferior venae cavae (pre- and postcava). If the heart has been injected with latex you can extend the incision about one-quarter inch along each of the caval vessels, pull up on the latex mass and cut it across. Now extend the incision across the atrium toward the ventricle and remove the latex. It may adhere, especially where some of it extends into the right auricle or into the ventricle, but more cutting will free it. Extend the incision next along the lateral wall of the right ventricle to the apex of the heart, then obliquely craniad toward the pulmonary trunk or artery. At this juncture of heart and artery is the PULMONARY (semilunar) VALVE. If you cut the latex injection mass in the pulmonary artery you may be able to pull it out of the vessel and valve, giving you a good model of the pulmonary valve.

   Open the left atrium and ventricle in much the same way as you did the right side and compare the relative thickness of the myocardium of the four chambers.

   Why is there such a variation in the thickness of the myocardium of the various heart chambers?

   Examine a prepared slide of cardiac muscle tissue and review its characteristics. Refer to the section on the muscular system for a description of cardiac muscle.

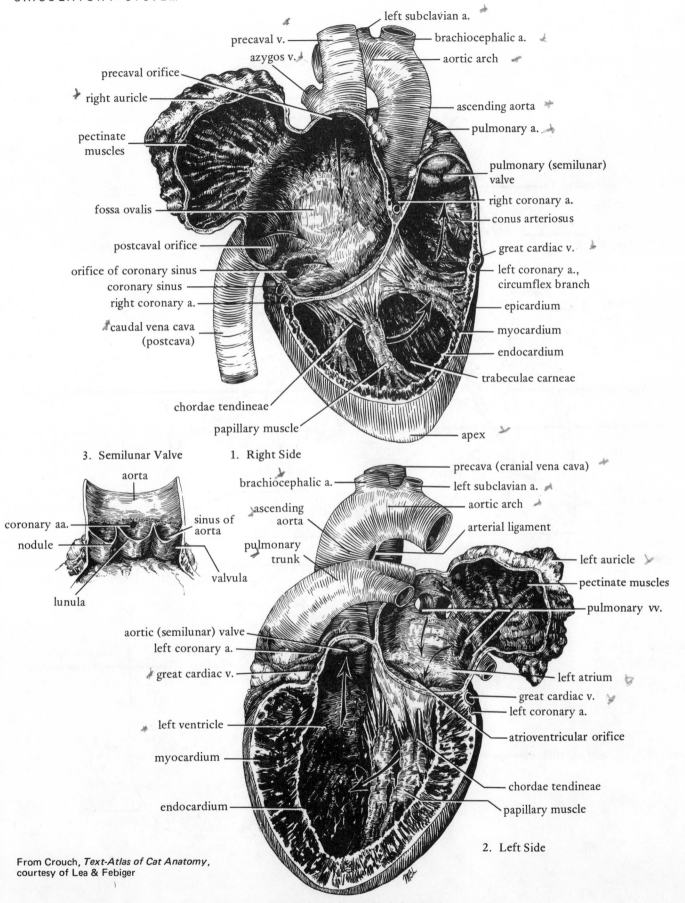

left subclavian a.

precaval v.

brachiocephalic a.

azygos v.

aortic arch

precaval orifice

right auricle

ascending aorta

pulmonary a.

pectinate
muscles

pulmonary (semilunar)
valve

right coronary a.

conus arteriosus

fossa ovalis

great cardiac v.

postcaval orifice

left coronary a.,
circumflex branch

orifice of coronary sinus

coronary sinus

epicardium

right coronary a.

myocardium

caudal vena cava
(postcava)

endocardium

trabeculae carneae

chordae tendineae

papillary muscle

apex

3. Semilunar Valve

1. Right Side

aorta

precava (cranial vena cava)

brachiocephalic a.

left subclavian a.

coronary aa.

ascending
aorta

aortic arch

sinus of
aorta

arterial ligament

nodule

pulmonary
trunk

left auricle

valvula

pectinate muscles

lunula

pulmonary vv.

aortic (semilunar) valve

left coronary a.

left atrium

great cardiac v.

great cardiac v.

left coronary a.

left ventricle

atrioventricular orifice

myocardium

endocardium

chordae tendineae

papillary muscle

2. Left Side

From Crouch, *Text-Atlas of Cat Anatomy*,
courtesy of Lea & Febiger

Plate 6-1. Internal Structure of the Heart of the Cat

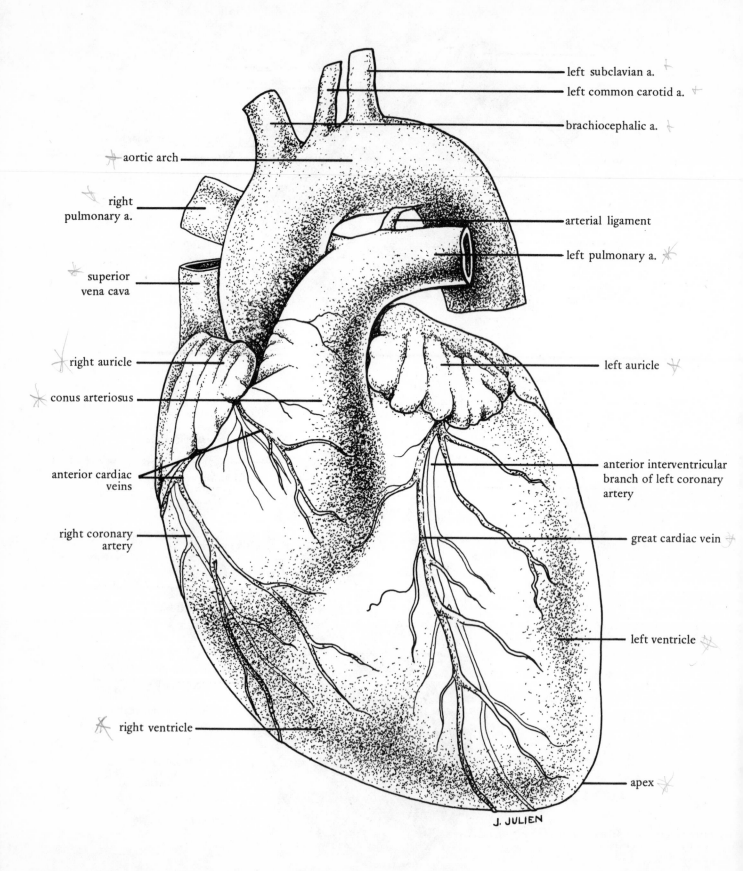

left subclavian a.

left common carotid a.

brachiocephalic a.

aortic arch

right pulmonary a.

arterial ligament

left pulmonary a.

superior vena cava

right auricle

left auricle

conus arteriosus

anterior cardiac veins

anterior interventricular branch of left coronary artery

right coronary artery

great cardiac vein

left ventricle

right ventricle

apex

J. JULIEN

Plate 6-2. Human Heart—Anterior View

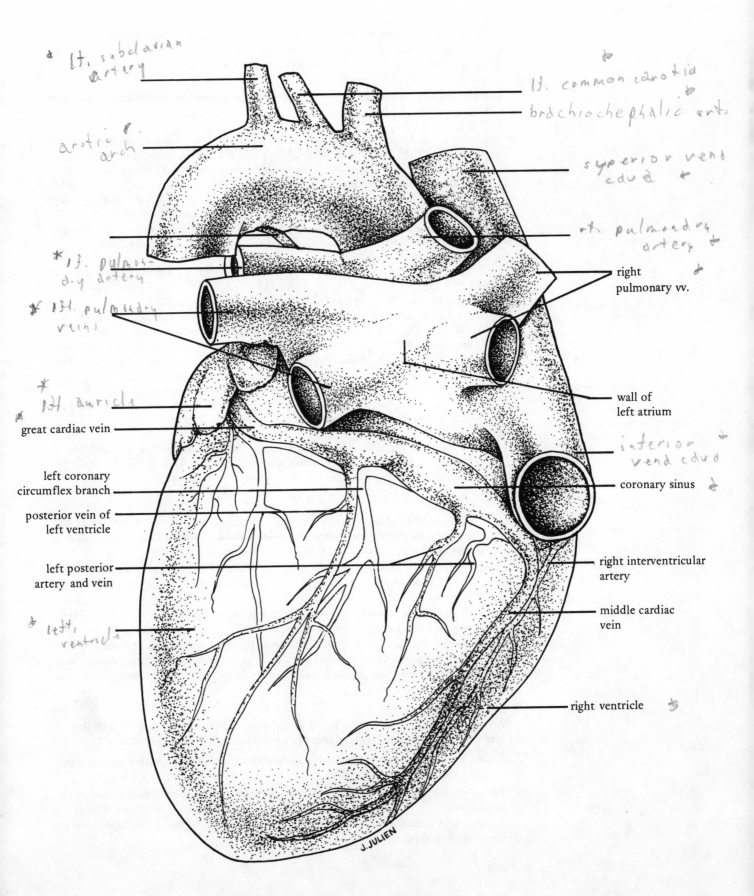

* lt. subclavian artery

aortic arch

*lt. pulmonary artery

*lt. pulmonary veins

*lt. auricle

great cardiac vein

left coronary circumflex branch

posterior vein of left ventricle

left posterior artery and vein

*left ventricle

lt. common carotid

brachiocephalic art.

superior vena cava

rt. pulmonary artery

right pulmonary vv.

wall of left atrium

inferior vena cava

coronary sinus

right interventricular artery

middle cardiac vein

right ventricle

J. JULIEN

Plate 6-3. Human Heart—Posterior View

4. Endocardium. The endocardium consists of a thin membrane, the ENDOTHELIUM (simple squamous epithelium), supported by connective tissue fibers. It forms the lining of the heart and the valves. The endothelium continues out into the vessels and forms an unbroken lining for the circulatory system.

5. Heart chambers and valves. These chambers have already been opened. Locate the following:

a. Right atrium

Notice the openings of the SUPERIOR VENA CAVA (precava) which drains the upper part of the body, and the INFERIOR VENA CAVA (postcava) which drains the lower regions of the body. The other LARGE OPENING in the walls of this chamber is the ATRIOVENTRICULAR orifice which leads into the right ventricle. Between the inferior vena cava and the atrioventricular opening is the small opening of the CORONARY SINUS. It returns blood from the substance of the heart. In the lower part of the interatrial septum is a depression known as the FOSSA OVALIS which marks the position of the FORAMEN OVALE of the fetus.

b. Right ventricle

This chamber has two openings, the ATRIOVENTRICULAR to the right atrium, and the ORIFICE OF THE PULMONARY ARTERY. The former opening is guarded by the TRICUSPID VALVE and the latter by the SEMILUNAR VALVE (pulmonary). Attached to the edges of the flaps of the tricuspid valve are the CHORDAE TENDINEAE which attach at their opposite ends either to the PAPILLARY MUSCLES or the TRABECULAE CARNEAE. The chordae tendineae prevent the tricuspid valve from inverting when the ventricle contracts. The TRABECULAE CARNEAE are irregular muscular columns in the wall of the ventricle.

Examine carefully the two types of valves mentioned above, and be sure you know how they function and why they are necessary (Plate 6-1).

c. Left atrium

The left atrium is smaller than the right, and receives the four PULMONARY VEINS from the lungs and empties into the LEFT VENTRICLE through the atrioventricular opening. There are no valves at the entrances of the pulmonary veins.

d. Left ventricle

Compare this chamber with the right ventricle. Notice that the valve at the atrioventricular opening has only two cusps instead of three. This chamber directs the blood into the aorta past the AORTIC (semilunar) VALVES.

6. Coronary circuit. The CORONARY ARTERIES which nourish the heart arise at the base of the ASCENDING AORTA and are distributed over the heart. There are two of them, the RIGHT and the LEFT coronary arteries. The blood distributed through the heart by these vessels is returned to the heart primarily by the CORONARY SINUS. Find these on the cat's heart. See Plates 6-1 and 6-4.

7. Heart nerves. The heart is supplied by nerves from the autonomic nervous system— branches of the vagus (10th cranial) and branches from the sympathetic system. You may be able to see these if you examine carefully the connective tissues around the heart. (See Plate 11-1.)

B. Arteries

Arteries are vessels which carry blood away from the heart. Examine a cross section of an artery under the microscope and identify the following layers in its walls.

1. Tunica interna (intima)—the inner layer—consists of endothelium with a small amount of elastic tissue.

2. Tunica media—the middle layer—contains smooth muscle plus elastic tissue in the larger arteries.

3. Tunica externa (adventitia)—the outer layer—is composed of loose areolar connective tissue. Draw and label a cross section of an artery.

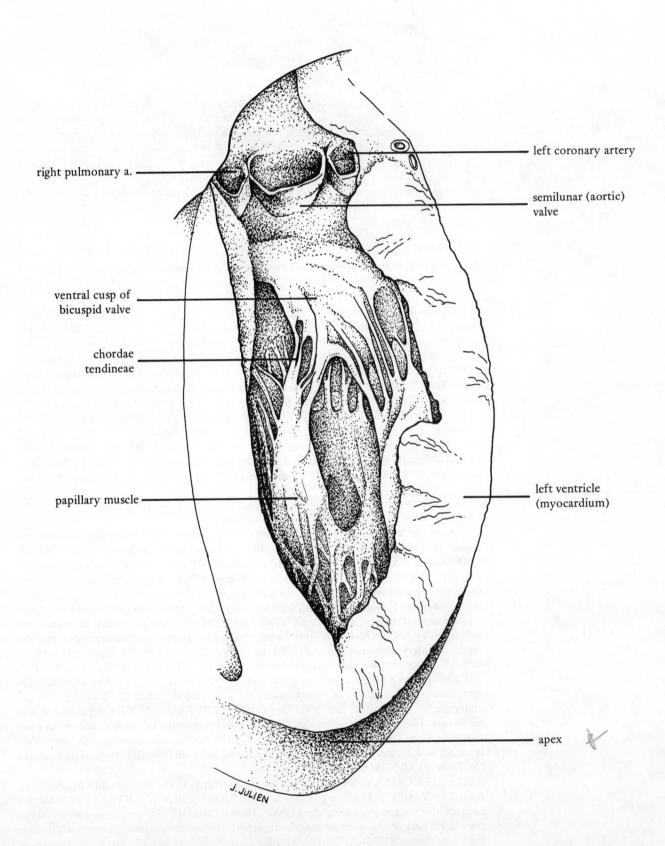

right pulmonary a.

left coronary artery

semilunar (aortic)
valve

ventral cusp of
bicuspid valve

chordae
tendineae

papillary muscle

left ventricle
(myocardium)

apex

J. JULIEN

Plate 6-4. Left Ventricle and Base of Aorta; Opened to Show Bicuspid Heart Valve

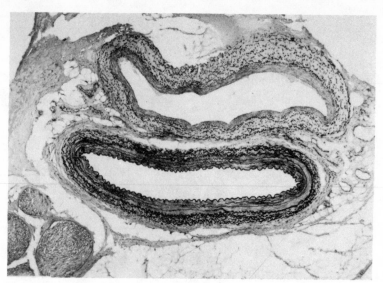

Figure 6-1. Photomicrograph of a Cross Section of an Artery and Vein

You should locate the following arteries on the cat. Study as many as possible on Plates 6-5 and 6-6. Refer to page 118 for a list of blood vessels you should learn. The AORTA has already been observed coming from the left ventricle of the heart. The first part of this vessel is the ASCENDING AORTA. It then curves dorsal to the heart as the AORTIC ARCH and then continues along the mid-dorsal line ventral to the spinal column as the DESCENDING AORTA. That part of the aorta in the thorax may be referred to as the THORACIC AORTA, and that below the diaphragm as the ABDOMINAL AORTA.

You have already seen the CORONARY arteries, right and left, coming from the ascending aorta. The aortic arch gives off two large vessels IN THE CAT; first, the BRACHIOCEPHALIC (innominate) which in turn divides into the RIGHT SUB-CLAVIAN going to the right forelimb and the RIGHT and LEFT COMMON CAROTIDS which supply the head and neck; second, the LEFT SUBCLAVIAN which goes to the left arm.

Compare these vessels arising from the aortic arch in the cat with those of man by using a model, chart, or cadaver (Plates 6-5 and 6-7).

Follow the RIGHT SUBCLAVIAN ARTERY as it branches from the brachiocephalic artery. It gives rise to four branches at about the level of the first rib; the INTERNAL THORACIC (MAMMARY), VERTEBRAL, COSTOCERVICAL, and THYROCERVICAL axis. The INTERNAL THORACIC ARTERY comes from the ventral side of the sub-clavian and passes with the vein of the same name to the chest wall. Its branches extend to the abdominal wall. The VERTEBRAL ARTERY arises from the dorsal side of the subclavian and passes into the VERTEBRARTERIAL CANAL, which is formed by successive TRANSVERSE FORAMINA of the cervical vertebrae. Reaching the atlas, the vertebral artery traverses the ATLANTAL FORAMEN and enters the VERTEBRAL CANAL where it joins the opposite vertebral artery to form the BASILAR ARTERY. The basilar artery runs craniad along the mid-ventral side of the spinal cord and the brain stem, giving off branches and finally joining the ARTERIAL CIRCLE (of WILLIS) on the underside of the brain (Plate 6-8). The COSTOCERVICAL ARTERY after leaving the subclavian divides into two branches. The branches supply the intercostal, back, and neck muscles. The THYROCERVICAL (omocervical) AXIS arises anterior to the other branches and supplies other muscles of the dorsal neck and shoulder regions. It becomes the TRANSVERSE SCAPULAR ARTERY.

The SUBCLAVIAN ARTERY now passes in front of the first rib and becomes the AXILLARY ARTERY which gives off a VENTRAL THORACIC ARTERY to the sternal ends of the pectoral muscles; the LONG THORACIC ARTERY going posteriorly along the lateral part of the pectoral muscles to supply the latissimus dorsi muscle; and, finally, the very large SUBSCAPULAR ARTERY (circumflex) which gives off numerous branches to the shoulder and superficial muscles of the back. The BRACHIAL ARTERY is the continuation of the axillary artery into the arm. The brachial artery, along with the

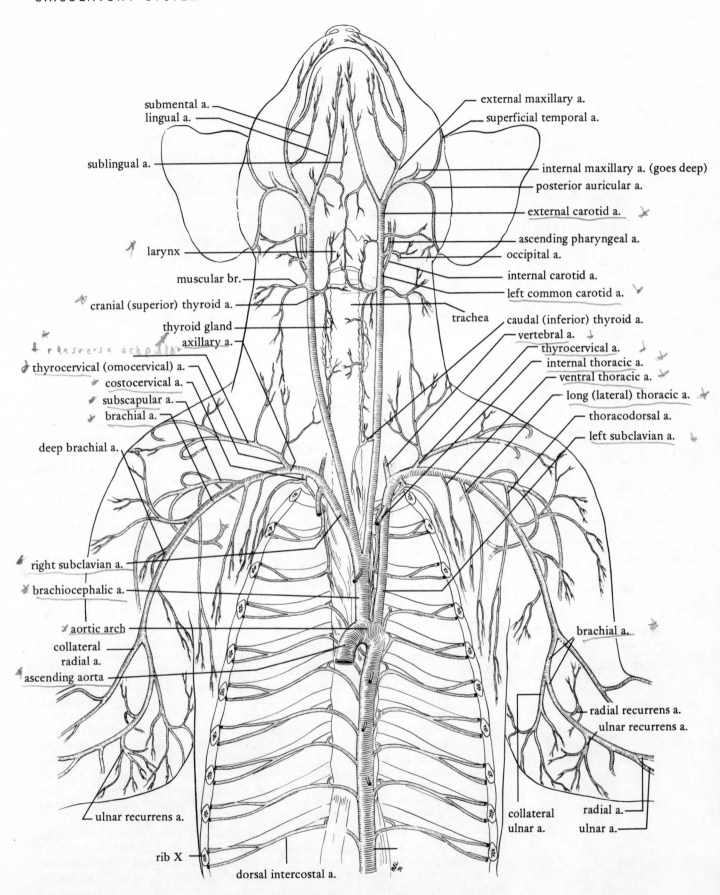

submental a.

lingual a.

sublingual a.

larynx

muscular br.

cranial (superior) thyroid a.

thyroid gland

axillary a.

transverse scapular

thyrocervical (omocervical) a.

costocervical a.

subscapular a.

brachial a.

deep brachial a.

right subclavian a.

brachiocephalic a.

aortic arch

collateral
radial a.

ascending aorta

ulnar recurrens a.

rib X

dorsal intercostal a.

external maxillary a.

superficial temporal a.

internal maxillary a. (goes deep)

posterior auricular a.

external carotid a.

ascending pharyngeal a.

occipital a.

internal carotid a.

left common carotid a.

trachea

caudal (inferior) thyroid a.

vertebral a.

thyrocervical a.

internal thoracic a.

ventral thoracic a.

long (lateral) thoracic a.

thoracodorsal a.

left subclavian a.

brachial a.

radial recurrens a.

ulnar recurrens a.

collateral
ulnar a.

radial a.

ulnar a.

Plate 6-5. Arterial System of the Cat—Superior Vessels

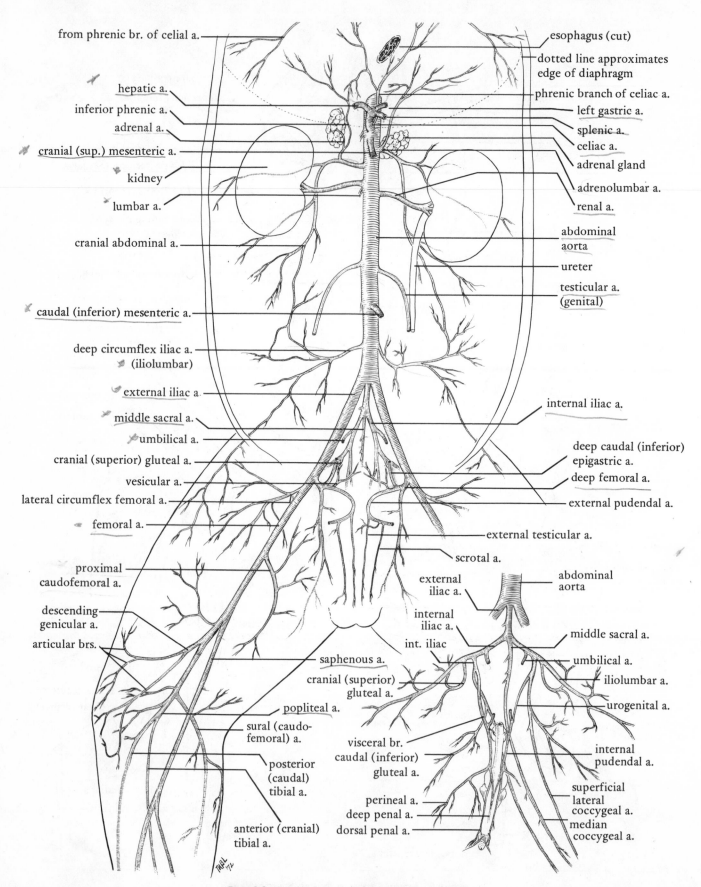

from phrenic br. of celial a.

esophagus (cut)

dotted line approximates edge of diaphragm

hepatic a.

inferior phrenic a.

adrenal a.

cranial (sup.) mesenteric a.

kidney

lumbar a.

cranial abdominal a.

caudal (inferior) mesenteric a.

deep circumflex iliac a. (iliolumbar)

external iliac a.

middle sacral a.

umbilical a.

cranial (superior) gluteal a.

vesicular a.

lateral circumflex femoral a.

femoral a.

proximal caudofemoral a.

descending genicular a.

articular brs.

phrenic branch of celiac a.

left gastric a.

splenic a.

celiac a.

adrenal gland

adrenolumbar a.

renal a.

abdominal aorta

ureter

testicular a. (genital)

internal iliac a.

deep caudal (inferior) epigastric a.

deep femoral a.

external pudendal a.

external testicular a.

scrotal a.

saphenous a.

cranial (superior) gluteal a.

popliteal a.

sural (caudo-femoral) a.

posterior (caudal) tibial a.

anterior (cranial) tibial a.

external iliac a.

internal iliac a.

int. iliac

visceral br. caudal (inferior) gluteal a.

perineal a.

deep penal a.

dorsal penal a.

abdominal aorta

middle sacral a.

umbilical a.

iliolumbar a.

urogenital a.

internal pudendal a.

superficial lateral coccygeal a.

median coccygeal a.

Plate 6-6. Arterial System of the Cat—Inferior Vessels

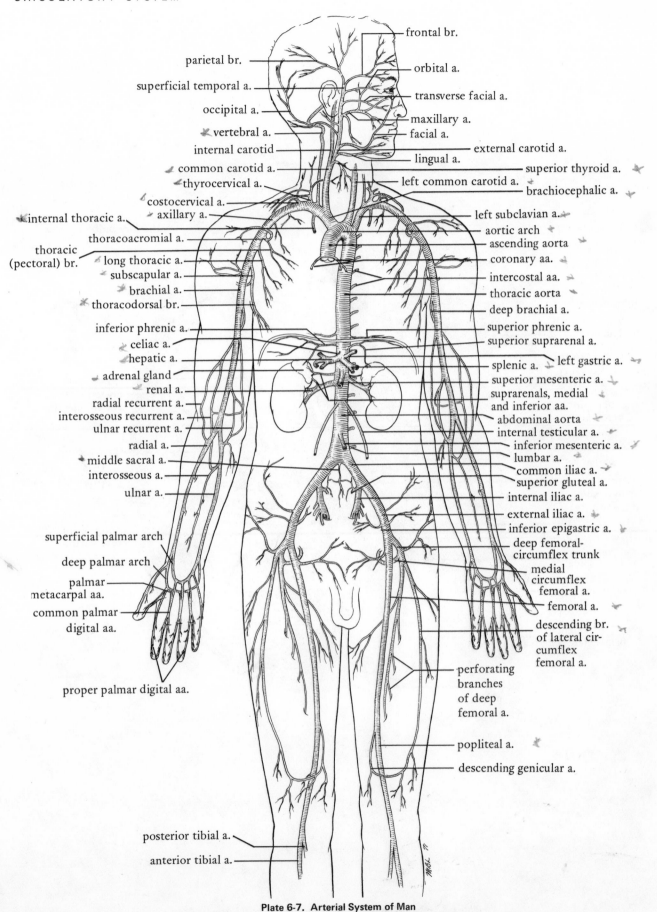

frontal br.

parietal br.

orbital a.

superficial temporal a.

transverse facial a.

occipital a.

maxillary a.

vertebral a.

facial a.

internal carotid

external carotid a.

common carotid a.

lingual a.

superior thyroid a.

thyrocervical a.

left common carotid a.

brachiocephalic a.

costocervical a.

left subclavian a.

internal thoracic a.

axillary a.

aortic arch

thoracoacromial a.

ascending aorta

thoracic (pectoral) br.

long thoracic a.

coronary aa.

subscapular a.

intercostal aa.

brachial a.

thoracic aorta

thoracodorsal br.

deep brachial a.

inferior phrenic a.

superior phrenic a.

celiac a.

superior suprarenal a.

hepatic a.

splenic a.

left gastric a.

adrenal gland

superior mesenteric a.

renal a.

suprarenals, medial and inferior aa.

radial recurrent a.

interosseous recurrent a.

abdominal aorta

ulnar recurrent a.

internal testicular a.

radial a.

inferior mesenteric a.

middle sacral a.

lumbar a.

interosseous a.

common iliac a.

ulnar a.

superior gluteal a.

internal iliac a.

external iliac a.

inferior epigastric a.

superficial palmar arch

deep femoral-circumflex trunk

deep palmar arch

medial circumflex femoral a.

palmar metacarpal aa.

common palmar digital aa.

femoral a.

descending br. of lateral circumflex femoral a.

proper palmar digital aa.

perforating branches of deep femoral a.

popliteal a.

descending genicular a.

posterior tibial a.

anterior tibial a.

Plate 6-7. Arterial System of Man

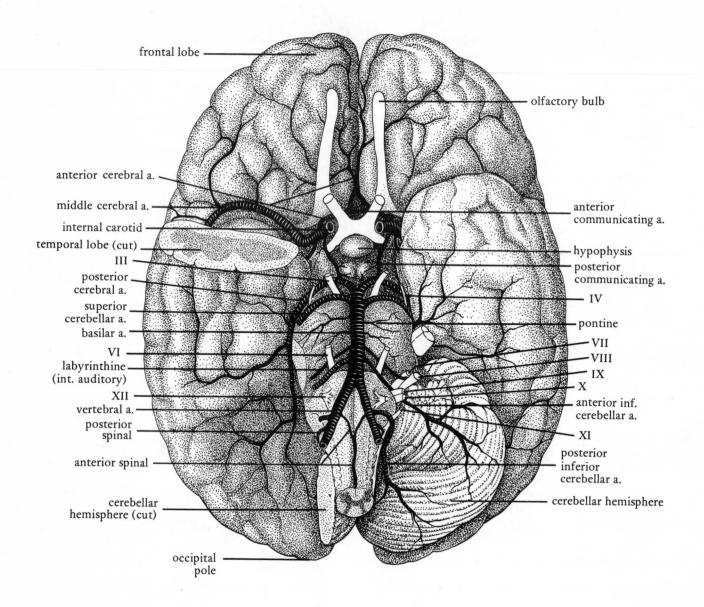

frontal lobe

olfactory bulb

anterior cerebral a.

middle cerebral a.

internal carotid

temporal lobe (cut)

III

posterior
cerebral a.

superior
cerebellar a.

basilar a.

VI

labyrinthine
(int. auditory)

XII

vertebral a.

posterior
spinal

anterior spinal

cerebellar
hemisphere (cut)

occipital
pole

anterior
communicating a.

hypophysis

posterior
communicating a.

IV

pontine

VII

VIII

IX

X

anterior inf.
cerebellar a.

XI

posterior
inferior
cerebellar a.

cerebellar hemisphere

Plate 6-8. Inferior Surface of Brain Showing Arterial Circle (Willis)

MEDIAN NERVE, passes through the SUPRACONDYLOID FORAMEN at the distal end of the humerus—a structure not present on the human humerus. At the elbow the brachial artery forms two main branches, the RADIAL and ULNAR arteries which supply the forearm and hand regions.

Now follow the COMMON CAROTID ARTERIES as they diverge from the brachiocephalic artery and pass, one to either side of the trachea. They give off small branches to the trachea and at the level of the thyroid gland each gives off a SUPERIOR THYROID ARTERY. Other branches are given off to the larynx and to the dorsal neck muscles and at the level of the larynx the common carotids branch to form the internal and external carotid arteries. The INTERNAL CAROTID, a diminutive artery in the cat, passes through a foramen in the tympanic bulla and enters the cranial cavity. The EXTERNAL CAROTID continues forward to supply the external structures of the head and face.

As the aorta arches to the left it passes close to the left pulmonary artery to which it is joined by a strong band. This is the ARTERIAL LIGAMENT and is what remains of a connecting vessel between the aorta and pulmonary artery of the fetus. The aorta now becomes the thoracic aorta as it goes dorsally to pass just to the left of the midline through the thoracic region. It gives off branches to the lungs, esophagus, and muscles of the back. At its lower end it penetrates the diaphragm and enters the peritoneal cavity where it is called the ABDOMINAL AORTA.

The ABDOMINAL AORTA gives off the CELIAC ARTERY (axis) just caudad of the diaphragm, and it in turn divides into the HEPATIC, SPLENIC (lienal), and LEFT GASTRIC arteries going to the liver, spleen, and stomach, respectively. The SUPERIOR (cranial) MESENTERIC artery comes off of the aorta just caudad of the celiac and sends branches to the small and large intestines and to the pancreas.

The next branches of the aorta are the ADRENOLUMBAR (phrenicoabdominal) ARTERIES which pass close to the ADRENAL (suprarenal) GLANDS to which they send a branch. They then pass to the body wall and also give off a PHRENIC ARTERY to the diaphragm. The RENAL ARTERIES to the kidneys are easily seen coming from the aorta between the kidneys. Small GENITAL (ovarian or testicular) ARTERIES come off caudad of the renals to supply the gonads. Moving caudad again the next large branch from the abdominal aorta is the INFERIOR (caudal) MESENTERIC which is distributed to the large intestine. The muscles of the iliac region are supplied by a pair of ILIOLUMBAR (deep circumflex iliac) ARTERIES and four or five pairs of LUMBAR ARTERIES come off of the dorsal side of the aorta at regular intervals between the diaphragm and the caudal end of the aorta. They go to the muscles of the back and the spinal cord. Near its caudal end the aorta divides into the large EXTERNAL ILIAC ARTERIES and almost immediately again into the INTERNAL ILIACS. The aorta continues into the tail as the MIDDLE SACRAL ARTERY.

The EXTERNAL ILIAC ARTERY passes caudad and just before penetrating the body wall gives rise to the DEEP FEMORAL ARTERY. The deep femoral artery gives off a branch, the INFERIOR (caudal deep) EPIGASTRIC, which passes forward on the dorsal surface of the rectus abdominis muscle and anastomoses with the terminal branches of the internal thoracic artery. Other branches of the deep femoral artery are the vesicular to the urinary bladder and the external pudendal which pierces the body wall and goes to the medial aspect of the thigh. The main vessel supplies the adductor and semimembranosus muscles.

After penetrating the body wall at the MIDDLE ILIOPECTINEAL ARCH the external iliac artery becomes the femoral artery. The FEMORAL ARTERY continues into the thigh along with the femoral vein and the femoral and saphenous nerves in a depression called the femoral triangle. The femoral artery gives off one large branch, the LATERAL CIRCUMFLEX FEMORAL ARTERY, supplying muscles of the thigh and hip, and muscular branches to the adductor muscles, a SAPHENOUS ARTERY to the medial leg and a descending genicular artery to the knee. The femoral artery then goes deep to the popliteal space (behind knee) where it becomes the popliteal artery. The POPLITEAL ARTERY gives off two MAIN branches, the SURAL and the CAUDAL (POSTERIOR) TIBIAL, and then continues as the CRANIAL (ANTERIOR) TIBIAL into the leg.

The INTERNAL ILIAC (hypogastric) artery gives off first an UMBILICAL ARTERY to the urinary bladder, then a cranial (superior) gluteal to the gluteal muscle and muscles of the thigh, a middle hemorrhoidal artery to the rectum, and finally its terminal branch, the caudal (inferior) gluteal following the sciatic nerve.

The illustrations show more blood vessels than we expect you to learn in this course. The following are most important. The vessels of the limbs may be colored; arteries red, veins blue on Plates 11-7 through 11-11.

ARTERIES TO KNOW

aorta	celiac
ascending	hepatic
arch	splenic (lienal)
descending	gastric
thoracic	superior mesenteric
abdominal	adrenolumbar
pulmonary	phrenic
coronary	renal
brachiocephalic	genital (ovarian, testicular)
common carotid	inferior mesenteric
subclavian	iliolumbar (deep circumflex iliac)
internal thoracic	lumbar
vertebral	common iliac
costocervical	external iliac
thyrocervical	internal iliac
basilar	umbilical
transverse scapular	middle sacral
axillary	deep femoral
ventral thoracic	inferior epigastric
long thoracic	femoral
subscapular	lateral circumflex femoral
brachial	saphenous
radial	popliteal
ulnar	sural
superior thyroid	caudal (posterior) tibial
internal carotid	cranial (anterior) tibial
external carotid	

Notice the similarity of these branches of the aorta in the cat to those of man. Label the diagrams provided on Plates 6-5, 6-6, 6-7 and 6-8.

VEINS TO KNOW

In general, know the veins which accompany the arteries you have learned and which have the same names.

In addition, learn the following:

superior vena cava (precava)
inferior vena cava (postcava)
azygos
common iliac
(hepatic) portal
coronary sinus
cardiac
thoracodorsal
posterior circumflex humeral
cephalic
external jugular
internal jugular
anterior facial
posterior facial
transverse facial (jugular)

C. Veins (Plates 6-9 through 6-11)
    Veins are vessels which carry blood toward the heart.

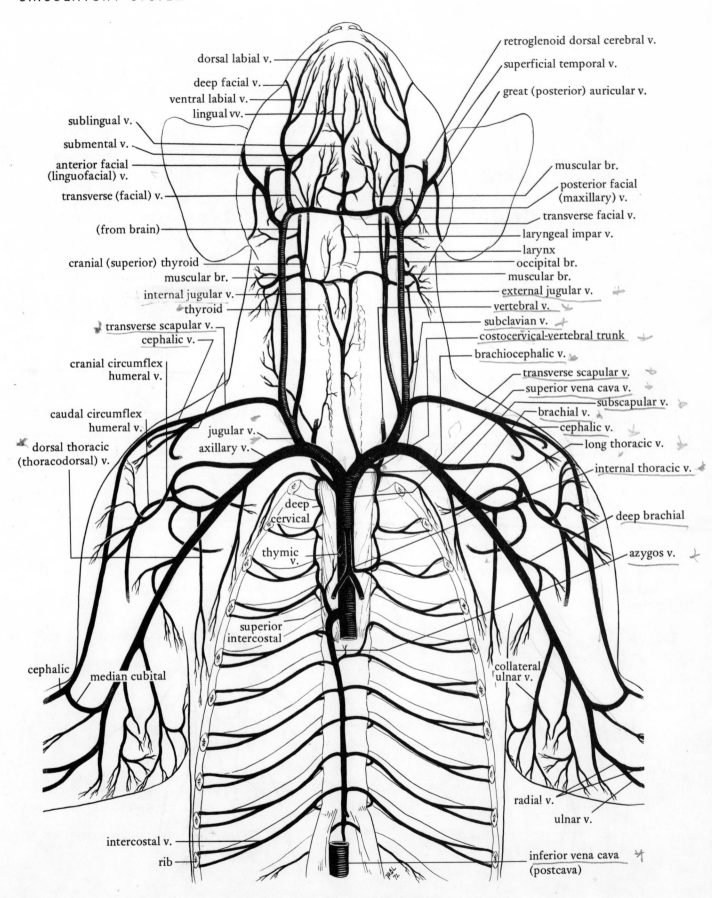

dorsal labial v.
deep facial v.
ventral labial v.
lingual vv.
sublingual v.
submental v.
anterior facial (linguofacial) v.
transverse (facial) v.
(from brain)
cranial (superior) thyroid
muscular br.
internal jugular v.
thyroid
transverse scapular v.
cephalic v.
cranial circumflex humeral v.
caudal circumflex humeral v.
dorsal thoracic (thoracodorsal) v.
jugular v.
axillary v.
deep cervical
thymic v.
superior intercostal
cephalic
median cubital
intercostal v.
rib

retroglenoid dorsal cerebral v.
superficial temporal v.
great (posterior) auricular v.
muscular br.
posterior facial (maxillary) v.
transverse facial v.
laryngeal impar v.
larynx
occipital br.
muscular br.
external jugular v.
vertebral v.
subclavian v.
costocervical-vertebral trunk
brachiocephalic v.
transverse scapular v.
superior vena cava v.
subscapular v.
brachial v.
cephalic v.
long thoracic v.
internal thoracic v.
deep brachial
azygos v.
collateral ulnar v.
radial v.
ulnar v.
inferior vena cava (postcava)

Plate 6-9. Veins of the Cat—Superior Vessels

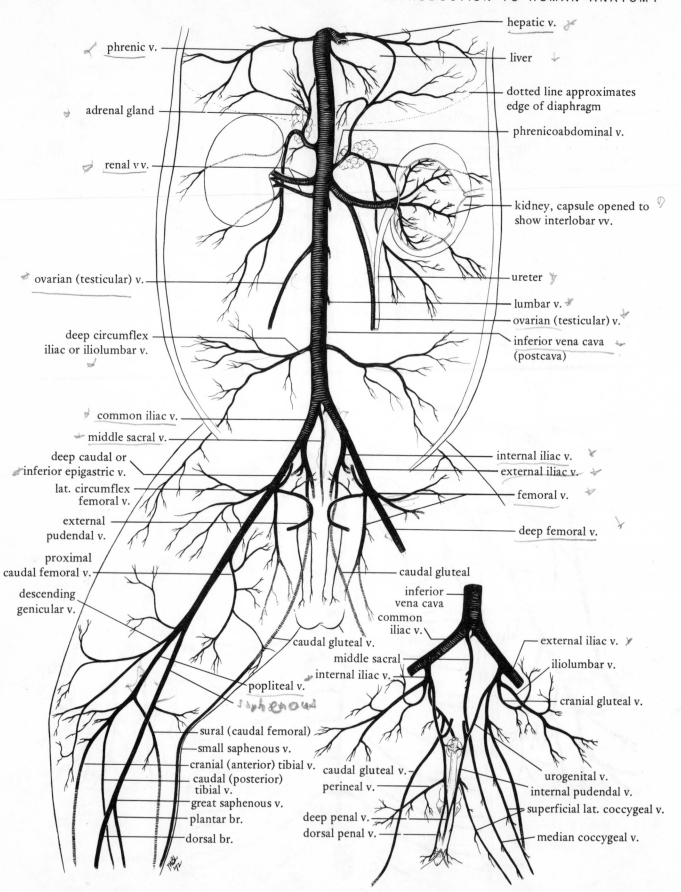

phrenic v.

hepatic v.

liver

dotted line approximates
edge of diaphragm

adrenal gland

phrenicoabdominal v.

renal v v.

kidney, capsule opened to
show interlobar vv.

ovarian (testicular) v.

ureter

lumbar v.

ovarian (testicular) v.

deep circumflex
iliac or iliolumbar v.

inferior vena cava
(postcava)

common iliac v.

middle sacral v.

deep caudal or
inferior epigastric v.

internal iliac v.

external iliac v.

lat. circumflex
femoral v.

femoral v.

external
pudendal v.

deep femoral v.

proximal
caudal femoral v.

caudal gluteal

descending
genicular v.

inferior
vena cava

common
iliac v.

caudal gluteal v.

external iliac v.

middle sacral

iliolumbar v.

internal iliac v.

popliteal v.

cranial gluteal v.

saphenous

sural (caudal femoral)

small saphenous v.

cranial (anterior) tibial v.

caudal gluteal v.

urogenital v.

caudal (posterior)
tibial v.

perineal v.

internal pudendal v.

great saphenous v.

superficial lat. coccygeal v.

plantar br.

deep penal v.

dorsal br.

dorsal penal v.

median coccygeal v.

Plate 6-10. Veins of the Cat—Inferior Vessels

Examine a slide of a cross section of a vein and compare it with the artery. Label the photomicrograph (Figure 6-1).

Do veins have valves? Do arteries?

You have already seen the pulmonary veins entering the left atrium and the superior and inferior venae cavae (precava and postcava) entering the right atrium.

As you study the veins, remember that they are named and identified for the areas they drain, not by the point at which they join other veins. These points of joining often vary.

Follow the INFERIOR VENA CAVA caudad of the heart where it lies in the free edge of the CAVAL FOLD of the pleura. It passes through the diaphragm and receives the PHRENIC VEINS from that structure. HEPATIC VEINS enter the inferior vena cava as it passes through the right median lobe of the liver. The liver tissue should be dissected away to see these vessels. As the inferior vena cava leaves the liver it runs alongside of the dorsal aorta and soon receives a right ADRENOLUMBAR (PHRENICOABDOMINAL) VEIN from the adrenal gland and adjacent body wall. You will need to remove some fat and connective tissue to see these well. The RIGHT RENAL VEIN is also apparent in this area. The LEFT ADRENOLUMBAR and RENAL VEINS may unite before they enter the vena cava. The left renal vein also receives a LEFT INTERNAL TESTICULAR VEIN from the scrotal region, or if a female, the LEFT OVARIAN VEIN from the ovary. The RIGHT INTERNAL TESTICULAR or OVARIAN VEINS enter the inferior vena cava posterior to the renal vein. Paired LUMBAR VEINS from the body wall enter the vena cava as it passes caudad. They come in on the dorsal side and so the vena cava must be freed and lifted up to see them. ILIOLUMBAR (DEEP CIRCUMFLEX EPIGASTRIC) VEINS enter the inferior vena cava about a centimeter cephalad of its formation by the COMMON ILIACS and the MIDDLE SACRAL (CAUDAL) VEIN.

Variations in the connections of the above veins are common and should be called to the attention of the instructor and other students. The inferior vena cava caudad of the kidneys may be double, for example. These variations are understandable on the basis of the complicated embryology and evolutionary history of this region.

The COMMON ILIAC VEINS are formed by the INTERNAL (hypogastric) and EXTERNAL ILIACS. The internal iliac veins receive branches from the gluteal region, the rectum, anus, and urinary bladder. The external iliac leaves the peritoneal cavity and passes to the leg where it receives on its medial side the DEEP FEMORAL VEIN. The deep femoral collects from the thigh, the fat between the thighs, the external genital region, and receives an INFERIOR (caudal deep) EPIGASTRIC VEIN from the rectus abdominis muscles. The external iliac now becomes the FEMORAL VEIN and receives branches from the thigh, lower leg, and foot. Note that these, in general, follow the arteries.

Return now to the peritoneal cavity to examine the HEPATIC PORTAL SYSTEM. A large HEPATIC PORTAL VEIN leads into the liver running in the LESSER OMENTUM (hepatoduodenal ligament). Clean the connective tissue from its surface and follow it and its branches into the liver. In the liver these branches lead into capillaries (sinusoids) and this blood is finally collected into the HEPATIC VEINS which, by way of the inferior vena cava, reach the right atrium of the heart. Following the hepatic portal vein in the other direction, notice that it receives many branches from the viscera. By removing fat and other connective tissue, trace out some of the vessels to get a general picture of the system.

Note that the names of the vessels correspond mostly to the names of the organs drained by them. Also recall that the blood drained from these organs was that delivered to them initially by the single median arteries of the abdominal aorta—the celiac, superior mesenteric, and inferior mesenteric.

The portal system serves as a direct route by which absorbed food materials reach the liver. Study Plate 6-11 carefully and label.

Turn your attention now to the SUPERIOR VENA CAVA (precava) which you have already identified. Note that there is but one of these. Many animals have two. The proximal part of the left one in the cat is represented by the CORONARY SINUS on the dorsal side of the heart which receives CARDIAC VEINS and which empties into the right atrium. The distal part of the left vena cava joins the right one to form the superior vena cava. This is also the pattern which we find in man.

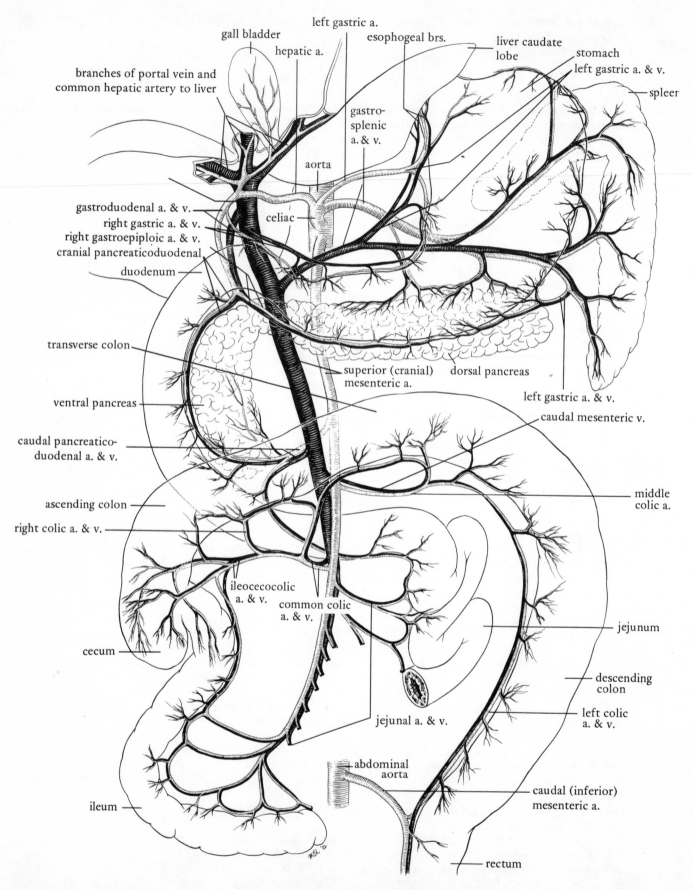

Plate 6-11. Hepatic Portal System of the Cat

The superior vena cava is joined just cephalad of the right atrium by an AZYGOS VEIN which can be found lying along the dorsal thoracic wall. It receives veins from the intercostal areas, the esophagus, and bronchi. The next major vein to enter the superior vena cava is the common stem of the INTERNAL THORACIC (MAMMARY) VEINS which drain the chest and abdominal walls. Small veins enter the superior vena cava from the thymus gland, and it is formed anteriorly by the joining of the two BRACHIO-CEPHALIC (INNOMINATE) VEINS. The branches of the BRACHIOCEPHALIC VEINS are the same, so only one may be followed. You may expect some variations from the description which follows.

The first branch, at the level of the first rib, is the VERTEBRAL which goes dorsally to enter the vertebrarterial canal. It drains the spinal cord and brain. Just before the vertebral vein enters the brachiocephalic it receives a COSTOCERVICAL VEIN which drains the muscles of the back and chest wall. It may enter the brachiocephalic independently of the vertebral vein.

The brachiocephalic (innominate) vein is formed anteriorly by the union of two large veins—the EXTERNAL JUGULAR from the neck region, and the SUBCLAVIAN from the arm. The subclavian passes in front of the first rib to the arm and is then called the AXILLARY VEIN. You will need to cut through the pectoral muscles, if you have not already done so, to expose the branches of the axillary vein. You should note also the nerves of the brachial plexus and lymph nodes in the axilla. Do not injure them. The first branch of the axillary vein is the large SUBSCAPULAR VEIN which runs through the proximal part of the upper arm to collect from the muscles of the upper arm and shoulder. It is joined by the POSTERIOR CIRCUMFLEX HUMERAL VEIN from the outer surface of the upper arm. Lateral to the entrance of the subscapular vein the axillary vein receives the small VENTRAL THORACIC VEIN from the medial portions of the pectoral muscles. The next branch is the LONG THORACIC VEIN which extends caudad along the pectoral muscles. The last branch of the axillary is the THORACO-DORSAL VEIN which collects from the latissimus dorsi muscle. A large branch connects the thoracodorsal and the subscapular vein. Beyond these four branches the axillary vein becomes the BRACHIAL VEIN which accompanies the brachial artery and nerves along the medial side of the upper arm.

The EXTERNAL JUGULAR VEIN soon receives on its medial side the very small INTERNAL JUGULAR VEIN. The INTERNAL JUGULAR accompanies the common carotid artery and the vagosympathetic trunk along the side of the trachea. The external jugular receives small branches from neighboring muscles and then a large TRANSVERSE SCAPULAR VEIN from the shoulder. The latter anastomoses with the CEPHALIC VEIN of the arm and also connects with the POSTERIOR CIRCUMFLEX HUMERAL VEIN mentioned above. Anteriorly the external jugular is formed by the union of ANTERIOR and POSTERIOR FACIAL VEINS and at this point is connected across the midline to the opposite external jugular vein by the TRANSVERSE VEIN. The anterior facial vein collects from face, jaws, submaxiliary, lymph glands, and region of the eye. The posterior facial vein collects from the parotid gland, the pinna, back of the head, and the temporal region. Label Plate 6-12 which shows the above veins as they are found in man.

D. Capillaries (see Plate 6-13, figure 3.)
    Where are the capillaries found? What functions do they serve?

E. Blood
    Examine a prepared slide of blood tissue. Using your textbook, identify the red corpuscles and the different kinds of leucocytes. Label Figure 6-2.

FETAL CIRCULATION

The fetus, carried in the uterus of the mother, is attached through the umbilical cord to the placenta. The placenta is a nutritive, respiratory, and excretory organ formed in part from maternal tissue and in part from the fetal tissue. It is reasonable to suppose, therefore, that the circulatory system of the fetus would differ from that of the adult.

The fetal heart has an opening between right and left atria known as the FORAMEN OVALE. Also there is a vessel, the DUCTUS ARTERIOSUS, connecting the aorta and pulmonary artery. A vessel, the DUCTUS VENOSUS, connects the UMBILICAL VEINS from the placenta to the inferior vena cava. Finally, there are UMBILICAL ARTERIES which connect the fetus with the mother through the umbilical cord.

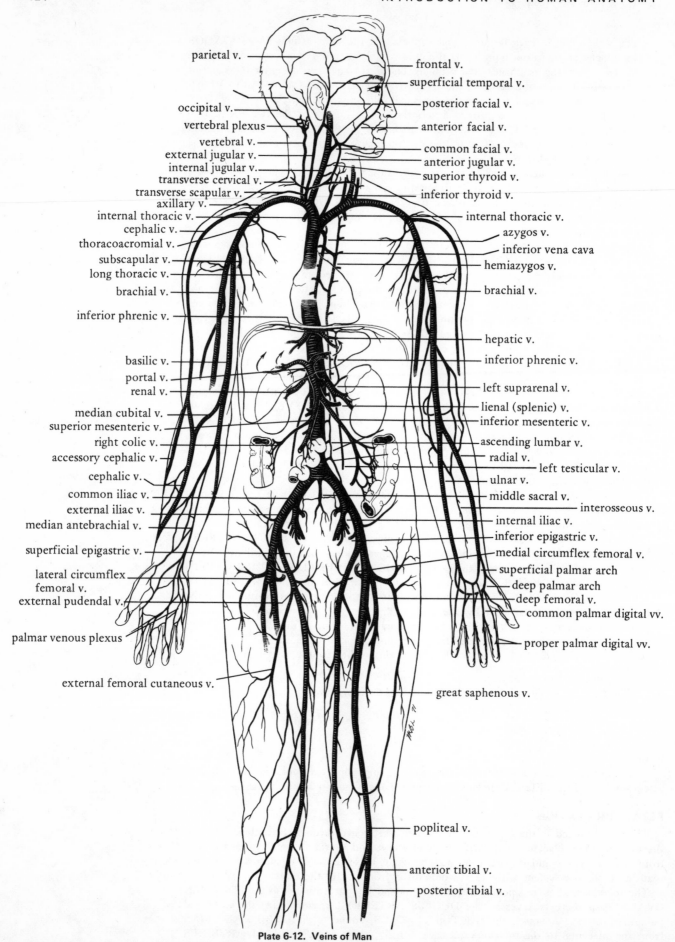

parietal v.
frontal v.
superficial temporal v.
occipital v.
posterior facial v.
vertebral plexus
anterior facial v.
vertebral v.
external jugular v.
common facial v.
internal jugular v.
anterior jugular v.
transverse cervical v.
superior thyroid v.
transverse scapular v.
inferior thyroid v.
axillary v.
internal thoracic v.
internal thoracic v.
cephalic v.
azygos v.
thoracoacromial v.
inferior vena cava
subscapular v.
hemiazygos v.
long thoracic v.
brachial v.
brachial v.
inferior phrenic v.
hepatic v.
inferior phrenic v.
basilic v.
portal v.
left suprarenal v.
renal v.
lienal (splenic) v.
median cubital v.
inferior mesenteric v.
superior mesenteric v.
ascending lumbar v.
right colic v.
radial v.
accessory cephalic v.
left testicular v.
cephalic v.
ulnar v.
common iliac v.
middle sacral v.
external iliac v.
interosseous v.
median antebrachial v.
internal iliac v.
inferior epigastric v.
superficial epigastric v.
medial circumflex femoral v.
superficial palmar arch
lateral circumflex
femoral v.
deep palmar arch
external pudendal v.
deep femoral v.
common palmar digital vv.
palmar venous plexus
proper palmar digital vv.
external femoral cutaneous v.
great saphenous v.
popliteal v.
anterior tibial v.
posterior tibial v.

Plate 6-12. Veins of Man

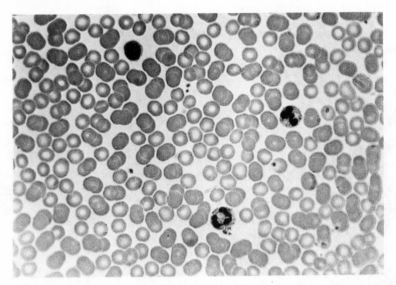

Figure 6-2. Photomicrograph of Blood

Since the blood entering the heart, through the inferior vena cava, has come largely from the placenta, it is oxygenated and does not need to go to the lungs. It passes instead through the foramen ovale into the left atrium, then to the left ventricle and out through the aorta. The blood from the superior vena cava enters the right atrium, goes to the right ventricle and then out through the aorta. Since the pulmonary artery is connected to the aorta by the ductus arteriosus, the bulk of this blood takes that route. A smaller amount continues into the lungs, giving them a minimal circulation. This is adequate since they are not yet serving the function of external respiration.

At birth, of course, the oval foramen closes and the ductus arteriosus becomes fibrous and circulation in this area is converted to that which you have just studied—that of the adult.

Refer to a textbook of human anatomy for diagrams and for an elaboration of the above important facts.

LYMPH-VASCULAR SYSTEM

A. Examine a prepared slide of a lymph node. Study Plate 6-13, figure 1. What are the functions of the lymphatic system?

The lymphatic system, because of the thin-walled condition of its vessels, cannot be dissected. However, you may be able to see the main vessel of the system, the THORACIC DUCT, as it comes up through the thorax just to the left of the mid-dorsal line. It appears to be segmented because of the presence of valves in it. It joins the veins at the junction of the left subclavian and the external jugular veins.

If a cat is available with a special injection in the lymphatic system, other vessels and the CHYLE CISTERN may be seen. Study Plate 6-14. Color the lymphatic structures green, arteries red, and veins blue.

Read carefully the section on the lymphatics in your textbook.

B. Lymph

What is its nature? Where does it come from? (See Plate 6-13, figure 3.)

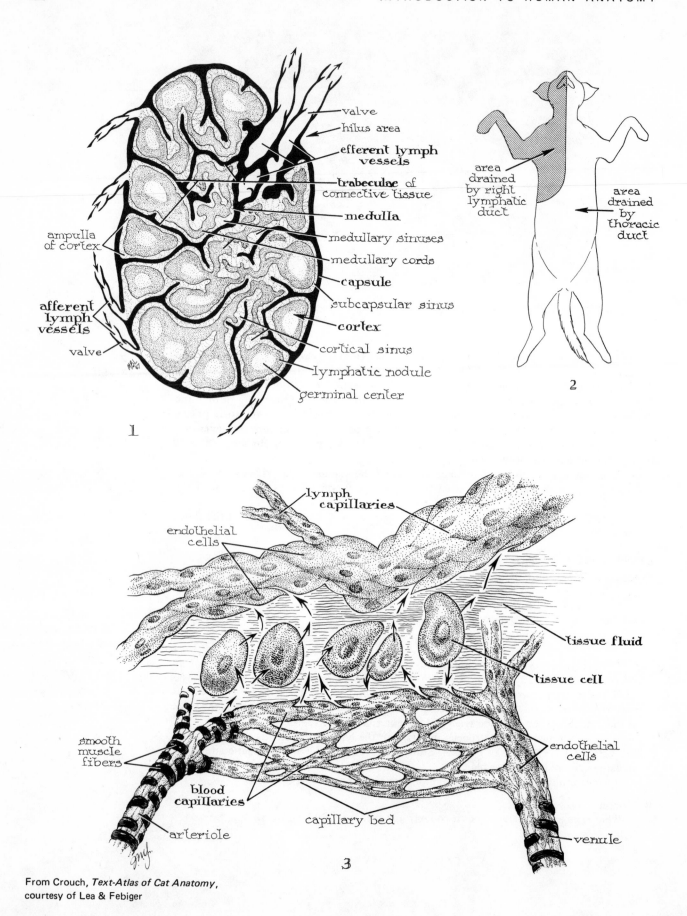

valve
hilus area
**efferent lymph
vessels**
trabeculae of
connective tissue
medulla
medullary sinuses
medullary cords
capsule
subcapsular sinus
cortex
cortical sinus
lymphatic nodule
germinal center

ampulla
of cortex

**afferent
lymph
vessels**

valve

1

area
drained
by right
lymphatic
duct

area
drained
by
thoracic
duct

2

lymph
capillaries

endothelial
cells

tissue fluid

tissue cell

endothelial
cells

smooth
muscle
fibers

blood
capillaries

arteriole

capillary bed

venule

3

From Crouch, *Text-Atlas of Cat Anatomy,*
courtesy of Lea & Febiger

Plate 6-13. The Lymphatic System

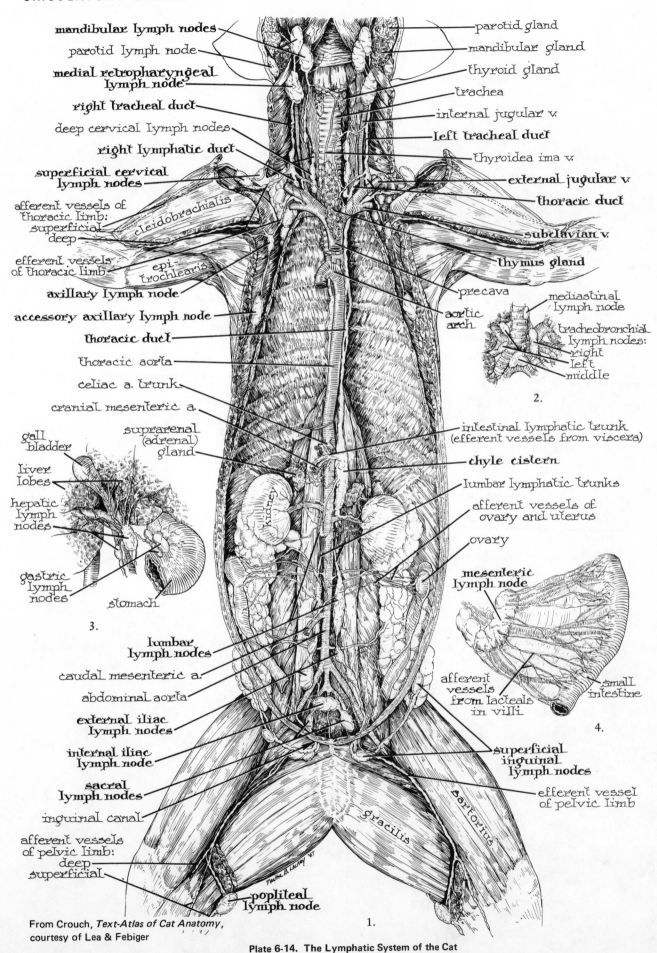

mandibular lymph nodes
parotid lymph node
medial retropharyngeal lymph node
right tracheal duct
deep cervical lymph nodes
right lymphatic duct
superficial cervical lymph nodes
afferent vessels of thoracic limb: superficial deep
efferent vessels of thoracic limb
axillary lymph node
accessory axillary lymph node
thoracic duct
thoracic aorta
celiac a. trunk
cranial mesenteric a.

parotid gland
mandibular gland
thyroid gland
trachea
internal jugular v.
left tracheal duct
thyroidea ima v.
external jugular v.
thoracic duct
subclavian v.
thymus gland
precava
aortic arch

cleidobrachialis
epi-trochlearis

mediastinal lymph node
tracheobronchial lymph nodes: right left middle

2.

gall bladder
liver lobes
hepatic lymph nodes
gastric lymph nodes
stomach

3.

suprarenal (adrenal) gland

kidney

intestinal lymphatic trunk (efferent vessels from viscera)
chyle cistern
lumbar lymphatic trunks
afferent vessels of ovary and uterus
ovary
mesenteric lymph node

lumbar lymph nodes
caudal mesenteric a.
abdominal aorta
external iliac lymph nodes
internal iliac lymph node
sacral lymph nodes
inguinal canal
afferent vessels of pelvic limb: deep superficial

afferent vessels from lacteals in villi

small intestine

4.

superficial inguinal lymph nodes
efferent vessel of pelvic limb

gracilis
sartorius

popliteal lymph node

1.

From Crouch, *Text-Atlas of Cat Anatomy*, courtesy of Lea & Febiger

Plate 6-14. The Lymphatic System of the Cat

GLOSSARY — Chapter 6

aorta (a ôr′tȧ): G., aorte, to lift, the great artery.

atrium (ā′tri um): L., a count, chamber.

auricle (ô′ri k'l): L., auricula, a little ear.

azygos (az′i gus): G., a, without; zygon, yoke.

capillary (kap′i ler′i): L., capillus, hair.

caudal (kô′d'l): L., cauda, tail.

chyle (kīl): G., chylos, juice.

circumflex (sûr′kum fleks): L., circum, round about; flectere, to bend.

celiac (sē′li ak): G., koilos, hollow.

coronary (kor′o ner i): L., crown or wreath.

endocardium (en do kär′di um): G., endon, within; kardia, heart.

epicardium (ep i kär′di um): G., epi, upon; kardia, heart.

epigastric (ep′i gas′trik): G., epi, upon; gaster, belly.

innominate (i nom′i nāt): L., innominatus, without a name.

intima (in′timȧ): L., intimus, innermost.

lymph (limf): L., lympha, water.

mesenteric (mes′en ter′ik): G., mesos, middle; enteron, gut.

myocardium (mī′o kär′di um): G., myos, muscle; kardia, heart.

phrenic (fren′ik): G., phren, phrenos, the diaphragm, the heart, the mind.

subclavian (sub clā′vi an): L., sub, under; clavis, key.

trabecula, pl. ae (trȧ bek′u lȧ, -lā): L., little beam.

tricuspid (trī kus′pid): L., tres, three; cuspis, point.

tunica (tū′ni kȧ): L., tunica, tunic.

umbilicus (um bil′i kus): L., umbilicus, navel.

vascular (vas′ku lēr): L., vasculum, a small vessel.

7

DIGESTIVE SYSTEM

GENERAL

The digestive system consists of those organs that are responsible for the ingestion, digestion, and absorption of food and the elimination of feces. In the human it is about 30 feet in length, extending from mouth to anus. The main organs of the system are the mouth, pharynx, esophagus, stomach, small intestine, large intestine, rectum and anus. Label Figure 7-1 and Plate 7-1.

Numerous glands empty into the digestive organs which provide the enzymes, water, mucus, and other agents required for digestion. Of these glands the salivary glands, liver, and pancreas are large and extend beyond the walls of the digestive tract. Other glands lie within the walls of the various organs and can be seen in prepared sections under the microscope.

A. Procedure

1. Identify as many of the digestive organs of the cadaver as possible.
2. Dissect the digestive system of the cat, noting especially the relationship of the organs to mesenteries, peritoneum, and celom.
3. Study the models of the digestive organs.
4. Study the slides of the digestive system.

All of the descriptions of organs below are of those found in the human body. The directions for dissection are for the work on the cat. Use your text and other books as needed.

MOUTH AND ACCESSORY STRUCTURES (Plate 7-2)

A. Salivary glands

These glands are not located in the mouth, but their ducts empty there. You may expose the SALIVARY GLANDS by picking away the connective tissue at the angle of the jaw and below the ear and back of the masseter muscle.

The PAROTID GLAND lies in front of and below the ear. Its duct, STENSEN'S DUCT, can be seen as it passes over the surface of the masseter muscle to the angle of the mouth. Here it passes through the buccal glands and opens into the mouth opposite the third premolar.

Behind the angle of the jaw is the SUBMANDIBULAR GLAND and just medial to it is the SUBLINGUAL GLAND. These should not be confused with the lymph nodes which lie along the anterior facial vein. The ducts of the submandibular and sublingual glands run quite deep and parallel one another and empty into the mouth on either side of the frenulum of the tongue.

Examine a section of the submandibular gland under the microscope, and note the granular serous cells and the open, clear mucous cells. Some of the tubules of the gland have both types of cells (Figure 7-2).

B. Mouth

The following structures should be observed. You may use a mirror and examine your

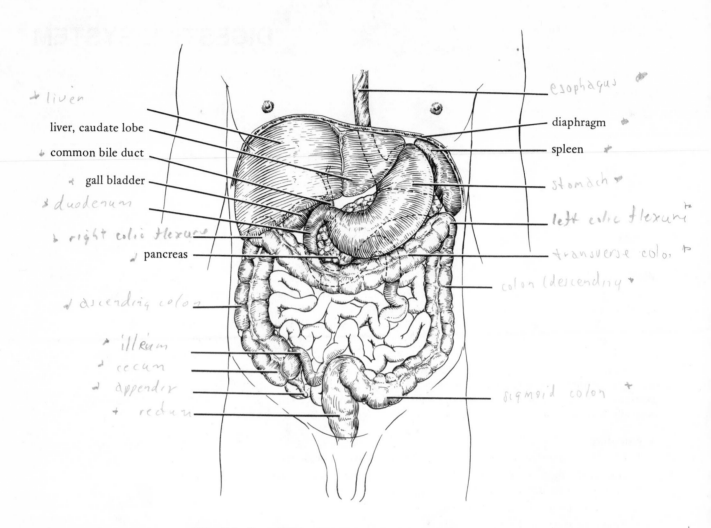

Figure 7-1. General View of the Digestive System of Man

Handwritten labels on the figure:

liver
liver, caudate lobe
common bile duct
gall bladder
duodenum
right colic flexure
pancreas
ascending colon
illeum
cecum
appendix
rectum

esophagus
diaphragm
spleen
stomach
left colic flexure
transverse colon
colon (descending)
sigmoid colon

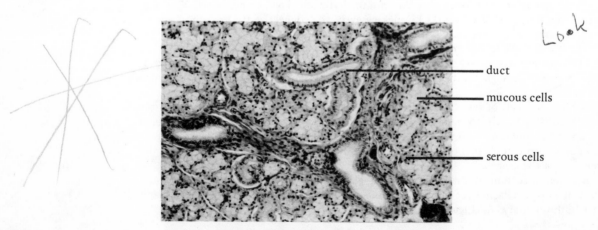

Look

duct
mucous cells
serous cells

Figure 7-2. Photomicrograph of Submandibular Gland of the Monkey (120X)

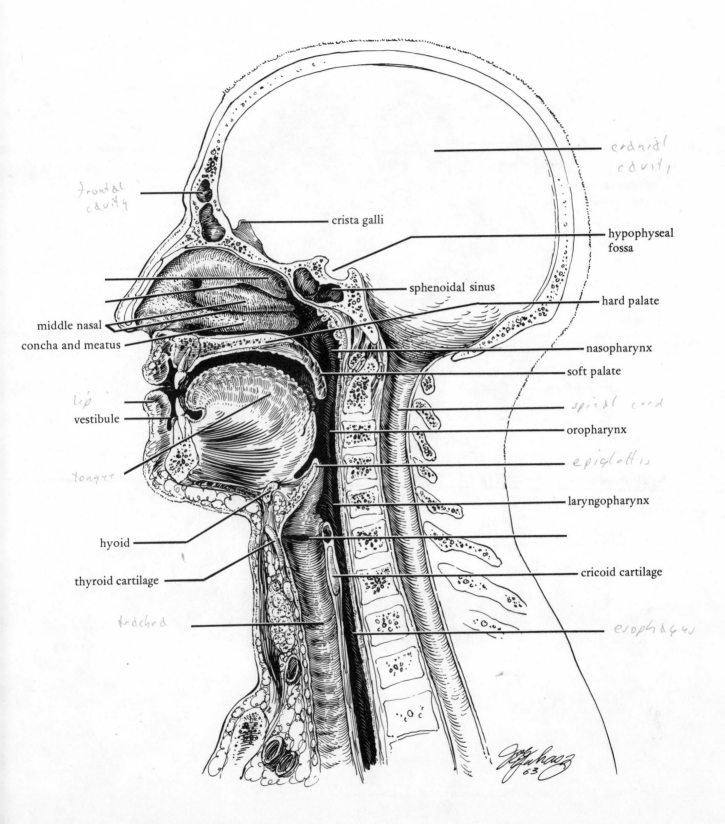

frontal cavity

crista galli

cranial cavity

hypophyseal fossa

sphenoidal sinus

hard palate

middle nasal concha and meatus

nasopharynx

soft palate

lip

spinal cord

vestibule

oropharynx

epiglottis

tongue

laryngopharynx

hyoid

thyroid cartilage

cricoid cartilage

trachea

esophagus

From Crouch, *Functional Human Anatomy,*
courtesy of Lea & Febiger

Plate 7-1. Sagittal Section of Head and Neck

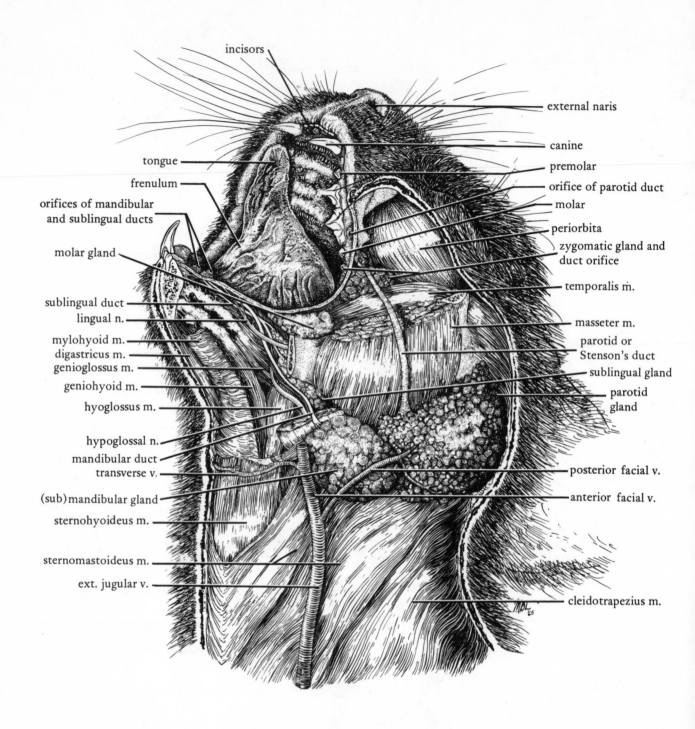

incisors

external naris

tongue

canine

frenulum

premolar

orifice of parotid duct

orifices of mandibular
and sublingual ducts

molar

periorbita

molar gland

zygomatic gland and
duct orifice

temporalis m.

sublingual duct

lingual n.

masseter m.

mylohyoid m.

parotid or
Stenson's duct

digastricus m.

genioglossus m.

sublingual gland

geniohyoid m.

parotid
gland

hyoglossus m.

hypoglossal n.

mandibular duct

transverse v.

posterior facial v.

(sub)mandibular gland

anterior facial v.

sternohyoideus m.

sternomastoideus m.

ext. jugular v.

cleidotrapezius m.

From Crouch, *Text-Atlas of Cat Anatomy*, courtesy of Lea & Febiger

Plate 7-2. Salivary Glands of the Cat

own mouth, or study your partner's mouth. The superficial layer of the mucous membrane of the mouth is STRATIFIED SQUAMOUS EPITHELIUM. To see these structures in the cat, it will be necessary to cut the corners of the mouth. First cut the soft tissues around the angle of the jaw to expose the bone. Then, using the bone cutters, cut through the mandible in front of the ramus, being careful not to destroy the muscles in the floor of the mouth. Extend the cut caudad on one side to open the pharynx and anterior end of the esophagus. You should now be able to identify most of the following structures in the cat (see Plate 7-2). Also refer to Plate 7-1 for these same structures in man.

1. Cheeks.
2. Lips.
3. Palate.

   What bones form the hard palate?

   a. Hard.
   b. Soft
      1) Uvula.
      2) Glossopalatine arch.
      3) Pharyngopalatine arch.
      4) Tonsilar fossae.
   c. Palatine tonsils.

4. Tongue (Plate 7-2)
   a. Primarily a muscular organ.
   b. Covered with mucous membrane with stratified squamous epithelium as surface layer.
   c. Papillae—modifications of tongue surface.
      1) Filiform.
      2) Fungiform.
      3) Vallate.
      4) Foliate.
      5) Conical.
   d. Taste buds (to be studied later).
   e. Frenulum—a fold or ridge between midline of tongue and floor of the mouth.

5. Teeth (Plate 7-2). Study the microscope slide.
   a. Crown, neck, root.
   b. Ivory substance (dentine).
   c. Adamant substance (enamel).
   d. Substantia ossea (cement).
   e. Pulp cavity.
      1) Contains nerves, blood vessels, and connective tissue.

6. Muscles of mouth (Plate 7-2)
   a. Temporal.
   b. Masseter.
   c. Pterygoideus lateralis.
   d. Pterygoideus medialis
   e. Digastricus.
   f. Mylohyoid.
   g. Geniohyoid.

These muscles have been mentioned on page 79. You should now attempt to find them on the cat. Remove the rest of the skin from the head of the cat. The TEMPORAL muscle will be seen on the lateral side of the skull. It lies behind the eye and above the ear. It inserts on the outer and inner surfaces of the coronoid process of the mandible. What is its function?

The MASSETER MUSCLE you saw as you studied the salivary glands. Where are its origin and insertion?

The PTERYGOIDEUS LATERALIS arises from the pterygoid process and neighboring parts of the palatine bone, and inserts on the medial aspect of the angle of the mandible. The PTERYGOIDEUS MEDIALIS lies caudal to the lateralis originating on the pterygoid process and inserting with the lateralis. What are the functions of these two muscles?

The DIGASTRICUS inserts on the ventral surface of the mandible, and has its origin near the mastoid process of the temporal and the jugular process. It helps to open the mouth. The remaining two muscles, the MYLOHYOID and the GENIOHYOID, are in the floor of the mouth. The MYLOHYOID is the superficial one, which inserts on the midventral raphe. Its fibers are transverse in direction. The GENIOHYOID can be exposed by cutting through the mylohyoid. It inserts on the hyoid apparatus and has its origin on the symphysis of the mandible. These muscles pull the hyoid bone forward and the mylohyoid elevates the floor of the mouth. See Plates 7-1 and 7-2.

PHARYNX

On Plate 7-1, locate and label the following structures:

A. Nasopharynx: upper part, behind nasal cavities. The PHARYNGEAL TONSILS (adenoids) are found here. The auditory (Eustachean) tubes open here, also.

B. Oropharynx: opens into mouth. The PALATINE TONSILS are on its lateral walls and the LINGUAL TONSILS, on the base of the tongue, are also in this region.

C. Laryngopharynx: lower part, the glottis and esophagus open from it.

D. What are the superior, middle, and inferior constrictors of the pharynx?

CROSS SECTION OF THE SMALL INTESTINE

A study of this cross section will serve to give an understanding of the nature of the walls of the digestive tract from esophagus to colon. Minor differences, however, are to be found in the various organs.

1. Study the photomicrographs and slides of the small intestine, and identify the following (Figures 7-3 and 7-4).
    a. Mucosa.
        1) simple columnar epithelium.
        2) goblet cells.
        3) villi.
        4) crypts of Liberkuhn.
        5) lamina propria (connective tissue).
        6) muscularis mucosae.
    b. Submucosa.
        1) composed of areolar connective tissue.
        2) contains Brunner's glands in duodenal region.
        3) Peyer's patch.
    c. Muscular layers (smooth).
        1) circular muscle—inner layer.
        2) longitudinal muscle—outer layer.
        3) oblique muscle (in stomach wall only).
    d. Serosa (visceral peritoneum).
        1) mesothelium (simple squamous epithelium).

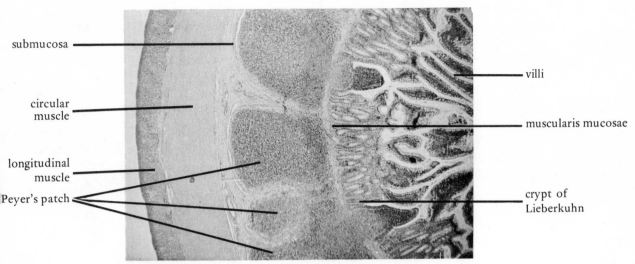

submucosa

circular
muscle

longitudinal
muscle

Peyer's patch

villi

muscularis mucosae

crypt of
Lieberkuhn

**Figure 7-3. Photomicrograph of a Cross Section
Through the Ileum (48X)**

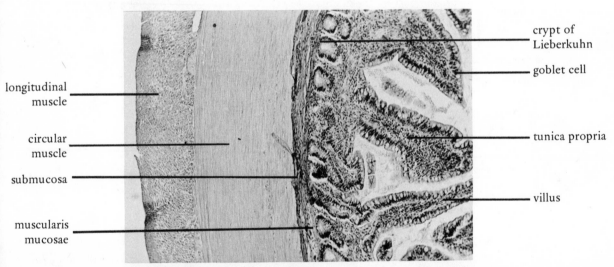

longitudinal
muscle

circular
muscle

submucosa

muscularis
mucosae

crypt of
Lieberkuhn

goblet cell

tunica propria

villus

**Figure 7-4. Photomicrograph of a Cross Section
Through the Ileum (120X)**

ESOPHAGUS (Plate 7-1)

This is a muscular tube passing from the pharynx through the neck, the thorax, and the diaphragm and into the abdominal cavity where it joins the stomach.

By removing some of the fascia and by pushing the organs to one side, the esophagus can be seen dorsal to the trachea and heart just in front of the vertebral column. Notice where it passes through the diaphragm.

A. Study a slide of a cross section of the esophagus.

    1. What kind of epithelium lines the esophagus?

    2. What kinds of muscles are found in the walls of the esophagus?

    3. Does the esophagus have a serosa?

    4. Where are the glands of the esophagus found?

STOMACH (Figure 7-1)

The stomach varies in position depending upon the body type of the individual and other factors. The border of the stomach to the left is called the GREATER CURVATURE, and that to the right is the LESSER CURVATURE. The larger, bulging left end of the stomach is the FUNDUS, the more constricted right end is the PYLORIS. The valve between the stomach and the duodenum is the PYLORIC SPHINCTER. Cut open the cat's stomach and locate the above valves. Notice also the character of the mucosa. What are rugae?

A. Study slides of the stomach wall and note the following (see Figures 7-5 and 7-6).

    1. Lining of simple columnar epithelium.

    2. Gastric glands—tubular, branched.

    3. Muscle layers—how many are there?

    4. Gastric pits.

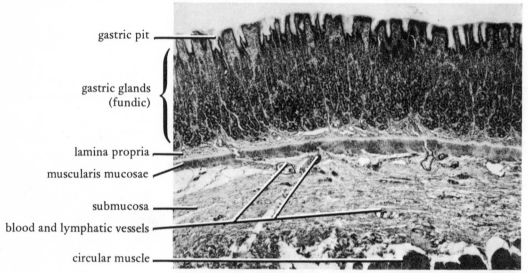

Figure 7-5. **Photomicrograph of a Longitudinal Section of the Fundic Stomach**

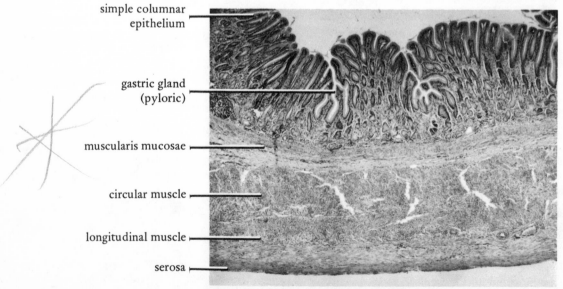

Figure 7-6. **Photomicrograph of a Longitudinal Section of the Pyloric Stomach (32X)**

SMALL INTESTINE (Figures 7-3 and 7-4; Plates 7-3 and 7-4)

A section of the small intestine has been studied. The small intestine is about 20 feet in length, and is divided into three parts.

A. Duodenum (Figures 7-1, 7-7, 7-8 and 7-9)

1. Notice the Brunner's glands in the submucosa of the cross section of the duodenum.

2. It is about 10 inches in length, and receives the ducts from the pancreas and liver. Locate these ducts and their opening into the duodenum. Label them on Figure 7-9.

B. Jejunum

1. About 8 feet in length.

C. Ileum (Figures 7-1, 7-3, 7-4; Plates 7-3 and 7-4)

1. It makes up the remainder of the small intestine and empties into the colon by the ileo-cecal valve. Locate the valve and label it on Figure 7-10.

2. What are Peyer's patches? Can you locate them on the histological sections of the ileum?

3. Study particularly the villi and label them on Plates 7-3 and 7-4. What is their function?

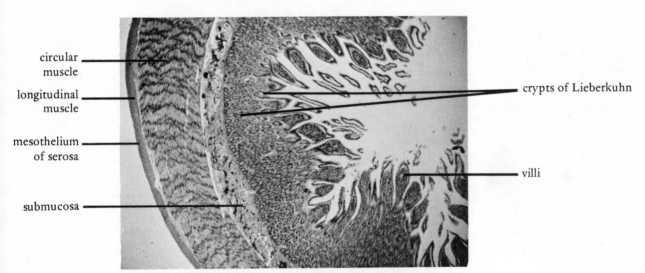

Figure 7-7. Photomicrograph of a Cross Section of the Duodenum of the Kitten (48X)

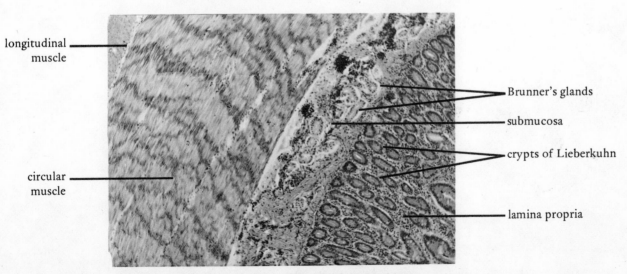

Figure 7-8. Photomicrograph of a Cross Section of the Duodenum of the Kitten (80X)

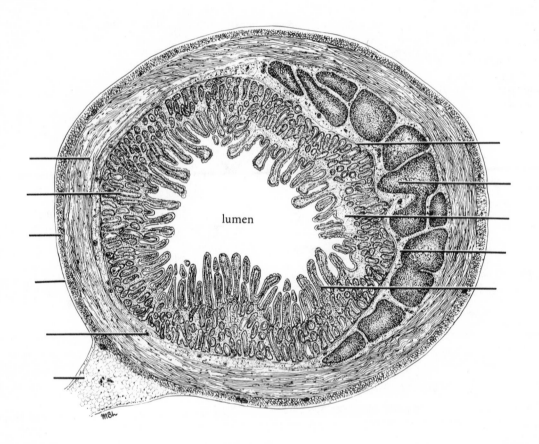

lumen

Plate 7-3. Drawing of a Cross Section of the Ileum

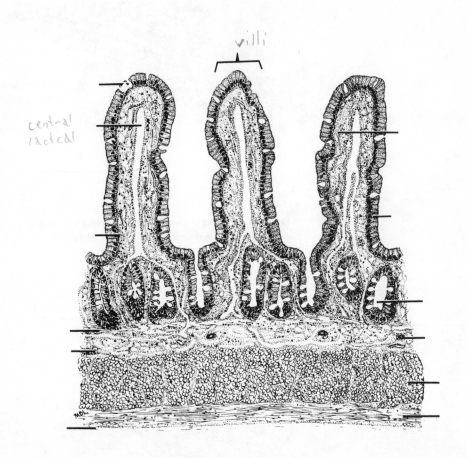

villi

central
lacteal

Plate 7-4. Schematic Diagram of a Longitudinal Section of the Ileum

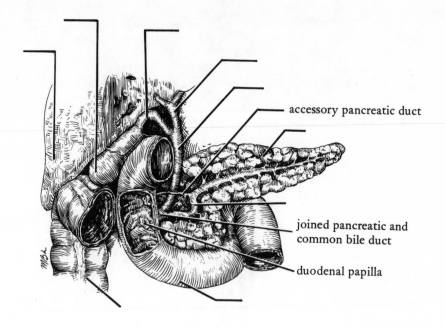

accessory pancreatic duct

joined pancreatic and
common bile duct

duodenal papilla

Figure 7-9. Drawing of Liver and Pancreas Showing Their
Relationship to the Duodenum and Colon

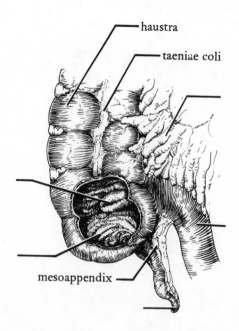

haustra

taeniae coli

mesoappendix

Figure 7-10. Drawing of Ileum, Colon, Cecum and Appendix
to Show Their Relationships

LARGE INTESTINE (Colon) (Figure 7-1)

The ileum enters the colon to one side rather than on its end, and hence leaves a small pouch, the CAECUM, at the end of which is found the VERMIFORM PROCESS or APPENDIX. Label Figure 7-10.

The colon is about five feet in length, and its parts take a definite course through the abdominal and pelvic cavities.

The colon is of greater diameter than the small intestine. Its walls are thrown into SACCULATIONS (haustra) because the longitudinal smooth muscles, laid down in three distinct bands around the colon, are not as long as the other layers of the colon. These bands of smooth muscle are called TAENIAE (taeniae coli). Label these on Figure 7-10.

A. Caecum and appendix
1. The appendix is attached to the mesentery of the small intestine by a small mesentery, the mesoappendix. Label Figure 7-10.

B. Ascending colon
1. It ascends on right side from the caecum to the inferior surface of the liver.
2. It lies against the posterior wall of the abdomen, and is covered anteriorly and laterally by peritoneum. It has no mesentery.
3. It bends to the left to form the transverse colon. This is the RIGHT COLIC FLEXURE.

C. Transverse colon
1. It crosses the abdominal cavity from right to left below the liver and stomach.
2. It has a mesentery, the mesocolon.
3. At the left end of the transverse colon there is an abrupt turn, the LEFT COLIC FLEXURE, leading into the descending colon.

D. Descending colon
1. It descends along the posterior abdominal wall on the left side of the iliac crest where it becomes the sigmoid colon.
2. It adheres to the posterior abdominal wall and hence has no mesentery.

E. Sigmoid colon (iliac and pelvic)
1. It makes an S-shaped curve from the left side to the midline where it joins the rectum.
2. It has a mesentery at the medial end.

F. Examine a cross section of the colon (Figure 7-11).
1. Mucosa.
   a. Notice the CRYPTS OF LIEBERKUHN which have many GOBLET CELLS.
   b. It has a simple columnar epithelium.
2. Submucosa.
   a. Large amounts of lymphoid tissue are present.

RECTUM

The rectum will be seen when the excretory system is studied.

This is the terminal portion of the digestive tube which passes in front of the sacrum and coccyx to empty at the ANUS.

The lower part of the rectum passes through the pelvic floor and is called the ANAL CANAL.

The anus is closed and operated by INTERNAL and EXTERNAL SPHINCTER MUSCLES.

LIVER (Plate 7-5)

This is the largest gland in the body and lies beneath the diaphragm with its greater bulk on the right side. It is divided into right and left lobes, the larger right lobe being further subdivided to form quadrate and caudate lobes.

The bile from the liver is received by two hepatic ducts, right and left, which unite to form a COMMON HEPATIC DUCT. The common hepatic duct soon joins a CYSTIC DUCT

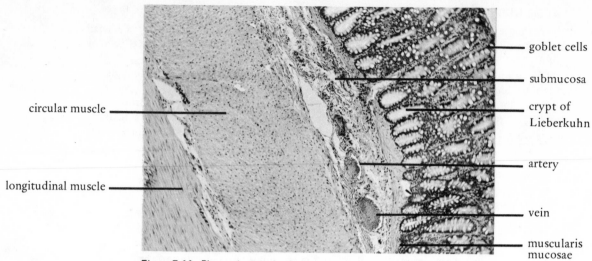

Figure 7-11. Photomicrograph of a Longitudinal Section of the Large Intestine (80X)

from the GALL BLADDER. The COMMON BILE DUCT, which empties into the duodenum, is formed by the union of the common hepatic and cystic ducts.

Locate the gall bladder and common bile duct in the cat. The common bile duct passes through the LESSER OMENTUM to reach the duodenum.

Notice the ligaments of the liver. Refer to your textbook.

Study a section of the liver, and note its microscopic structure.

Label Plate 7-5.

PANCREAS (Figures 7-1 and 7-9)

This gland lies with its head in the loop formed by the duodenum, and its tail extends to the left behind the stomach on the posterior abdominal wall.

It has a PANCREATIC DUCT running the length of the gland and emptying along with the common bile duct into the duodenum. An ACCESSORY DUCT may be present. Label Figure 7-9.

Locate this gland in the cat.

The pancreatic juice from this gland contains important digestive enzymes. Also, the gland contains special groups of cells known as the ISLANDS OF LANGERHANS which empty their secretion INSULIN into the blood directly. Insulin takes part in the regulation of sugar metabolism. Study a slide of the pancreas and find the islands of Langerhans.

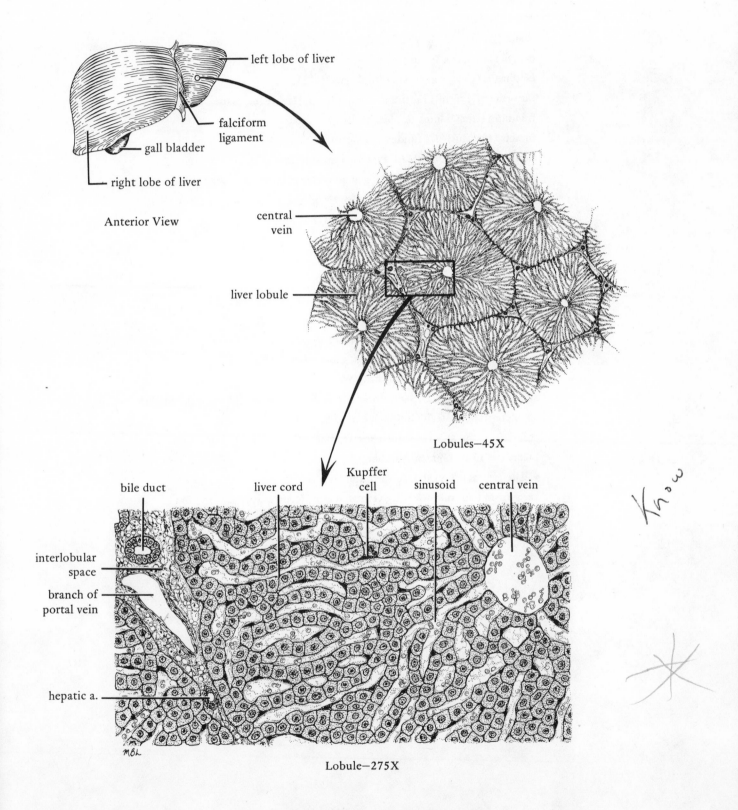

left lobe of liver

falciform
ligament

gall bladder

right lobe of liver

Anterior View

central
vein

liver lobule

Lobules—45X

bile duct

Kupffer
cell

liver cord

sinusoid

central vein

interlobular
space

branch of
portal vein

hepatic a.

Lobule—275X

Plate 7-5. The Liver—Gross and Microscopic Anatomy

GLOSSARY — Chapter 7

adamant (ad´ȧ mant): L., adamas, the hardest metal.

caecum (se´kum): L., caecus, blind.

crypt (kript): L., crypta, hidden.

cystic (sis´tik): G., kystis, a bladder.

enzyme (en´zim): G., en, in; zyme, leaven.

esophagus (e sôf´ȧ gus): G., oisophagos, gullet.

filiform (fil´i fôrm): L., filum, thread; form. Having the shape of a thread.

frenulum (fren´u lum): L., bit, bridle.

fundus (fun´dus): L., fundus, the bottom.

fungiform (fun´ji fôrm): L., fungus, a mushroom; forma, shape.

geniohyoid (je ni´o hī´oid): G., geneion, chin; upsilon, a Y-shaped letter.

glossopalatine (glos´o pal´ȧ tīn; –tin): G., glossa, tongue; L., palatum, palate.

haustrum (haws´trum): L., haustor, drawer.

ileum (il´e um): G., eilo, twist.

jejunum (je jōō´num): L., hungry.

lamina (lam´i nȧ): L., lamina, a thin plate.

mylohyoid (mī´lo hī´oid): G., myle, mill; upsilon, the letter "Y."

pharynx (far´ingks): G., pharynx, throat.

pterygoid (ter´i goid, pter–): G., pteron, wing.

pylorus (pī lō´rus, pi–): G., pyloros, gatekeeper.

rectum (rek´tum): L., rectus, straight.

sigmoid (sig´moid): G., sigmoeides, Greek letter corresponding to the English "S."

sphincter (sfingk´tēr): G., sphingein, to bind tight.

stomach (stum´ȧk): G., stomachos, stomach, throat, gullet, from stoma, mouth.

taenia (tē´ni ȧ): L., taenia, ribbon.

vallate (val´at): L., vallo, to surround with a wall.

vermiform (vûr´mi fôrm): L., vermis, worm; form, shape.

8

RESPIRATORY SYSTEM

GENERAL

One of the basic needs of all living things is oxygen for carrying on metabolism. In the simpler forms of animals this is readily obtained through the cell membranes directly from the external environment. In higher forms, with their more complex bodies, special systems of organs have evolved to take care of this requirement. In higher vertebrates including man the lungs are the essential organs of respiration, for it is through their thin membranes that the oxygen of the air passes into the blood and is distributed to the body as a whole. Carbon dioxide passes through these same membranes, but in the opposite direction, and the elimination of this waste product of metabolism is the second important function of the respiratory system. The remaining organs of the respiratory system serve for the passage of air into and out of the lungs—inspiration and expiration. A third function, in part at least attributed to this system, is voice production. Some water and heat are lost through the lungs.

PROCEDURE

A. Locate the following organs on the cadaver. (Demonstration.)

    1. Larynx.

    2. Trachea.

    3. Bronchi.

    4. Root of lung.

    5. Lungs.

    6. Pleura.
        a. Visceral pleura.
        b. Parietal pleura.

    7. Pleural cavity.

    8. Mediastinum.

    9. Diaphragm.

  10. On Plates 8-1 and 8-2 color the blood vessels red or blue to show oxygen content of blood carried.

B. Locate the above organs on your cat (Plate 8-2).

C. Study the following slides.

    1. Cross section of trachea.

    2. Section of lung.

    3. Section of injected lung.

D. Make full use of your textbook and any reference books which may be available.

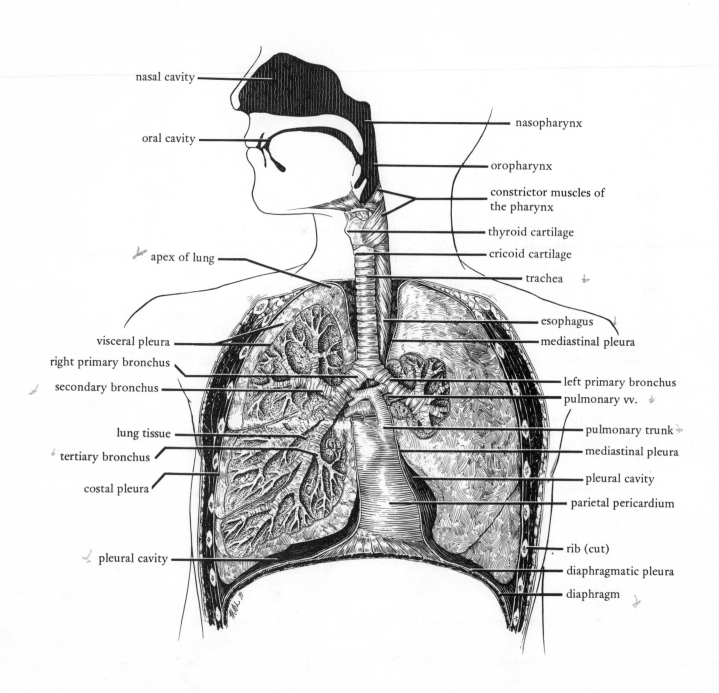

nasal cavity

oral cavity

apex of lung

visceral pleura
right primary bronchus
secondary bronchus

lung tissue
tertiary bronchus

costal pleura

pleural cavity

nasopharynx

oropharynx

constrictor muscles of
the pharynx

thyroid cartilage

cricoid cartilage

trachea

esophagus

mediastinal pleura

left primary bronchus
pulmonary vv.

pulmonary trunk

mediastinal pleura

pleural cavity

parietal pericardium

rib (cut)

diaphragmatic pleura

diaphragm

Plate 8-1. The Respiratory System of Man

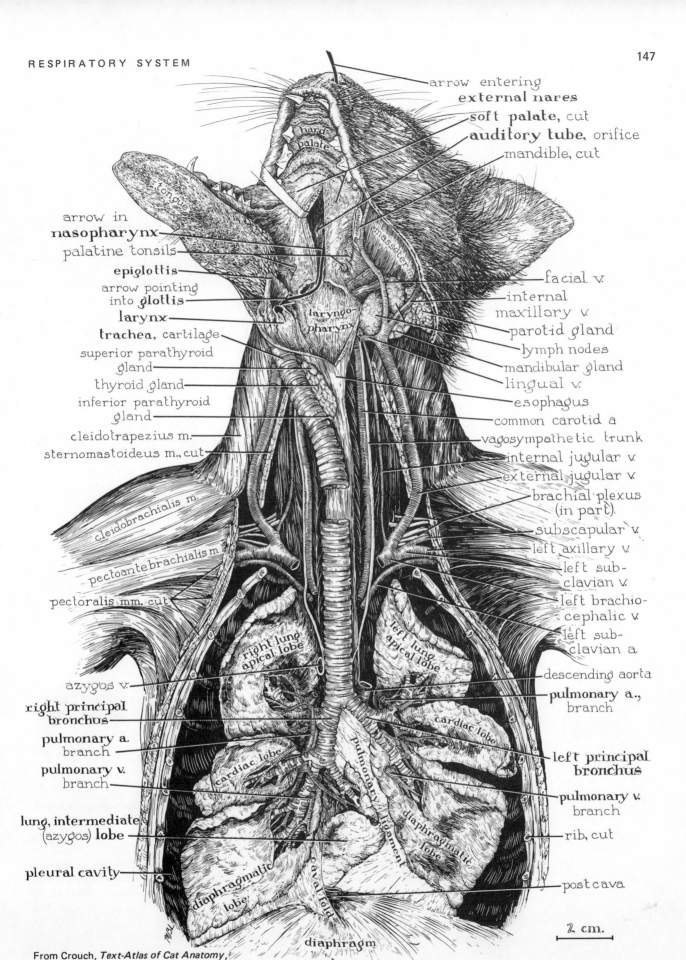

arrow entering
external nares
soft palate, cut
auditory tube, orifice
mandible, cut

hard palate

tongue

masseter

arrow in
nasopharynx
palatine tonsils
epiglottis
arrow pointing
into **glottis**
larynx
trachea, cartilage
superior parathyroid
gland
thyroid gland
inferior parathyroid
gland
cleidotrapezius m.
sternomastoideus m., cut

laryngo-
pharynx

facial v.
internal
maxillary v.
parotid gland
lymph nodes
mandibular gland
lingual v.
esophagus
common carotid a.
vagosympathetic trunk
internal jugular v.
external jugular v.
brachial plexus
(in part)
subscapular v.
left axillary v.
left sub-
clavian v.
left brachio-
cephalic v.
left sub-
clavian a.

cleidobrachialis m.

pectoantebrachialis m

pectoralis mm. cut

right lung
apical lobe

left lung
apical lobe

azygos v.
**right principal
bronchus**
pulmonary a.
branch
pulmonary v.
branch

**lung, intermediate
(azygos) lobe**

pleural cavity

cardiac lobe

cardiac lobe

pulmonary
ligament

diaphragmatic
lobe

descending aorta
pulmonary a.,
branch

**left principal
bronchus**

pulmonary v.
branch

rib, cut

post cava

diaphragmatic
lobe

caval fold

diaphragm

2 cm.

From Crouch, *Text-Atlas of Cat Anatomy,*
courtesy of Lea & Febiger

Plate 8-2. The Respiratory System of the Cat

E. Make use of models
  1. Of human torso.
  2. Of human head—cut in parasagittal section.
  3. Of human larynx.

NOSE AND PHARYNX (Plate 7-1 and 8-2)

A. The skeletal framework of the nose should be reviewed.

B. The relations of the nasal passageways and nasopharynx to the sinuses, auditory tube, middle ear and mastoid cells should be reviewed.

C. The pharyngeal tonsils are located on the posterior wall of the nasopharynx.
  1. What is the condition of their enlargement called, and what are the consequences?

D. What other functions, besides the passage of air, are centered in the nose?

E. The remaining portions of the pharynx are the oropharynx and laryngopharynx.
  1. What are their functions?

LARYNX (Voice Box) (Figure 8-1, Plates 8-1 and 8-2)

The larynx is located at the top of the trachea or wind pipe and ventral (anterior) to the laryngopharynx. It has a framework of nine cartilages, the most prominent of which are the thyroid, cricoid, and epiglottis. Dissect the larynx of the cat and identify the following.

A. Thyroid cartilage
  1. This is evidenced externally as the Adam's apple. It is the largest of the cartilages.

B. Cricoid
  1. This lies below the thyroid and is shaped like a signet ring with the signet part of the ring placed posteriorly.

C. Epiglottis
  1. This is a fairly large cartilage at the base of the tongue and at the top of the larynx. The epiglottis serves to shut off the larynx when the individual is swallowing. Actually, the larynx is lifted against the epiglottis.

D. The other cartilages of the larynx are: ARYTENOIDS (2), CORNICULATES (2), and CUNEIFORMS (2). (Refer to your textbook.)

E. Vocal cords
  1. The vocal cords consist of two folds on each side which are stretched across the larynx from anterior to posterior. They attach to the thyroid cartilage in front and to the two arytenoid cartilages behind. The upper folds are the SUPERIOR or FALSE VOCAL CORDS; the lower ones are the INFERIOR or TRUE VOCAL CORDS.
    The TRUE VOCAL CORDS consist of elastic and fibrous ligaments and are covered by mucous membrane. The tension on the cords is regulated by small muscles which move the arytenoid cartilages and hence stretch or relax the cords. The FALSE VOCAL CORDS or VENTRICULAR FOLDS help to keep the true vocal cords moist and in holding the breath.
  2. What other structures serve in voice or speech in man?

3. The opening between the vocal cords is the GLOTTIS. Label Figure 8-1.

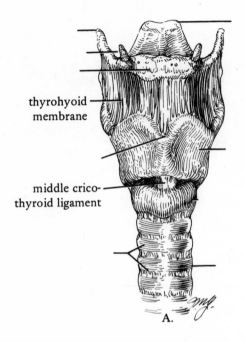

thyrohyoid
membrane

middle crico-
thyroid ligament

A.

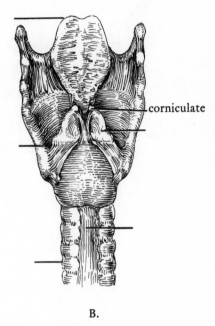

corniculate

B.

Figure 8-1. Larynx of Man

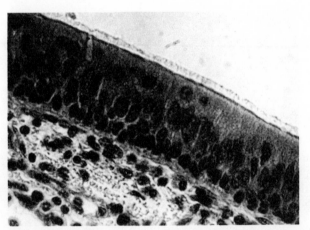

**Figure 8-2. Photomicrograph of Pseudostratified Ciliated Columnar
Epithelium of the Trachea (450X)**

`RACHEA (Plates 8-1 and 8-2)

Examine a cross section of the trachea, and be able to answer the following questions:

1. What kind of epithelium lines the trachea? Label Figure 8-2.

2. Describe a tracheal cartilage.

   3. What is the purpose of the tracheal cartilages?

BRONCHI (Plates 8-1 and 8-2)

   The bronchi diverge from the base of the trachea to the ROOTS of the lungs. The right bronchus is shorter, wider, and more nearly vertical than is the left one. Note that the pulmonary artery and veins also enter and leave the lungs at the root.

LUNGS (Plates 8-1 and 8-2, Figures 8-3 and 8-4)

A. Examine the lungs of the cadaver.
   1. How many lobes has each lung?

   2. Locate the root of each lung.
   3. Do the lungs have ligaments?

B. Examine the lungs of the cat (Plate 8-2).
   1. Note their relationships to the heart and other thoracic structures.
   2. How many lobes do they have?

   3. Do the lungs have ligaments?

   4. Using a hose or glass tube and the compressed air, inflate the cat's lung.

C. Examine slides of the lungs to study their histology. Compare with Figures 8-3 and 8-4.
   1. Injected section of lung.
      a. Note the capillary networks.
   2. Uninjected section of lung.
      a. Notice relationships of alveoli and other minute structures of the lung.

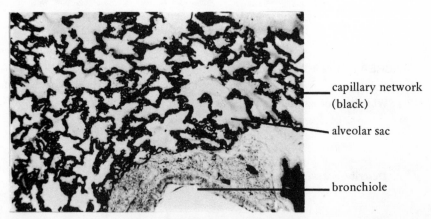

Figure 8-3. Photomicrograph of an Injected Lung of Man (80X)

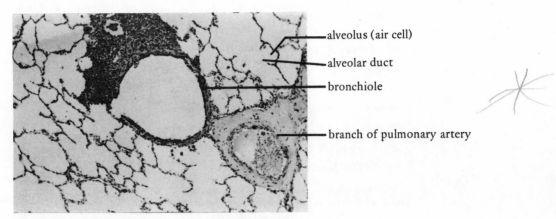

Figure 8-4. Photomicrograph of Lung of the Cat (80X)

PLEURA AND PLEURAL CAVITIES (A Review—See Plate 8-2)

A. Each lung is covered by a serous membrane known as the VISCERAL PLEURA which is reflected onto the wall of the thorax as the PARIETAL PLEURA. The potential space between these two membranes is the PLEURAL CAVITY.

   1. What is pleurisy?

   2. What is the mediastinum?

      a. How is the mediastinum related to the parietal pleura?

BREATHING MUSCLES

A. Diaphragm (Plates 8-1 and 8-2)
   1. Locate this muscle.
      a. Where is its tendon?

      b. What is its relationship to the parietal pleura?

B. Intercostal muscles.
   1. Locate external and internal intercostal muscles.
C. Abdominal muscles.
   1. By compressing the abdomen, force the expiration of air.

GLOSSARY — Chapter 8

adenoid (ad ′e noid′): G., aden, gland; eidos, like, form.

alveolar (al vē′ō lār): L., alveolus, a little cavity.

arytenoid (ar′i tē′noid): G., arytaina, funnel, pitcher.

bronchiole (brong′ki ȯl): L., bronchus, windpipe (little).

bronchus (bron′kus): G., bronchus, windpipe.

corniculate (kôr nik′ū lāt): L., cornu, horn.

cricoid (krī′koid): G., kriksos, ring.

cuneiform (kū nē′i fôrm): L., cuneus, wedge; forma, shape.
(Note: Long u is pronounced like the word "you.")

epiglottis (ep′i glȯt′is): G., epi, upon; glotta, tongue.

larynx (lar′inks): G., laryngx, the organ of voice.

mediastinum (mē′di as tī′num): L., mediastinus, being in the middle.

oral (ô′ral): L., os, mouth.

pleura (plū′rȧ): G., pleura, rib, side.

respiratory (re spir′ȧ to ry): L., re, again; spirare, to breathe.

tonsil (ton′sil): L., tonsilla, a small rounded mass.

trachea (trā′ki ȧ): L., trachia, rough.

9

EXCRETORY SYSTEM

GENERAL

The excretory system consists of the essential organs, the KIDNEYS, and the accessory organs, the URETERS, URINARY BLADDER, and URETHRA.

This system has the following functions:

1. Elimination of metabolic wastes.
2. Regulation of the water balance in the body.
3. Regulation of hydrogen ion concentration (acid-base balance).

Other systems such as the skin and the respiratory, supplement the excretory system in the elimination of metabolic wastes. Except for the urethra, the system in the male and the female are essentially alike

PROCEDURE

A. Study the gross anatomy of the system as seen in the cadaver.

B. Study the models and charts of this system.

C. Dissect these organs in the cat. Observe them in both male and female.

D. Study microscopic anatomy, using prepared slides.

KIDNEYS

These are called the essential organs of excretion because they actually remove the wastes and other material from the blood.

A. Locate these organs which lie against the posterior or dorsal body wall outside of the peritoneum (retroperitoneal). Locate the renal artery and vein and the ureter. Remove one kidney by loosening the peritoneum and supporting tissues. Make a frontal section of this kideny to show the pelvis, medulla, and cortex. Label these structures on Plate 9-1.

B. Examine slides of sections of a kidney and locate the following structures: glomerulus, glomerular (Bowman's) capsule, renal corpuscle, blood vessels, medulla, cortex. What kinds of epithelia make up the kidney tubule?

Reference to Plate 9-2 will aid you in the identification of structures on the slides. These structures constitute a renal tubule (nephron), the structural and functional unit of the kidney. Each kidney contains about 1,000,000 of these units.

What are the pyramids of the kidneys? Label on Plate 9-1.

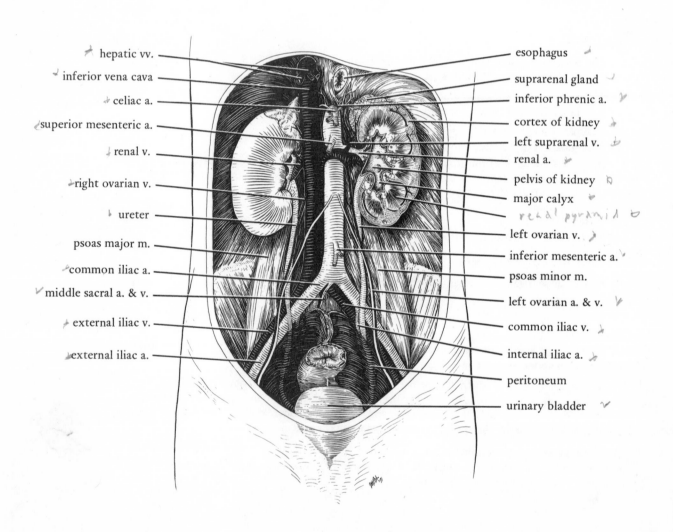

hepatic vv.
inferior vena cava
celiac a.
superior mesenteric a.
renal v.
right ovarian v.
ureter
psoas major m.
common iliac a.
middle sacral a. & v.
external iliac v.
external iliac a.

esophagus
suprarenal gland
inferior phrenic a.
cortex of kidney
left suprarenal v.
renal a.
pelvis of kidney
major calyx
renal pyramid
left ovarian v.
inferior mesenteric a.
psoas minor m.
left ovarian a. & v.
common iliac v.
internal iliac a.
peritoneum
urinary bladder

Plate 9-1. Excretory System of Man—Anterior View

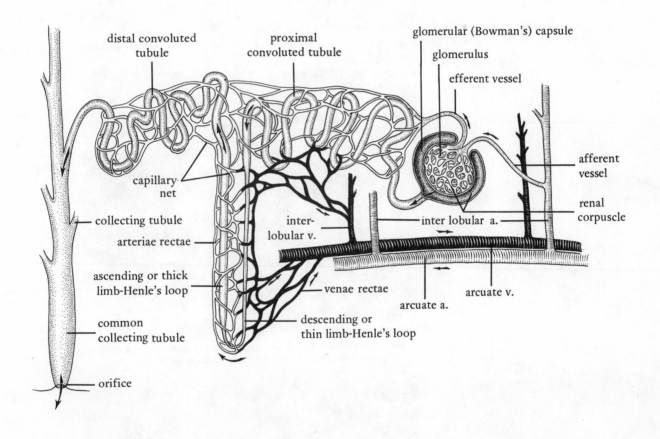

distal convoluted
tubule

proximal
convoluted tubule

glomerular (Bowman's) capsule

glomerulus

efferent vessel

afferent
vessel

renal
corpuscle

capillary
net

collecting tubule

arteriae rectae

ascending or thick
limb-Henle's loop

common
collecting tubule

orifice

inter-
lobular v.

inter lobular a.

venae rectae

descending or
thin limb-Henle's loop

arcuate a.

arcuate v.

Plate 9-2. Diagram of a Kidney Tubule and Its Blood Supply

Study Closely

proximal
convoluted tubules

*smaller lumen
lots of cytoplasm*

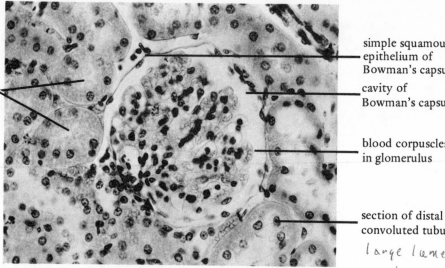

simple squamous
epithelium of
Bowman's capsule

cavity of
Bowman's capsule

blood corpuscles
in glomerulus

section of distal
convoluted tubule

*large lumen
small amount
of cytoplasm*

Figure 9-1. Photomicrograph of a Section of a Kidney Through the Cortex

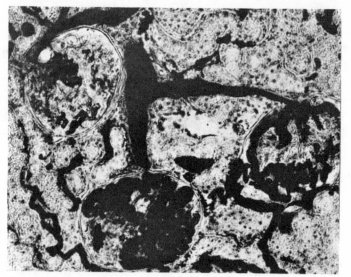

**Figure 9-2. Photomicrograph of a Section of an Injected Kidney Showing
Three Renal Corpuscles (Blood Vessels are Black)**

Look

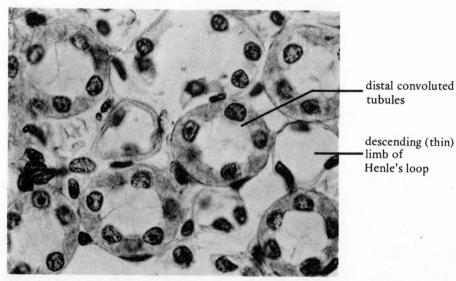

distal convoluted
tubules

descending (thin)
limb of
Henle's loop

**Figure 9-3. Photomicrograph of Kidney Tubules Showing Convuluted
Tubules and the Thin Limb of Henle's Loop**

URETER

A. Follow the course of the ureter from the kidney to the bladder in the cat. Where does the ureter enter the bladder?

What is the relationship of the ureter to the parietal peritoneum?

B. Examine a cross section of the ureter under the microscope. Be able to describe the layers in the walls of the ureter (Figure 9-4).

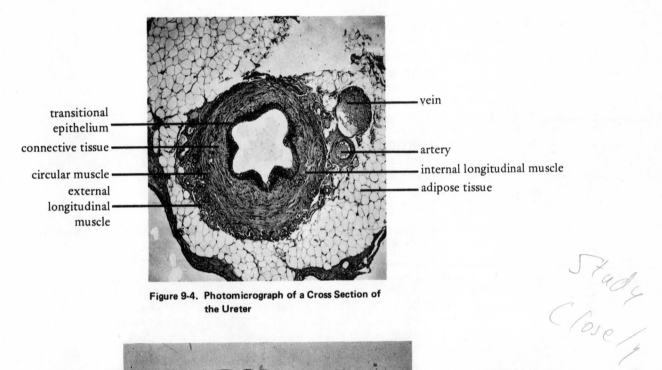

transitional epithelium

connective tissue

circular muscle

external longitudinal muscle

vein

artery

internal longitudinal muscle

adipose tissue

Figure 9-4. Photomicrograph of a Cross Section of the Ureter

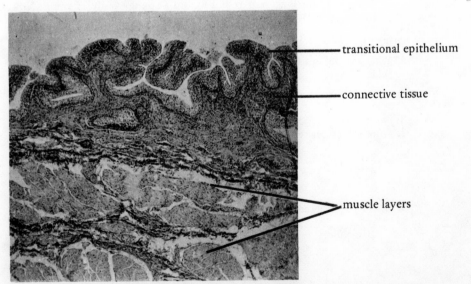

transitional epithelium

connective tissue

muscle layers

Figure 9-5. Photomicrograph of a Section of the Urinary Bladder

Study Closely

BLADDER

A. Study the position of the bladder in relationship to other organs in the male and female cats. Examine the bladder in the cadaver. What ligaments support the bladder? See Plate 5-1, page 99.

B. Examine a section of the urinary bladder and compare the layers of tissue with those of the ureter (Figure 9-5).

URETHRA

A. Urethra in the Cat (Plate 10-6)

To expose the full length of the urethra, it will be necessary to separate the ISCHIOPUBIC SYMPHYSIS. If your cat is a male, care must be taken to avoid injuring the SPERMATIC CORDS which lie close beneath the skin and to either side of the midventral line. Using a scalpel, cut through the thick muscle lying over the ischiopubic symphysis. Having cut through this, insert the scalpel into the midline of the symphysis and separate the bones. This may be more difficult in the male than in the female cat. Take care not to cut more than through the bone, for the urogenital canal lies close to the symphysis. Now you can dissect out the terminal portions of the urogenital systems. In the male the URETHRA can be traced to the PENIS through which it passes to open to the outside. In the female the urethra will be joined by the VAGINA and the two have a common passage to the outside (Plate 10-5, figures 1 and 4)

B. Urethra in Man (Plates 10-1 and 10-3)

1. Female

The URETHRA in the human female is about one and one-half inches long. It opens INDEPENDENTLY of the VAGINA to the outside.

2. Male

The human male has a urethra about eight inches long. It is divided into three parts. The portion just below the bladder is surrounded by the PROSTATE GLAND and is called the PROSTATIC URETHRA. The next part, the MEMBRANOUS URETHRA, passes through the floor of the pelvis (UROGENITAL DIAPHRAGM) and is very short. The final and longest part lies within a spongy body of the PENIS and is called the SPONGY URETHRA.

QUESTIONS

1. What kind of epithelium lines the bladder and ureters?

2. What structures regulate the flow of urine from the bladder?

3. Could you diagram and label a longitudinal section of a kidney?

4. What components of the kidney tubule lie within the cortex of the kidney? Within the medulla?

5. Trace the course of a drop of urine from the collecting tubule of a nephron to the external orifice of the male urethra, naming in logical order all structures through which it would pass.

GLOSSARY — Chapter 9

adrenal (à drē′nàl): L., ad, upon; renes, kidneys.

arcuate (âr′kū āt): L., arcue, bow, curvature.

calyx (kā′liks): L., calyx, cup of a flower.

convolute (kon′vo lūt): L., cum, together; volvere, to wind.

corpuscle (kôr′pu sul): L., corpusculus, small body.

cribrosa (krib′rō sà): L., cribrum, sieve.

glomerulus (glôm ēr′ū lus): L., glomus, ball (little).

hilum or hilus (hī′lum or hī′lus): L., hilum, trifle (depression or notch).

lobar (lo′bär): G., lobos, lobe (any rounded projection of an organ).

lobular (lob′ū lär): G., lobos, lobe (little).

nephros (nef′ros): G., nephros, kidney.

pyramid (pir′à mid): L., pyramis, pyramid, conical structure.

ureter (ū rē′tẽr): G., oureter, ureter.

urethra (ū rē′thrà): G., from ouron, urine.

10

REPRODUCTIVE SYSTEM

GENERAL

This system is composed of those organs whose specific function is to reproduce the individual and thus to maintain the species. The essential organs of reproduction, those which produce the germ cells, are the ovaries and the testes. The accessory organs of reproduction are those which transport, house or otherwise serve the germ cells in their later development.

PROCEDURE

1. Study the models and charts of the male and female pelves.
2. Examine the system in the cadaver and be able to identify the organs, as outlined below.
3. Dissect the system in the cat and identify the organs. Be sure to see both sexes.
4. Study the slides as indicated in the discussion below.
5. Be able to list the homologies between the male and female systems.

FEMALE REPRODUCTIVE SYSTEM—MAN

A. General (Plate 10-1).

1. Internal organs.
   a. Ovaries: produce eggs and hormones.
   b. Uterine tubes: conduct eggs to uterus.
   c. Uterus: receives egg or embryo. If the egg has been fertilized the uterus houses the embryo and fetus until birth.
   d. Vagina: allows passage of blood and debris of menstrual period, and serves as birth canal. Opens into the area called the VESTIBULE.
2. External organs (pudendum—vulva).
   a. Mons pubis: rounded fatty eminence covered after puberty with hair.
   b. Labia majora: two large longitudinal skin folds extending backward from the mons pubis, one on each side of the vestibule. Homologous to scrotum.
   c. Labia minora: small skin folds which lie mediad to b. Anteriorly, they pass around the clitoris.
   d. Clitoris: homologous to penis, contains erectile tissue.
   e. (Urethral opening.)
   f. Vaginal orifice.
   g. Hymen: a semilunar or annular fold of mucous membrane which partially closes the vaginal orifice.
   h. Perineum: corresponds to the outlet of the pelvis.

The student should be able to identify the above organs and structures. Their relative positions in the body should be understood. Label the diagrams of the female reproductive system (Plate 10-1).

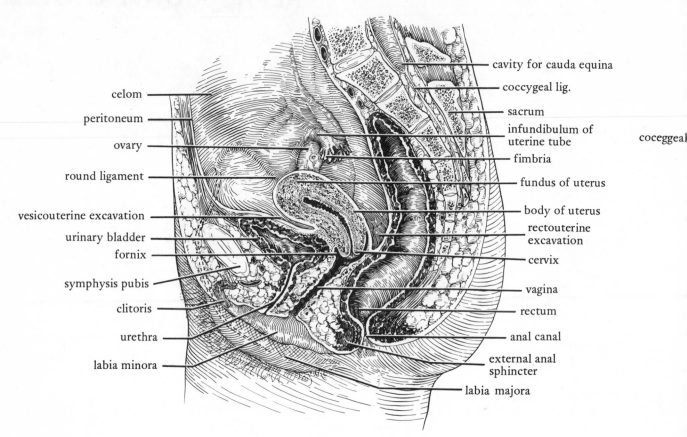

celom

peritoneum

ovary

round ligament

vesicouterine excavation

urinary bladder

fornix

symphysis pubis

clitoris

urethra

labia minora

cavity for cauda equina

coccygeal lig.

sacrum

infundibulum of
uterine tube

fimbria

fundus of uterus

body of uterus

rectouterine
excavation

cervix

vagina

rectum

anal canal

external anal
sphincter

labia majora

coceggeal

1. Sagittal Section of the Female Pelvis

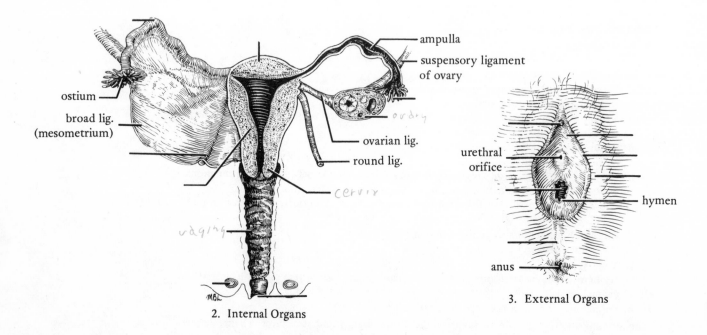

ampulla

suspensory ligament
of ovary

ostium

broad lig.
(mesometrium)

ovary

ovarian lig.

round lig.

cervir

vagina

2. Internal Organs

urethral
orifice

hymen

anus

3. External Organs

Plate 10-1. Reproductive Organs of the Human Female

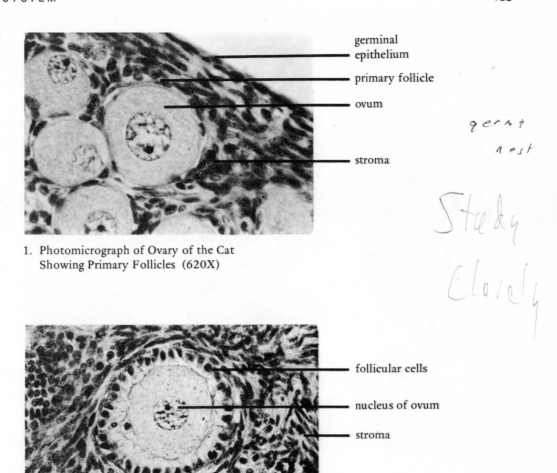

germinal epithelium

primary follicle

ovum

stroma

germ nest

Study Closely

1. Photomicrograph of Ovary of the Cat
   Showing Primary Follicles (620X)

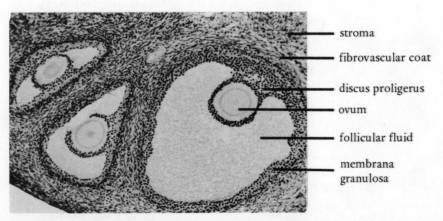

follicular cells

nucleus of ovum

stroma

2. Photomicrograph of a Growing Follicle
   of the Ovary of a Cat (360X)

stroma

fibrovascular coat

discus proligerus

ovum

follicular fluid

membrana granulosa

3. Photomicrograph of Vesicular
   (Graafian) Follicle (80X)

Plate 10-2. Stages in Growth and Development of Ovarian Follicles

B. Ovaries. Examine a section of an ovary under the microscope and locate the following (Plate 10-2):

1. Germinal epithelium: covers surface of ovary.
2. Primary follicles: the small cells around the ova.
3. Vesicular (Graafian) follicles: the mature follicles.
4. Stroma: the connective tissue component of the ovary.
5. Corpus luteum: formed from the cells of a vesicular follicle after the ovum is discharged.

Draw and label a vesicular (Graafian) follicle.

C. Uterine tube.
1. What is the relationship of the ovary and uterine tube?

2. What is the infundibulum?

3. What are fimbriae?

4. What kind of tissue lines the uterine tubes?

D. Uterus (womb).
1. Identify the body and cervix of the uterus.
2. What and where are the broad and round ligaments of the uterus?

3. The three layers in the wall of the uterus are as follows:
   a. Endometrium: the lining or mucosa.
   b. Middle muscular layer: the thickest.
   c. Serous coat: visceral peritoneum.

E. Vagina (birth canal).
1. What are the anterior, lateral, and posterior fornices?

MALE REPRODUCTIVE SYSTEM—MAN

A. General (Plate 10-3).
1. Testis and epididymis: for production of sperm and male sex hormone, and for conduction of sperms.
2. Ductus deferens (sperm duct): conveys sperms from epididymis.
3. Seminal vesicles: secrete a fluid conducive to sperm vitality. Their ducts join the ductus deferens to form the ejaculatory duct.
4. Ejaculatory duct: empties sperms into urethra.

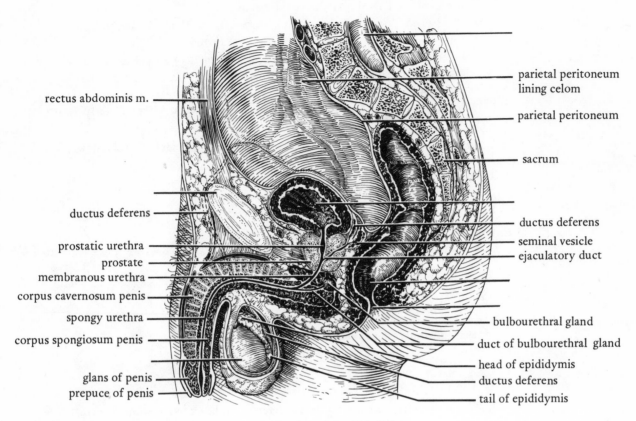

rectus abdominis m.

parietal peritoneum lining celom

parietal peritoneum

sacrum

ductus deferens

ductus deferens
seminal vesicle
ejaculatory duct

prostatic urethra
prostate
membranous urethra
corpus cavernosum penis
spongy urethra
corpus spongiosum penis

bulbourethral gland
duct of bulbourethral gland
head of epididymis
ductus deferens
tail of epididymis

glans of penis
prepuce of penis

1. Section of the Male Pelvis

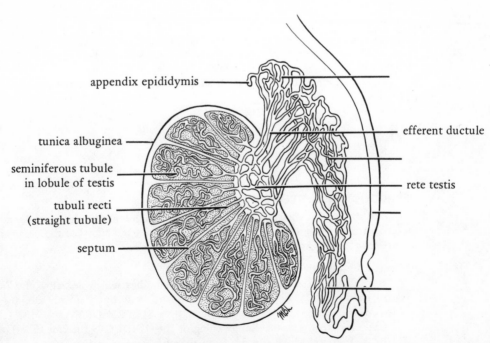

appendix epididymis

efferent ductule

tunica albuginea

seminiferous tubule
in lobule of testis

rete testis

tubuli recti
(straight tubule)

septum

2. Diagram of Section of the Testis, Epididymis,
   and Ductus Deferens

Plate 10-3. Reproductive Organs of the Human Male

    5. Scrotum: houses the testes.

    6. Spermatic cord: composed of the ductus deferens, blood vessels, and nerves. Passes through the INGUINAL CANAL to the celom.

    7. Prostate gland: located around upper urethra—secretes fluid into urethra.

    8. Urethra: common duct for passage of urine and sperms.

    9. Bulbourethral glands (Cowper's glands): located in floor of pelvis; empty secretion into membranous urethra.

  10. Penis: copulatory organ.

Complete the labeling of the diagram of the male reproductive system (Plate 10-3).

B. Testes. Label Plate 10-3, figure 2.

    Examine a section of a testis under the microscope, and identify the following (Plate 10-4, figures 1 and 2):

    1. Spermatogenic cells: give rise to sperm (spermatozoa).

    2. Interstitial cells: produce the male sex hormone.

Examine the slide of human sperm cells and draw and label one (Plate 10-4, Figure 3).

C. Epididymis and ductus deferens.

    Examine a slide of the epididymis. What kind of tissue lines it? Label Plate 10-4, figure 4.

    1. What constitutes the spermatic cord?

    2. What is the relationship of the ductus deferens to the ejaculatory duct in man?

D. Penis.

    Examine a slide of a cross section of the penis of the bull or other mammal. Identify the urethra and the cavernous bodies.

    Make a sketch of this organ, to show the relationships of the urethra and cavernous bodies.

REPRODUCTIVE SYSTEM OF THE CAT

    Having studied the charts and models of the human reproductive system, and having seen the cadaver, you should dissect the system in your cat. Many of the organs have already been revealed through previous dissection.

A. Female reproductive system. Study Plate 10-5.

    The OVARIES are small, elongate, ovoid bodies which lie below the kidney on the dorsal body wall. They are attached to the wall by a membrane, the OVARIAN LIGAMENT (mesovarium) and anteriorly by a SUSPENSORY LIGAMENT. The ovaries lie very close to the funnel-like opening of the OVIDUCTS (uterine tubes), the OSTIUM TUBAE. The eggs which rupture from the surface of the ovary (ovulation) normally pass into the ostium tubae due to the action of the cilia which create a MUCOUS CURRENT in that direction.

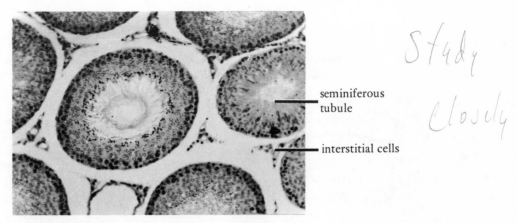

seminiferous
tubule

interstitial cells

Study Closely

1. Photomicrograph of Testis of the Rat (120X)

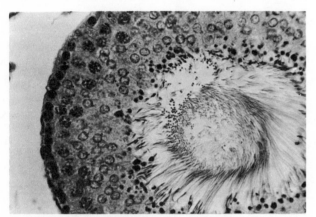

2. Photomicrograph of Testis of the Rat
Showing Stages in Maturation of Spermatozoa
(360X)

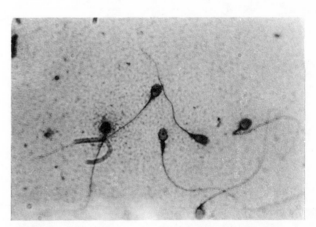

3. Photomicrograph of Human Spermatozoa (800X)

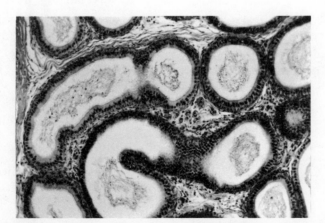

4. Photomicrograph of a Cross Section of
the Epididymis (80X)

Plate 10-4. Photomicrographs of Testis, Epididymis and Sperms

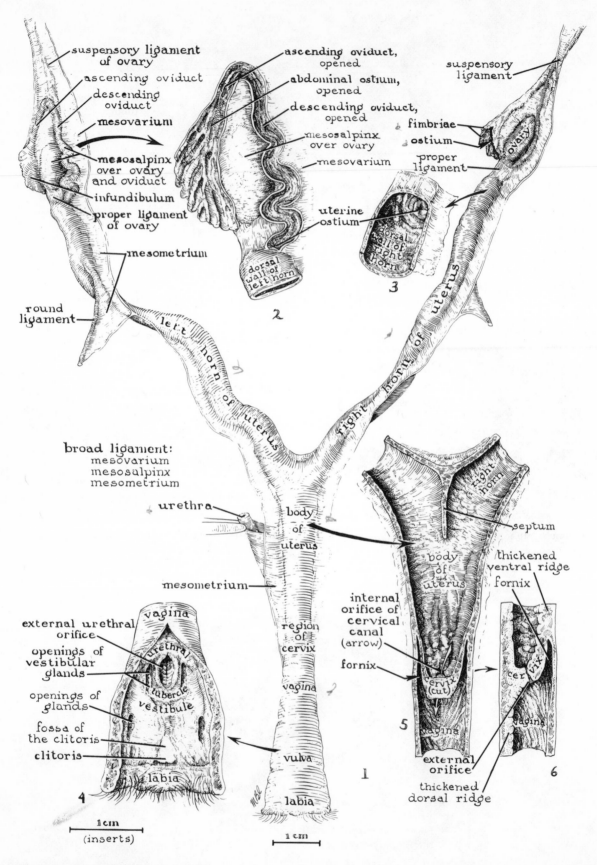

From Crouch, *Text-Atlas of Cat Anatomy*,
courtesy of Lea & Febiger

Plate 10-5. Reproductive System of Female Cat—Dorsal View

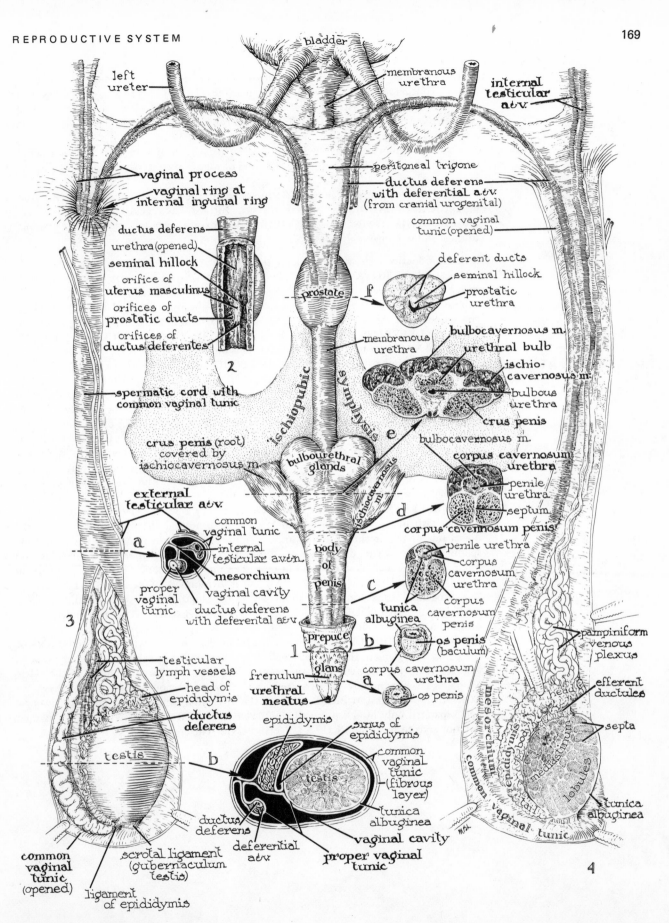

left ureter

bladder

membranous urethra

internal testicular a.&v.

vaginal process

vaginal ring at internal inguinal ring

ductus deferens

urethra (opened)

seminal hillock

orifice of uterus masculinus

orifices of prostatic ducts

orifices of ductus deferentes

spermatic cord with common vaginal tunic

crus penis (root) covered by ischiocavernosus m.

external testicular a.&v.

common vaginal tunic

internal testicular a.&v.

mesorchium

proper vaginal tunic

vaginal cavity

ductus deferens with deferental a.&v.

testicular lymph vessels

head of epididymis

ductus deferens

testis

common vaginal tunic (opened)

scrotal ligament (gubernaculum testis)

ligament of epididymis

peritoneal trigone

ductus deferens with deferential a.&v. (from cranial urogenital)

common vaginal tunic (opened)

deferent ducts

seminal hillock

prostatic urethra

prostate

membranous urethra

bulbocavernosus m.

urethral bulb

ischio-cavernosus m.

bulbous urethra

crus penis

bulbocavernosus m.

corpus cavernosum urethra

penile urethra

septum

corpus cavernosum penis

ischiopubic

symphysis

ischiocavernosus m.

bulbourethral glands

body of penis

penile urethra

corpus cavernosum urethra

corpus cavernosum penis

tunica albuginea

os penis (baculum)

corpus cavernosum urethra

os penis

prepuce

glans

frenulum

urethral meatus

epididymis

sinus of epididymis

common vaginal tunic (fibrous layer)

testis

tunica albuginea

vaginal cavity

proper vaginal tunic

ductus deferens

deferential a.&v.

pampiniform venous plexus

efferent ductules

septa

mediastinum

lobules

tunica albuginea

mesorchium

common vaginal tunic

From Crouch, *Text-Atlas of Cat Anatomy,* courtesy of Lea & Febiger

Plate 10-6. Reproductive System of the Male Cat

The oviducts are small and convoluted and pass craniad and then turn caudad to become continuous with the HORNS (cornua) OF THE UTERUS. The ovarian ligament is continuous with a BROAD LIGAMENT (mesometrium) which supports the horns of the uterus. There is also a ROUND LIGAMENT running from the broad ligament to attach into the inguinal region.

The two cornua or horns of the uterus come together into a single CORPUS or BODY OF THE UTERUS. This is a BIPARTITE kind of uterus in contrast to the SIMPLEX type in man.

The body of the uterus at its CERVIX leads into the VAGINA. The URETHRA from the URINARY BLADDER is bound to its ventral surface. The vagina and urethra open into the UROGENITAL SINUS or VESTIBULE. The external genitals, the vulva, are similar to those in the human.

B. Male reproductive system. Study Plate 10-6.

Locate the SCROTAL SAC which houses the testes. Open the scrotal sac, cutting deep enough to go through the TUNICA VAGINALIS which lies beneath the skin. This should expose the testis which can be delivered through the opening. The tunica vaginalis is continuous with the sheath of the SPERMATIC CORD. The spermatic cord encloses the DUCTUS DEFERENS (sperm duct) and the INTERNAL TESTICULAR ARTERY, VEIN, and NERVE. Color arteries red and veins blue.

Returning now to the testis, note the EPIDIDYMIS, a coiled mass of tubules on its dorsal side. The epididymis has a HEAD, BODY, and TAIL. Into the head empty the EFFERENT DUCTULES which convey sperm from the SEMINIFEROUS TUBULES of the testes. The HEAD OF THE EPIDIDYMIS leads to the body on the dorsal side of the testis and finally to the TAIL OF THE EPIDIDYMIS at the posterior end. From here the DUCTUS DEFERENS leads up into the spermatic cord in which it passes through the INGUINAL CANAL to the celom. The GUBERNACULUM, a ligament of the testis, attaches to the tail of the epididymis and to the posterior scrotal wall, and plays a part in the descent of the testis into the scrotal sac. The gubernaculum is homologous to the round ligament of the female.

The DEFERENT DUCTS or sperm ducts when they enter the celom separate from the internal testicular artery, vein, and nerve and loop around the ureters and pass to the dorsal side of the urethra. Cut the ureters and lift up the urinary bladder and follow the sperm ducts to where they enter the urethra. Note that the sperm ducts produce no seminal vesicles such as you found in man. The point of junction of urethra and sperm ducts forms the UROGENITAL CANAL and is surrounded by the PROSTATE GLAND. The urogenital canal or sinus, about an inch behind the prostate gland, has small swellings, the BULBOURETHRAL or COWPER'S GLANDS. The remainder of the urogenital canal is enclosed in the PENIS or copulatory organ. Cut the skin at the end of the penis, the PREPUCE, and discover the pointed projection within it, the GLANS of the penis. The glans in the cat has small spines on it and the urogenital canal opens at its end. By removing the skin from the rest of the penis, note its attachment to the pelvic region. A cross section of the penis reveals the three cavernous bodies. One of these, the CORPUS SPONGIOSUM PENIS, encloses the urogenital canal; the others, constituting a pair separated only by a septum, the CORPORA CAVERNOSA PENIS, diverge at their anterior ends to form the CRURA OF THE PENIS. The crura attach to the ischia.

GLOSSARY — Chapter 10

albicans (al´bi kanz): L., albicare, to grow white.

allantois (á lan´to is): G., allas, sausage (a membranous sack).

amnion (am´ni on): G., amnion, fetal membrane.

atretic (á trē´tik): G., a, not; tratos, perforated.

cavernous (kav´ēr nus): L., caverna, hollow.

cervix (sēr´viks): L., cervix, neck.

clitoris (klī´to ris or klit´o ris): G., kleio, to close.

corpus, pl. – corpora (kôr´pus, kôr´po rá): L., corpus, body.

crura, sing. – crus (krōo´rá, krus): L., crus, leg (any leg-like organ).

decidua (de sid´ū á): L., de, away; cadere, to fall.

deferens (def´ēr enz): L., defero, to carry away.

efferent (ef´ēr ent): L., ex, out; ferre, to carry.

endometrium (en´dō mē´tri um): G., endo, within; metra, womb.

epididymis (ep´i did´i mis): G., epi, upon; didymos, testis.

estrogen (es´trō jen): G., oistros, gad fly (sexual excitement); genos, produce.

fimbria (fim´bri á): L., fimbria, fringe.

follicle (fol´i kul): L., folliculus, small bag.

fornix (fôr´niks): L., fornix, vault, arch.

genital (jen´i tál): L., gignere, to beget (pert. to reproductive organs).

glans (glanz): L., glans, acorn.

gubernaculum (gū´bēr nák´ū lum): L., gubernare, to govern, to guide.

hymen (hī´men): G., hymen, skin, membrane.

infundibulum (in fun dib´ū lum): L., infundibulum, funnel.

inguinal (ing´gwin ál): L., inguen, groin.

labia (lā´bi á): L., labium, lip.

luteum (lū´tē um): L., luteus, yellow.

menses (men´sēz): L., mensis, month.

menstruation (men´strōo ā´shun): L., mensis, month; struere, to flow.

mesometrium (mez´ō mē´tri um): G., mesos, middle; metra, uterus.

ostium (os´ti um): L., ostium, door.

penis (pē´nis): L., penis, penis.

perineum (per i nē´um): L., perineon, uncertain origin (urogenital area).

placenta (plá sen´tá): L., placenta, flat cake (area of fetal attachment to uterus).

progesterone (pro jes′tēr ōn′): G., pro, for; gestare, to bear; one, hormone, to excite.

prostate (pros′tāt): G., pros, to, before; stat, standing, placed.

pudendum (pū den′dum): L., pudere, to be ashamed (external female genital organs).

seminiferous (sem′i nif′ēr us): L., semen, seed; fero, to bear.

scrotum (skro′tum): L., scrotum, bag.

stroma (strō′mȧ): G., stroma, couch, bed.

testis, pl. – testes (tes′tis, tes′tēz): L., testis, testicle.

testosterone (tes tôs′tēr ōn′): L., testo, testis; sterol, solid organic chemical.

tunica (tū′ni kȧ): L., tunica, coating.

vagina (va jī′na): L., vagin, a sheath.

vesicle (ves′i kul): L., vesica, bladder (little).

vestibule (ves′ti bul′): L., vestibulum, passage.

11

NERVOUS SYSTEM

Nature, even of the body, can only be understood as a whole.

—Plato

GENERAL

A. Structure (Plate 11-1).

This is the most complex system of the body. It is divided into (1) the central nervous system, (2) the PERIPHERAL NERVOUS SYSTEM, and (3) the VISCERAL AFFERENT FIBERS. The central nervous system is in turn subdivided into:

1. The BRAIN, which lies in the cranial cavity of the skull.

2. The SPINAL CORD, which connects with the brain through the foramen magnum and passes through the vertebral canal of the backbone.

The peripheral nervous system consists of:

1. CRANIAL NERVES, which attach to the ventral aspect of the brain and supply mostly the head and neck regions except for the 10th cranial, the vagus, which wanders to organs of the peritoneal cavity.

2. SPINAL NERVES, which arise from the spinal cord and supply the remainder of the body.

3. AUTONOMIC NERVOUS SYSTEM, which supplies the viscera, blood vessels, and glands.

The visceral afferent fibers carry impulses from the viscera.

B. Functions

The functions of the nervous system are (1) to aid in the orientation of the body, (2) control and coordinate body activities, and (3) intelligence.

PROCEDURE

A. The following sequence of study is recommended:

1. Study of nervous tissue to become familiar with structure and types of NEURONS and with the supportive elements called GLIAL (neuroglia) cells.

2. Study by use of charts, models and dissection to learn the distribution of spinal, cranial, and autonomic nerves.

3. Study of prepared slides, to learn the composition of nerves and ganglia.

4. Study of the spinal cord by dissection of the cat and use of models and slides.

5. Study of the brain by dissection of the cat, the preserved human brain, models, charts, and slides.

6. Study of the autonomic nervous system; much of it can be seen in the cat.

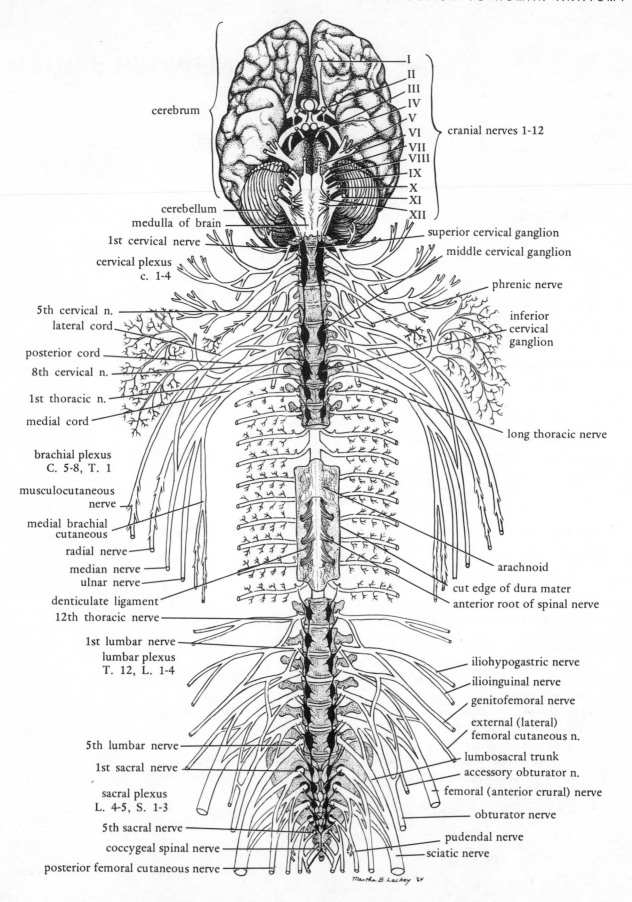

cerebrum

cranial nerves 1-12

I
II
III
IV
V
VI
VII
VIII
IX
X
XI
XII

cerebellum
medulla of brain
1st cervical nerve
cervical plexus
c. 1-4

superior cervical ganglion
middle cervical ganglion

phrenic nerve

5th cervical n.
lateral cord

inferior
cervical
ganglion

posterior cord
8th cervical n.

1st thoracic n.
medial cord

brachial plexus
C. 5-8, T. 1

long thoracic nerve

musculocutaneous
nerve
medial brachial
cutaneous
radial nerve
median nerve
ulnar nerve
denticulate ligament
12th thoracic nerve

arachnoid
cut edge of dura mater
anterior root of spinal nerve

1st lumbar nerve
lumbar plexus
T. 12, L. 1-4

iliohypogastric nerve
ilioinguinal nerve
genitofemoral nerve
external (lateral)
femoral cutaneous n.

5th lumbar nerve
1st sacral nerve

lumbosacral trunk
accessory obturator n.
femoral (anterior crural) nerve

sacral plexus
L. 4-5, S. 1-3

obturator nerve

5th sacral nerve
coccygeal spinal nerve

pudendal nerve
sciatic nerve

posterior femoral cutaneous nerve

Martha B. Lackey '64

Plate 11-1. General View of the Nervous System of Man

NERVOUS TISSUE

Study the prepared slides of neurons and nerves and sections of the spinal cord and brain, and identify as many as possible of the structures capitalized in the description below. Label Plate 11-2, figures 1 and 3. The photomicrographs below (Figures 11-1 and 11-2) should be helpful in understanding the nervous tissue.

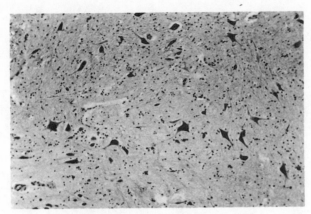

Figure 11-1. Photomicrograph of a Cross Section of the Anterior Column of the Gray Matter of the Spinal Cord (80X)

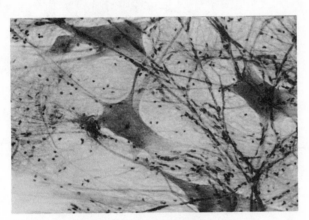

Figure 11-2. Photomicrograph of Nerve Cells of the Anterior Column of Gray Matter of the Spinal Cord of the Ox (120X)

A. Nervous system components

Two kinds of cells make up the nervous tissues: (1) NERVE CELLS or NEURONS, and (2) GLIAL or NEUROLOGIAL cells. The latter are connective tissue cells of two types. The MACROGLIAL CELLS, unlike most connective tissue cells, come from embryonic ectoderm and give support to neurons in the CENTRAL NERVOUS SYSTEM. The MICROGLIA are mesodermal in origin and are PHAGOCYTES.

B. Neurons

Neurons are specialized in the functions of irritability and conductivity; i.e., stimuli cause changes in the neurons, and these changes spread to other parts of the cell.

A neuron consists of a CELL BODY and several PROCESSES. In different parts of the nervous system they vary in shape and size and in the number of processes. The cell body may be stellate, round, pyramidal, or other shape. The nucleus is usually round and obvious and has a conspicuous nucleolus. The cytoplasm, although much like that in other cells, contains structures known as NISSL BODIES and NEUROFIBRILS. The Nissl bodies are related to the metabolism of the cell and when the cell is injured, they disintegrate. The neurofibrils are delicate structures which extend through the cell body and into the processes. They are involved in conduction.

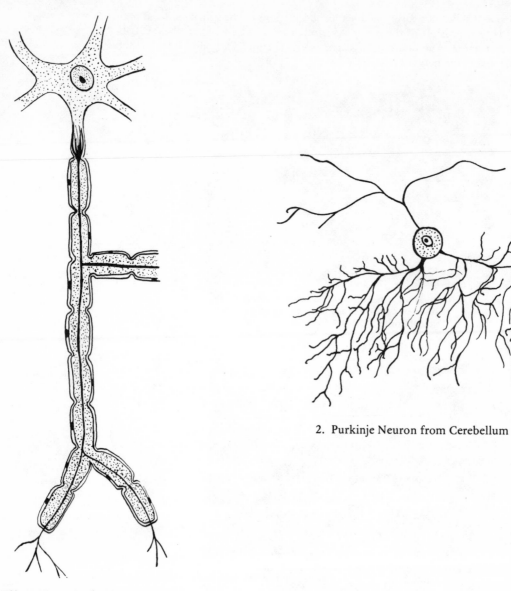

2. Purkinje Neuron from Cerebellum

1. Efferent Neuron from a Spinal Nerve

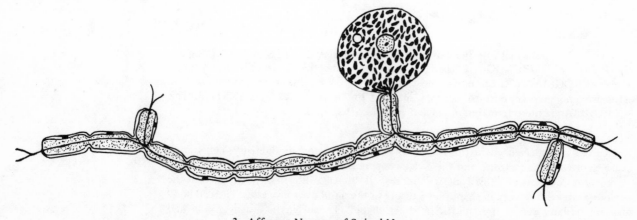

3. Afferent Neuron of Spinal Nerve

Plate 11-2. Types of Neurons

The processes of the cell body are of two kinds, DENDRITES and AXONS. DEN-DRITES under normal conditions conduct impulses toward the cell body. They have many branches, their attachments to the cell body are quite broad, and the Nissl substance extends into them. There may be one or many for each cell body. AXONS are limited to one per cell body. They conduct impulses away from the cell body, have few branches which are usually called collaterals, and lack Nissl substance. Neurons with only one process are called UNIPOLAR; those with two processes are called BIPOLAR and are found in only a few places in man. MULTIPOLAR neurons are the common type.

C. Sheaths

The processes of neurons (NERVE FIBERS) may be provided with coverings called SHEATHS which appear under the light microscope to be of two types: (1) quite thick and called MYELIN; (2) a thin cellular membrane called the NEURILEMMA or SCHWANN'S SHEATH. Studies with the electron microscope indicate that the myelin sheath is actually a doubled cell membrane of the neurilemmal (Schwann) cells wrapped spirally around the axon and not therefore a separate sheath. Though this be true we still continue to use the terms myelin sheath and neurilemma.

A process with a myelin sheath is called a MYELINATED or MEDULLATED FIBER; one without this sheath is called UNMYELINATED or UNMEDULLATED. The myelin sheath is often broken into segments. The intervals between the segments are called the NODES OF RANVIER.

Medullated fibers are found mainly in the SPINAL and CRANIAL nerves and in the WHITE MATTER of the SPINAL CORD and BRAIN. Unmedullated fibers are abundant in the AUTONOMIC NERVOUS SYSTEM.

The NEURILEMMA appears to fit closely against the myelin sheath and is continuous across the nodes of Ranvier. In unmyelinated fibers of the autonomic nervous system it lies directly against the fiber. The neurilemma may aid in the regeneration of nerve fibers.

Plate 11-2, figure 3, is a diagram of a SENSORY or AFFERENT NEURON. It would appear to be a unipolar neuron. However, study of its embryological development shows it to be bipolar, its two processes having joined near the cell body. The two branches coming from the common process are identical histologically. Since the branch from the body surface, the peripheral branch, carries impulses toward the cell body, it is func-tionally a dendrite, while the branch leading centrally to the spinal cord is a functional axon. What are terminal aborizations and internodes? Label them on Plate 11-2, figure 1.

D. Classification of Neurons on Basis of Function

1. Afferent (sensory) neurons. Those which carry impulses from the peripheral sense organs, the receptors to the central nervous system. If the receptors are in the viscera the neurons leading from them are VISCERAL AFFERENT; if from the receptors of the body surface, they are SOMATIC AFFERENT.(Plate 11-2, figure 3).

2. Efferent (motor or secretory) neurons. Those which carry impulses from the central system to the responding organs as the glands or muscles, the effectors (Plate 11-2, figure 1).

3. Internuncial or association neurons. Those which connect, mostly in the central system, the afferent and efferent neurons.

E. Synapses

These are the points where neurons come into functional continuity; i.e., when the terminal arborization of the axon of one neuron joins the dendrites or cell body of the next neuron so as to transfer the impulse. There is no protoplasmic continuity at the synapse, only a contact.

F. Nerves

Nerves are groups of nerve fibers outside of the central system, bound together by connective tissue. The connective tissue around a single nerve fiber is called the ENDO-NEURIUM. A bundle (fasciculus) of nerve fibers is bound by a PERINEURIUM of connective tissue and a number of fasciculi constituting the complete nerve is bound by the EPINEURIUM.

Label the cross section of a nerve and the cross section of a myelinated nerve fiber on Plate 11-3, figures 1-3.

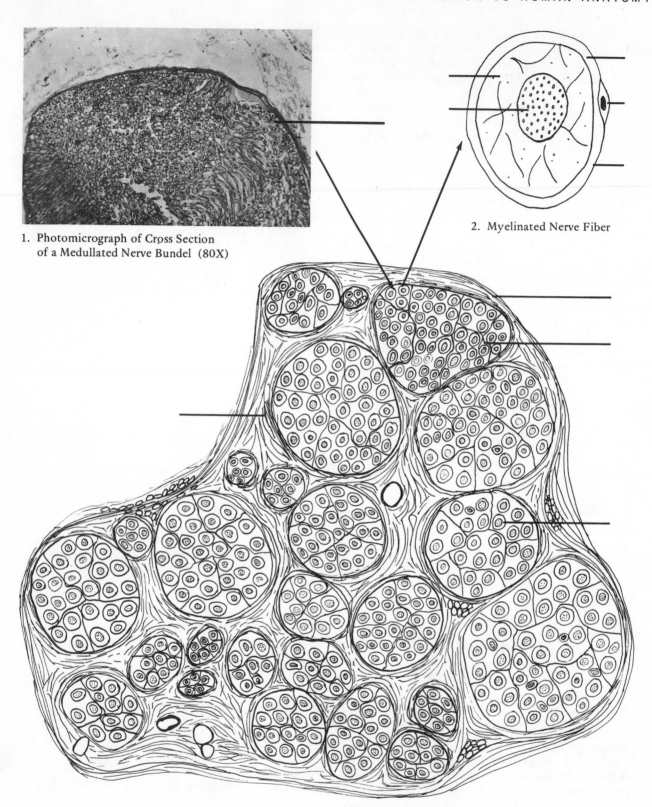

1. Photomicrograph of Cross Section
   of a Medullated Nerve Bundel (80X)

2. Myelinated Nerve Fiber

3. Cross Section of Nerve Trunk; One Axon Enlarged at Right

Plate 11-3. Microscopic Anatomy of a Nerve

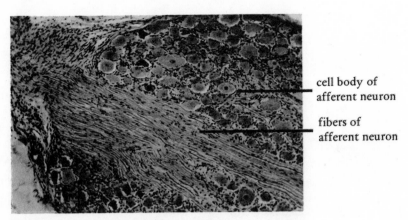

cell body of
afferent neuron

fibers of
afferent neuron

**Figure 11-3. Photomicrograph of a Section of
Spinal Ganglion (80X)**

G. Ganglion, Nucleus, Center

A GANGLION is a group of nerve cell bodies located outside of the central nervous system; i.e., along a nerve. Examine a slide of a ganglion (Figure 11-3).

A NUCLEUS is a group of nerve cells within the central nervous system, the fibers of which form a NERVE or TRACT.

A CENTER is a functional unit, whereas a ganglion and a nucleus are anatomical entities. A center therefore is a group of cell bodies and synapses regulating a certain function such as a heart center in the brain.

SPINAL CORD (Plates 11-1 and 11-4)

The SPINAL CORD is continuous with the brain through the FORAMEN MAGNUM of the skull. It continues down through the vertebral canal of the back bone, finally tapering off in the extreme caudal region into a non-nervous FILUM TERMINALE. In man the nervous part of the cord terminates at the level of the first lumbar vertebra and a filum terminale continues to the coccyx.

The spinal cord is a COMMUNICATION and ASSOCIATION CENTER. Many REFLEX CENTERS are located in it. Its fiber tracts carry impulses from one level of the cord to another, and to and from the brain.

The following description is adequate for the cord of the cat or of man. When there are important differences they will be mentioned. Recall that in human anatomy we use the term "anterior" for "ventral," "posterior" for "dorsal."

A. Dissection (Plate 11-4)

Carefully cut away the dorsal muscles on either side of the vertebral column and, with the bone cutters, remove the laminae of SEVERAL VERTEBRAE. This should be done with extreme care, to avoid injury to the spinal cord which lies underneath and to the spinal nerves which attach to the cord. As the laminae are removed, you find a layer of loose connective tissue and fat. The space in which this is located is called EPIDURAL. When this is removed the cord, covered with its meninges, will come to view.

B. Meninges (Plate 11-4)

The MENINGES (the singular is "meninx") are membranes—a series of three—which enclose the spinal cord and continue through the foramen magnum to cover the brain. Between the meninges are spaces that are filled with a lymph or CEREBROSPINAL FLUID. This combination of membranes and fluids forms a protective cushion around the central nervous system in addition to the bony framework. An infection of these membranes is MENINGITIS.

The outermost and toughest meninx is the DURA MATER. It is a fibrous membrane and forms a continuous sheath around the spinal cord. At the lower end of the cord it extends beyond the nervous cord itself to form a cul-de-sac, ending in man at the second sacral vertebra. The space outside of the dura mater is the EPIDURAL CAVITY and is, as stated above, filled with loose connective tissue and fat. Below the dura mater is the SUBDURAL CAVITY containing a small amount of fluid.

The next membrane is the ARACHNOID which is thin, web-like and transparent. It may be impossible to see in your cat. Beneath the arachnoid is a wide space, the SUBARACHNOID CAVITY, which is filled with CEREBROSPINAL FLUID.

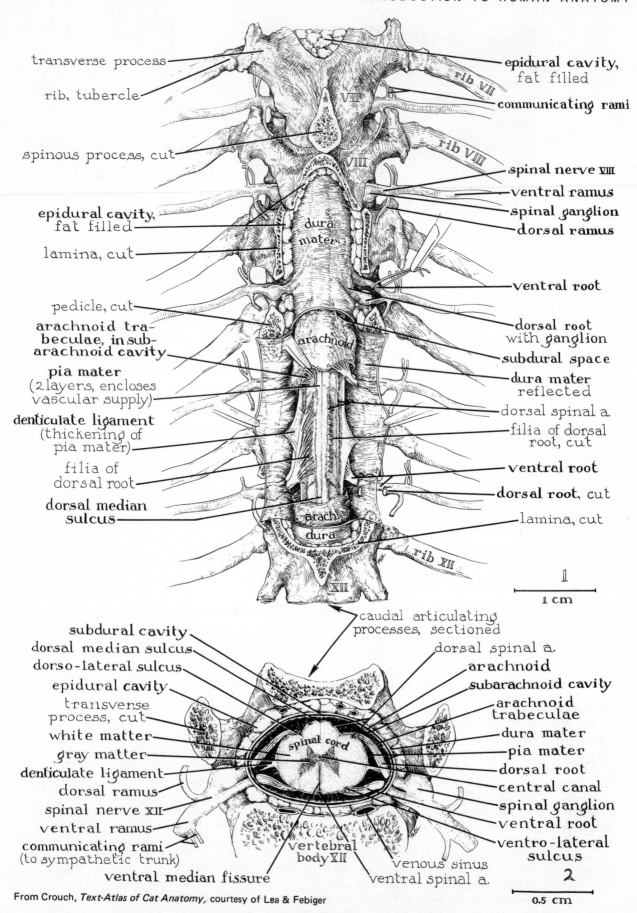

transverse process

rib, tubercle

spinous process, cut

epidural cavity, fat filled

lamina, cut

pedicle, cut

arachnoid trabeculae, in subarachnoid cavity

pia mater (2 layers, encloses vascular supply)

denticulate ligament (thickening of pia mater)

filia of dorsal root

dorsal median sulcus

epidural cavity, fat filled

communicating rami

rib VII

rib VIII

spinal nerve VIII

ventral ramus

spinal ganglion

dorsal ramus

ventral root

dorsal root with ganglion

subdural space

dura mater reflected

dorsal spinal a.

filia of dorsal root, cut

ventral root

dorsal root, cut

lamina, cut

rib XII

VII

VIII

dura mater

arachnoid

arach

dura

XII

1

1 cm

caudal articulating processes, sectioned

subdural cavity

dorsal median sulcus

dorso-lateral sulcus

epidural cavity

transverse process, cut

white matter

gray matter

denticulate ligament

dorsal ramus

spinal nerve XII

ventral ramus

communicating rami (to sympathetic trunk)

ventral median fissure

dorsal spinal a.

arachnoid

subarachnoid cavity

arachnoid trabeculae

dura mater

pia mater

dorsal root

central canal

spinal ganglion

ventral root

ventro-lateral sulcus

spinal cord

vertebral body XII

venous sinus

ventral spinal a.

2

From Crouch, *Text-Atlas of Cat Anatomy*, courtesy of Lea & Febiger

0.5 cm

Plate 11-4. The Spinal Cord and Spinal Nerves of the Cat to Show Their Relationships to the Vertebral Column, Intervertebral Foramina and Meninges

The final meninx is the PIA MATER, a delicate membrane which closely invests the spinal cord and sends septa into its substance. Outline, using colored pencils, the above meninges on Plate 11-5. Label. In dissection the meninges you may have noticed the delicate roots of the spinal nerves attached to the cord. We will return to these later.

C. Surface anatomy of spinal cord

Extend your dissection of the spinal cord by removing the laminae of the remaining vertebrae to expose the entire cord. Be careful to leave the spinal nerves intact. Remove the meninges dorsally to expose the naked cord. Note that it has two enlarged areas: the CERVICAL, in the region where the large spinal nerves go to the forelimb, and the LUMBAR ENLARGEMENT which supplies nerves to the hindlimbs. Below the lumbar enlargement the cord tapers down as the CONUS MEDULLARIS, to end in the FILUM TERMINALE.

Now remove a section about one inch long of the spinal cord in the thoracic region, by cutting it transversely. Examine the dorsal surface carefully to note a deep DORSAL FISSURE, and the ventral side to see the shallow VENTRAL FISSURE. These fissures together incompletely divide the cord into right and left halves. In man they are called the POSTERIOR MEDIAN SULCUS and the ANTERIOR MEDIAN FISSURE. The posterior median sulcus in man has extending from it into the substance of the cord a SEPTUM OF NEUROGLIA. Each half of the spinal cord is further subdivided by POSTERO-LATERAL and ANTERO-LATERAL sulci into three columns: the POSTERIOR (DORSAL) FUNICULUS, the LATERAL FUNICULUS, and the ANTERIOR (VENTRAL) FUNICULUS. The postero-lateral and antero-lateral sulci lie roughly at the points where the roots of the spinal nerves attach to the cord.

D. Cross section of spinal cord (Plates 11-4 and 11-5)

Examine the cut surface of the piece of spinal cord which you removed. Also observe under the microscope a prepared cross section of the spinal cord, and identify the following:

In the center of the cord may be seen a small canal, the CENTRAL CANAL, which contains CEREBROSPINAL FLUID. It extends the length of the cord and to the brain. Around it in the form of a capital "H" is the GRAY MATTER of the cord. The gray matter consists on each side of a DORSAL (POSTERIOR) COLUMN, a LATERAL COLUMN, and a VENTRAL (ANTERIOR) COLUMN. The two sides of the gray matter are connected by a gray matter commissure which is divided by the central canal into ANTERIOR and POSTERIOR GRAY COMMISSURES. Close examination of the gray matter of the spinal cord under the microscope shows it to be made up of CELL BODIES, NAKED FIBERS, SYNAPSES OF NEURONS, and NEUROGLIA. Since the fibers in this area are naked, it has a gray appearance in contrast to the surrounding areas of the cord which are made up of medullated fibers, the WHITE MATTER.

The white matter of the spinal cord is divided into three regions by the dorsal and ventral columns of gray matter. These are the DORSAL, LATERAL, and VENTRAL FUNICULI. The funiculi in turn are made up of FASCICULI (bundles) of nerve fibers forming the tracts of the spinal cord. These have a very definite organization for which you should refer to your textbook for more complete information.

Label as many as possible of the above structures on the cross section of the spinal cord (Plate 11-5).

SPINAL NERVES (Plate 11-6)

A. General

There are 38 pairs of spinal nerves in the cat, 31 in man. They are segmentally arranged and each is attached to the spinal cord by two roots, the DORSAL (POSTERIOR) ROOT, and the VENTRAL (ANTERIOR) ROOT. They make their exit from the vertebral canal by way of the INTERVERTEBRAL FORAMINA.

Return to your dissection of the cat and see if you can locate these structures. It will be necessary to remove some more bone from the vertebrae and to cut away more of the dura mater.

The dorsal roots attach along the dorsolateral sulcus and have a swelling on them, the SPINAL or DORSAL (POSTERIOR) ROOT GANGLION. The ganglion is where the cell bodies of afferent neurons are located. It lies in the invertebral foramen and the meninges cover and protect it.

The ventral (anterior) roots attach ventrolaterally over the area of the anterior gray column. They pass into the intervertebral foramina and join the dorsal roots to form the

COMMON SPINAL NERVES. The ventral roots consist of medullated fibers whose cell bodies are found in the ventral and lateral gray columns. These are EFFERENT NEURONS. The common spinal nerves are therefore called MIXED NERVES because they contain both AFFERENT and EFFERENT FIBERS.

The spinal nerves are named and numbered according to their relationship to the vertebrae. Hence, there are in the cat 8 pairs of CERVICAL SPINAL NERVES, 13 THORACIC, 7 LUMBAR, 3 SACRAL, and 7-8 CAUDALS. The number of caudals may vary. In man the numbers are 8, 12, 5, 5, 1, respectively. The first cervical spinal nerves exit between the skull and the atlas, the rest through the intervertebral foramina of the vertebral column.

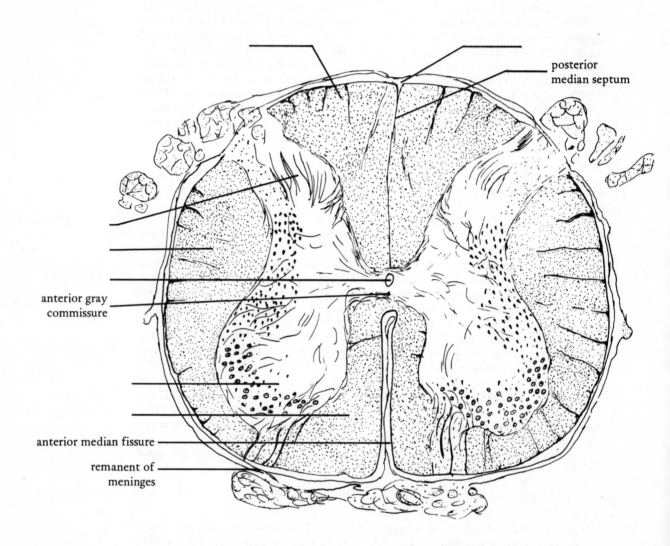

posterior
median septum

anterior gray
commissure

anterior median fissure

remanent of
meninges

Plate 11-5. Cross Section of Spinal Cord

Now follow the common spinal nerve and note that it divides just distad of its formation into a DORSAL RAMUS which goes to the muscles and skin of the back, a VENTRAL RAMUS to the muscles and skin of the lateral and ventral body wall and the limbs, and in the thoracic and lumbar nerves a third branch, a double one, the COM-MUNICATING RAMUS, to the SYMPATHETIC TRUNK GANGLIA of the autonomic system.

Label the above structures on Plate 11-6.

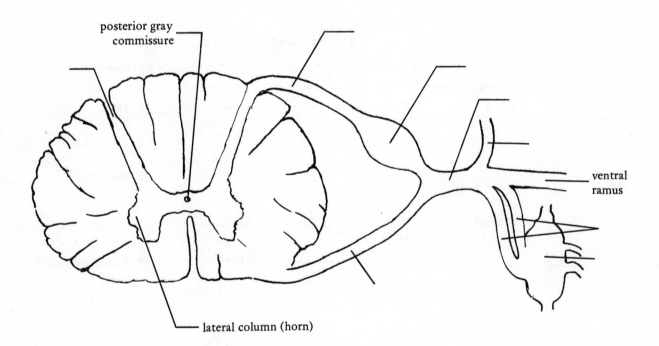

posterior gray
commissure

ventral
ramus

lateral column (horn)

Plate 11-6. Cross Section of Spinal Cord, a Spinal Nerve and Sympathetic Ganglion

B. Plexuses (Plates 11-1, 11-7 and 11-9)

The ANTERIOR RAMI of spinal nerves with the exception of most of the thoracics anastomose (intermingle) to form PLEXUSES. These are related to the enlargements of the spinal cord and the complex musculature of the fore and hindlimbs which you have already studied. You have seen parts of these plexuses also, as you were studying the circulatory system. Most of the anterior rami of the thoracic nerves and the posterior rami of ALL the spinal nerves DO NOT form plexuses. They maintain their segmental arrangement.

Table III names these plexuses and indicates the spinal nerves which contribute to them and the main nerves which are derived from them in the cat and in man. Appropriate letters are used to indicate cervical (C), thoracic (T), lumbar (L), and sacral (S) spinal nerves.

You should find the structures mentioned in Table III on your cat without taking time to trace or learn the complex interconnections of the plexuses. Give special attention to following distad the nerves capitalized in the table. Color them yellow on Plates 11-7 through 11-11 and label where needed.

TABLE III. Spinal Nerve Plexuses

| Name of Plexus | Spinal Nerves Involved | | Main Nerves Derived From Plexus | |
	Cat	Man	Cat	Man
Cervical	$C_1C_2C_3C_4$ (C_5)	$C_1C_2C_3C_4$	1. Nerves to certain head and neck regions. 2. PHRENIC C_5C_6.	1. Lesser occipital C_2C_3. 2. Anterior cervical cutaneous C_2C_3. 3. PHRENIC $C_3C_4C_5$.
Brachial	$(C_5)C_6C_7$ C_8T_1	$C_5C_6C_7C_8$ T_1	1. AXILLARY C_7. 2. RADIAL $C_7C_8(T_1)$. 3. MUSCULO-CUTANEOUS C_6C_7. 4. MEDIAN $C_7C_8(T_1)$. 5. ULNAR T_1.	1. Axillary $C_4C_5C_6$. 2. RADIAL C_5-T_1. 3. Musculocutaneous C_5C_7. 4. MEDIAN C_6-T_1. 5. ULNAR C_7-T_1.
Lumbar	$L_4L_5L_6L_7$	$(T_{12})L_1$ $L_2L_3L_4$	1. FEMORAL L_5L_6. a. SAPHENOUS. 2. Obturator L_6L_7. 3. Lateral femoral cutaneous L_4L_5.	1. Obturator L_2-L_4. 2. FEMORAL L_1-L_4. a. SAPHENOUS. 3. Lateral femoral cutaneous L_2L_3.
Sacral	L_6L_7S $S_1S_2S_3$	$(L_4)L_5$ $S_1S_2S_3$	1. SCIATIC (ischiatic) $L_6L_7S_1$. a. TIBIAL. b. COMMON PERONEAL. 1) Superficial. 2) Deep.	1. SCIATIC (ischiatic) L_4-S_3. a. TIBIAL L_4-S_3. b. COMMON PERONEAL L_4S_2.

Lumbosacral

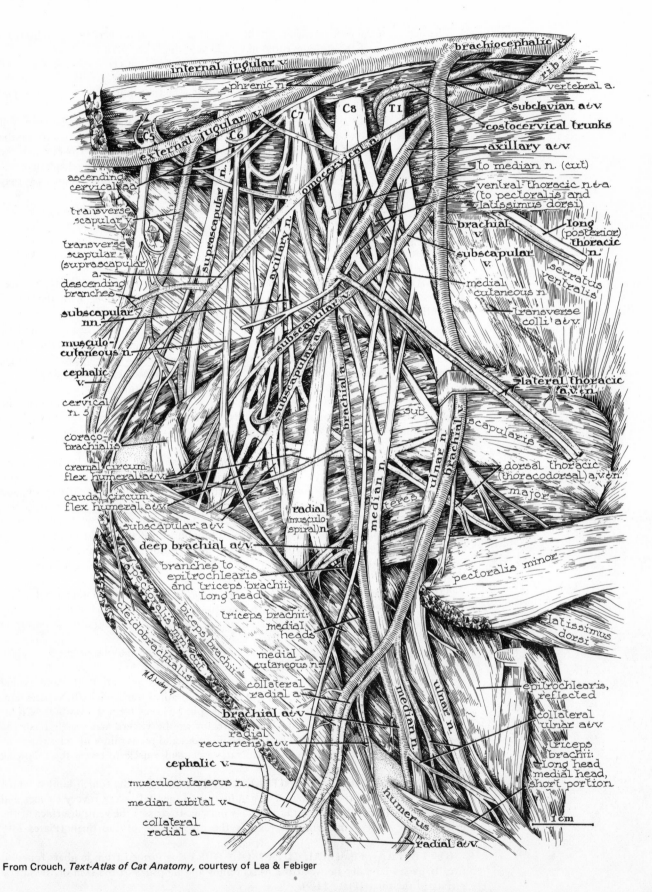

From Crouch, *Text-Atlas of Cat Anatomy,* courtesy of Lea & Febiger

Plate 11-7. Ventral View of the Brachial Plexus, Nerves and Blood Vessels of the Axilla and Arm of the Cat

The nerves of the cervical plexus can be traced back toward the vertebral column from the general region of the sternomastoid muscle. They supply the neck musculature.

The BRACHIAL PLEXUS is composed of the ventral rami of cervical nerves five-eight and of the first thoracic nerve. These nerves can be seen emerging from between the muscles of the neck, the longus capitis and scalenes. The first thoracic nerve emerges just in front of the first rib (Plate 11-7).

The fifth cervical nerve sends off a small branch which joins with a similar branch of the sixth cervical to form the PHRENIC NERVE which passes caudad to enter the thoracic cavity in front of the first rib and continues to the diaphragm. The fact that the diaphragm is supplied by a nerve from the cervical region suggests that the diaphragm was derived from cervical myotomes (muscle segments). Nerves tend to follow muscles as they migrate during development from their points of origin.

The MUSCULOCUTANEOUS NERVE is derived from the sixth and seventh cervical nerves. It passes to near the margin of the biceps brachii muscle where it divides, one branch supplying the coracobrachialis and the biceps muscles, the more posterior one passing along the medial edge of the biceps to supply the brachialis muscle and then it continues to the skin of the forelimb.

The AXILLARY NERVE originates also from the sixth and seventh cervical nerves and passes between the teres major and subscapularis muscles along with the caudal circumflex humeral artery and vein. It supplies some of the lateral shoulder muscles.

The RADIAL NERVE originates from the seventh and eighth cervical and the first thoracic nerves. It passes with the deep brachial artery through the middle head of the triceps muscle, divides forming superficial and deep branches which supply the triceps, supinator, and the extensor muscles of the lower forelimb (Plates 11-7 and 11-8).

The MEDIAN NERVE derived from the seventh and eighth cervical and the first thoracic nerves lies along the brachial artery and with it passes through the supracondyloid foramen of the humerus. It supplies the flexors and pronators of the lower forelimb except for the flexor carpi ulnaris. There is no supracondyloid foramen on the humerus of man (Plates 11-7 and 11-8).

The ULNAR NERVE arises primarily from the first thoracic but receives branches from the eighth cervical nerve. It lies medial and caudal to the brachial artery in the arm. It curves around the medial epicondyle of the humerus between it and the olecranon, and extends into the lower limb where it supplies the ulnar head of the flexor digitorum profundus and the flexor carpi ulnaris. It is often bumped at the elbow which causes a tingling in the hand referred to as "hitting the funny bone." (Plates 11-7 and 11-8.)

Other major nerves from the brachial plexus not described here are the suprascapular, the three subscapulars, the ventral thoracics, the long thoracic, and the medial cutaneous (Plate 11-7).

THORACIC NERVES (ventral rami), other than the first, are called intercostal nerves and pass between the ribs along with the intercostal arteries and veins to supply intercostal muscles, the superficial muscles of the lateral thorax, the transverse costarum and rectus abdominis muscles.

The dorsal rami of the thoracic nerves supply the skin and muscles of the back as do the dorsal rami of the lumbar and sacral nerves.

The ventral rami of the first three LUMBAR NERVES give off lateral and medial branches to the muscles of the lateral and ventral abdominal walls, while the ventral rami of the last four lumbars and the three sacral spinal nerves form a LUMBOSACRAL PLEXUS. This plexus can best be seen by removing the viscera and vessels from the abdominal and pelvic cavities and cutting the iliopsoas and psoas minor muscles which lie ventral to the vertebral column. Remove fat, fascia and muscle to reveal the following nerves:

The GENITOFEMORAL (GENITAL) NERVE comes from the fourth lumbar which also connects to the fifth lumbar. The genitofemoral (genital) nerve is very slender and lies along the medial surface of the iliopsoas muscle. It crosses the ventral surface of the external iliac artery and vein and reaches the medial side of the thigh (Plates 11-9 and 11-10).

The LATERAL FEMORAL CUTANEOUS NERVE is formed from lumbars four and five. It passes laterally between the psoas minor and iliopsoas to the skin of the lateral surface of the thigh (Plate 11-9).

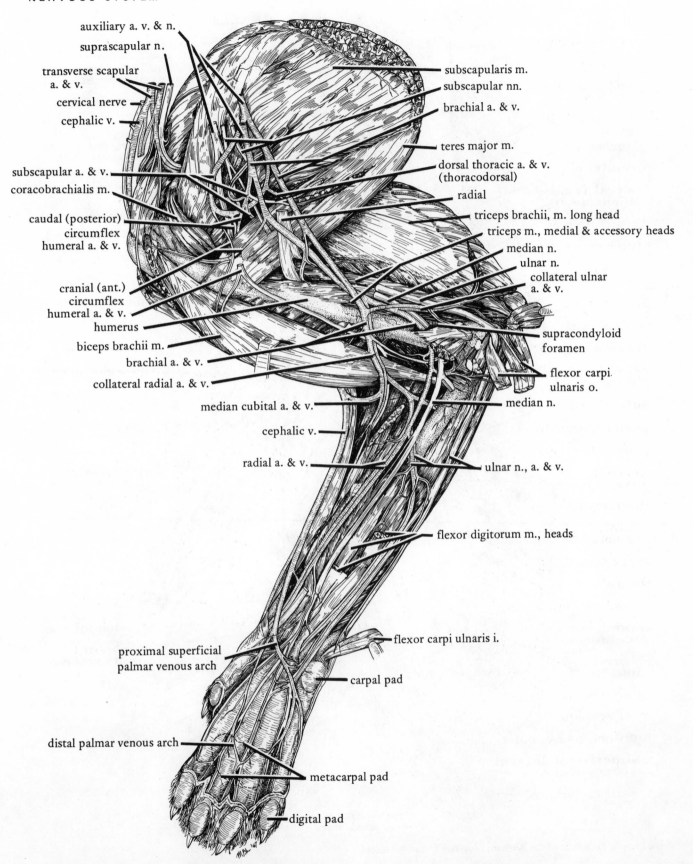

auxiliary a. v. & n.

suprascapular n.

transverse scapular
a. & v.

cervical nerve

cephalic v.

subscapular a. & v.

coracobrachialis m.

caudal (posterior)
circumflex
humeral a. & v.

cranial (ant.)
circumflex
humeral a. & v.

humerus

biceps brachii m.

brachial a. & v.

collateral radial a. & v.

median cubital a. & v.

cephalic v.

radial a. & v.

proximal superficial
palmar venous arch

distal palmar venous arch

subscapularis m.

subscapular nn.

brachial a. & v.

teres major m.

dorsal thoracic a. & v.
(thoracodorsal)

radial

triceps brachii, m. long head

triceps m., medial & accessory heads

median n.

ulnar n.

collateral ulnar
a. & v.

supracondyloid
foramen

flexor carpi
ulnaris o.

median n.

ulnar n., a. & v.

flexor digitorum m., heads

flexor carpi ulnaris i.

carpal pad

metacarpal pad

digital pad

From Crouch, *Text-Atlas of Cat Anatomy,* courtesy of Lea & Febiger

Plate 11-8. Medial View of Nerves and Blood Vessels of the Forelimb of the Cat

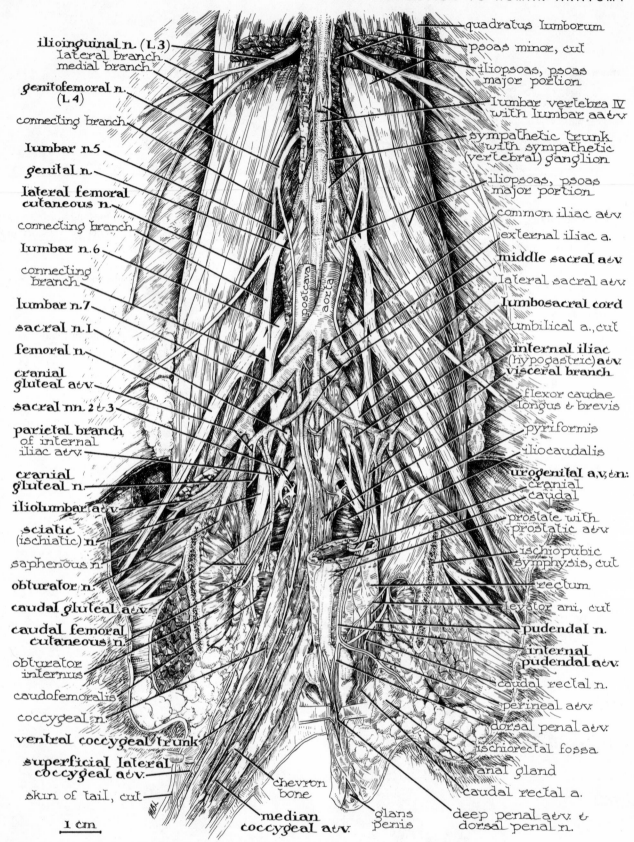

ilioinguinal n. (L3)
lateral branch
medial branch

genitofemoral n.
(L4)

connecting branch

lumbar n.5

genital n.

lateral femoral
cutaneous n.

connecting branch

lumbar n.6

connecting
branch

lumbar n.7

sacral n.1

femoral n.

cranial
gluteal a&v.

sacral nn. 2&3

parietal branch
of internal
iliac a&v.

cranial
gluteal n.

iliolumbar a&v.

sciatic
(ischiatic) n.

saphenous n.

obturator n.

caudal gluteal a&v.

caudal femoral
cutaneous n.

obturator
internus

caudofemoralis

coccygeal n.

ventral coccygeal trunk

superficial lateral
coccygeal a&v.

skin of tail, cut

1 cm

quadratus lumborum

psoas minor, cut

iliopsoas, psoas
major portion

lumbar vertebra IV
with lumbar aa&v.

sympathetic trunk
with sympathetic
(vertebral) ganglion

iliopsoas, psoas
major portion

common iliac a&v.

external iliac a.

middle sacral a&v.

lateral sacral a&v.

lumbosacral cord

umbilical a., cut

internal iliac
(hypogastric) a&v.
visceral branch

flexor caudae
longus & brevis

pyriformis

iliocaudalis

urogenital a, v, &n:
cranial
caudal

prostate with
prostatic a&v.

ischiopubic
symphysis, cut

rectum

levator ani, cut

pudendal n.

internal
pudendal a&v.

caudal rectal n.

perineal a&v.

dorsal penal a&v.

ischiorectal fossa

anal gland

caudal rectal a.

postcava   aorta

chevron
bone

median
coccygeal a&v.

glans
penis

deep penal a&v. &
dorsal penal n.

From Crouch, *Text-Atlas of Cat Anatomy,* courtesy of Lea & Febiger

Plate 11-9. Ventral View of the Lumbosacral Plexus, Some Nerves
and Blood Vessels of the Cat

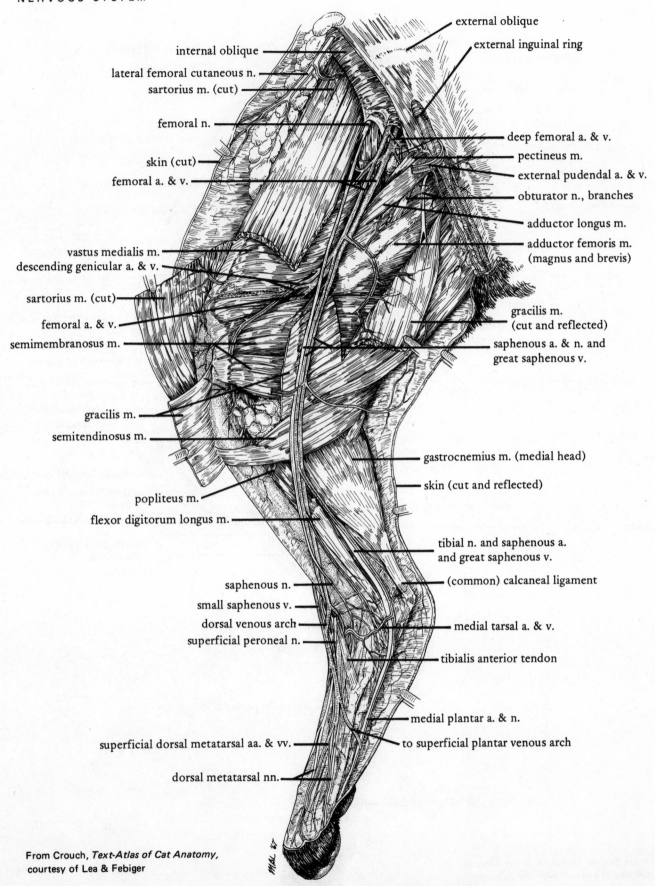

external oblique

external inguinal ring

internal oblique

lateral femoral cutaneous n.

sartorius m. (cut)

femoral n.

deep femoral a. & v.

pectineus m.

skin (cut)

external pudendal a. & v.

femoral a. & v.

obturator n., branches

adductor longus m.

adductor femoris m.
(magnus and brevis)

vastus medialis m.

descending genicular a. & v.

sartorius m. (cut)

gracilis m.
(cut and reflected)

femoral a. & v.

saphenous a. & n. and
great saphenous v.

semimembranosus m.

gracilis m.

semitendinosus m.

gastrocnemius m. (medial head)

skin (cut and reflected)

popliteus m.

flexor digitorum longus m.

tibial n. and saphenous a.
and great saphenous v.

saphenous n.

(common) calcaneal ligament

small saphenous v.

dorsal venous arch

medial tarsal a. & v.

superficial peroneal n.

tibialis anterior tendon

medial plantar a. & n.

superficial dorsal metatarsal aa. & vv.

to superficial plantar venous arch

dorsal metatarsal nn.

From Crouch, *Text-Atlas of Cat Anatomy,*
courtesy of Lea & Febiger

Plate 11-10. Nerves and Blood Vessels of the Right Hindlimb of the Cat—Medial View

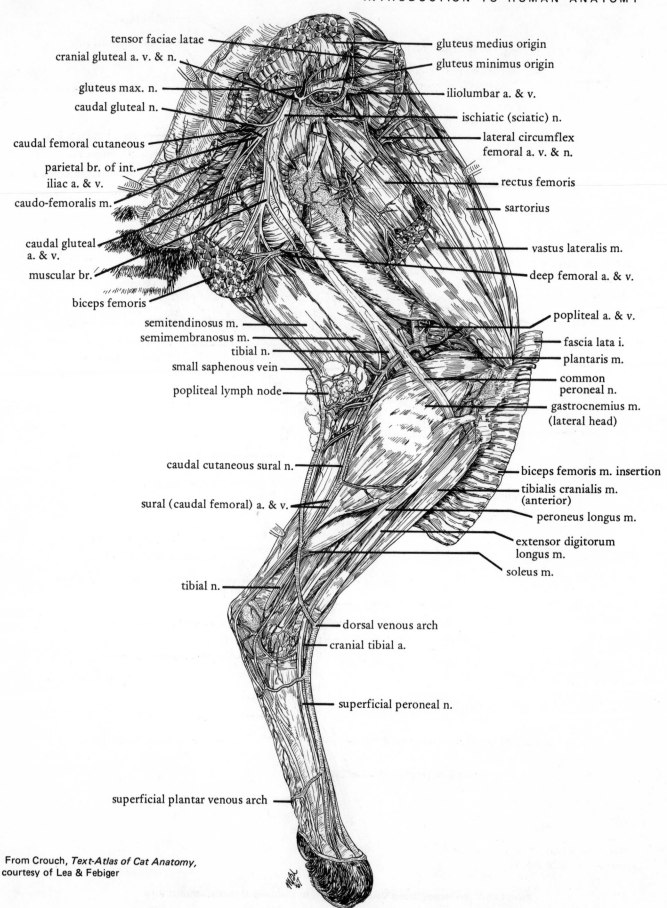

tensor faciae latae
cranial gluteal a. v. & n.
gluteus max. n.
caudal gluteal n.
caudal femoral cutaneous
parietal br. of int.
iliac a. & v.
caudo-femoralis m.
caudal gluteal
a. & v.
muscular br.
biceps femoris
semitendinosus m.
semimembranosus m.
tibial n.
small saphenous vein
popliteal lymph node
caudal cutaneous sural n.
sural (caudal femoral) a. & v.
tibial n.
superficial plantar venous arch

gluteus medius origin
gluteus minimus origin
iliolumbar a. & v.
ischiatic (sciatic) n.
lateral circumflex
femoral a. v. & n.
rectus femoris
sartorius
vastus lateralis m.
deep femoral a. & v.
popliteal a. & v.
fascia lata i.
plantaris m.
common
peroneal n.
gastrocnemius m.
(lateral head)
biceps femoris m. insertion
tibialis cranialis m.
(anterior)
peroneus longus m.
extensor digitorum
longus m.
soleus m.
dorsal venous arch
cranial tibial a.
superficial peroneal n.

Plate 11-11. Nerves and Blood Vessels of the Right Hindlimb of the Cat—Lateral View

The FEMORAL NERVE, derived from the fifth and sixth lumbar nerves, passes caudad over the ventral surface of the iliopsoas to which it gives off branches. It passes through the abdominal wall to the thigh where it gives branches to the sartorius. Another branch passes between the vastus medialis and rectus femoris. The femoral nerve then continues as the SAPHENOUS NERVE as far as the ankle, supplying the skin on the medial side of the leg (Plates 11-9 and 11-10).

The OBTURATOR NERVE has its origin from lumbar nerves six and seven. It travels caudad along the lateral pelvic wall, passes through the obturator foramen and sends branches to the gracilis, pectineus, and adductor muscles (Plates 11-9 and 11-10).

The sixth and seventh lumbar nerves are connected to the three sacral nerves of the sacral plexus by a broad band, the LUMBOSACRAL CORD (Plate 11-9).

The SCIATIC (ischiatic) and the cranial and caudal gluteal nerves are formed from the lumbosacral cord and the first sacral nerve (Plate 11-11). The second sacral nerve also contributes to the large sciatic nerve.

You first saw the sciatic nerve when you studied the muscles of the thigh. Remove the biceps femoris and tensor fascia lata muscles and transect the caudofemoralis, gluteus maximus and medius. Now cut away the ilium and the dorsal parts of the sacral vertebrae and the seventh lumbar to reveal the cranial relationships of the sciatic nerve and related sacral nerves. Also follow the sciatic nerve caudad and note that it gives off muscular branches to the biceps femoris, semitendinosus and semimembranosus. It then passes over the adductor femoris and semimembranosus muscles above the knee and gives off a sural nerve which travels along the lateral surface of the gastrocnemius muscle to the ankle. The sciatic nerve divides near the knee into TIBIAL and COMMON PERONEAL NERVES which supply the muscles of the leg (Plate 11-11).

REFLEX ARC (Plate 11-6)

In studying the spinal cord and nerves we have been dealing with structures which are involved in the reflex arc. The AFFERENT (SENSORY) NEURON connects at the body surface with a sense organ or RECEPTOR. The receptor may be a simple or very complex structure, as we shall see when we study it in Chapter 12. Centrally, the afferent neuron connects with the spinal cord where it synapses with a second neuron, the ASSOCIATION or INTERNUNCIAL NEURON. It, in turn, in the VENTRAL COLUMN of the gray matter, synapses with an EFFERENT (MOTOR) NEURON. The EFFERENT NEURON leaves the spinal cord through the anterior root of the spinal nerve to end in a SKELETAL MUSCLE (effector).

The REFLEX ARC is an important functional unit of the nervous system. Draw the components of a reflex arc into Plate 11-6 (page 183) to show their relationship to the spinal cord and spinal nerves. Indicate by arrows the direction in which conduction takes place. This reflex arc as you have drawn it would operate at only one "level" of the nervous system. How do you explain reflexes which cause responses at two or more "levels" of the system?

BRAIN

"The need is not really for more brains, the need is now for a gentler, a more tolerant people than those who won for us against the ice, the tiger, and the bear."

— L. Eiseley
The Immense Journey (Random House,
New York, 1946)

The spinal cord enters the FORAMEN MAGNUM of the skull and becomes continuous with the BRAIN. The central canal of the spinal cord widens out in the brain to form the VENTRICLES. The MENINGES which cover the cord continue over the brain with some modifications. CEREBROSPINAL FLUID is found in the ventricles of the brain and in the spaces between meninges.

The brain is a kind of control center for the nervous system. It contains FIBER TRACTS (WHITE MATTER) which interconnect its many parts and also connect it to the spinal cord and nerves. It has many NERVE CENTERS (GRAY MATTER) and its CORTEX AREAS (GRAY MATTER) which are centers of integration and control. It has its own set of nerves—the CRANIAL NERVES—which give it direct connections to certain RECEPTORS and EFFECTORS of the body.

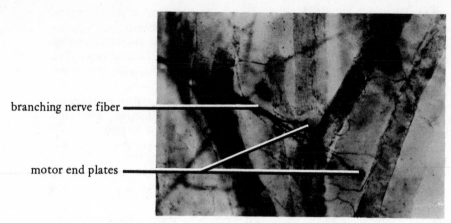

branching nerve fiber

motor end plates

**Figure 11-4. Photomicrograph of Motor End Plate
on Skeletal Muscle (120X)**

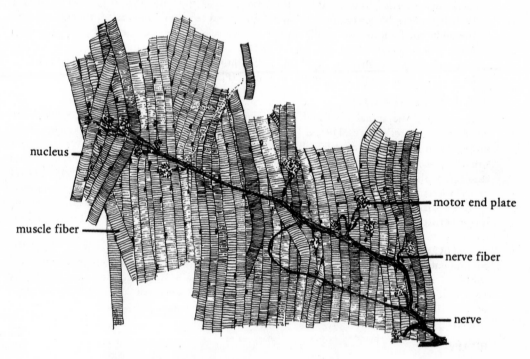

nucleus

muscle fiber

motor end plate

nerve fiber

nerve

Figure 11-5. Motor End Plates on Skeletal Muscle

Using bone cutters or bone saws, carefully remove the roof from the skull of the cat. Since the dura mater ossifies where it pushes down between the cerebrum and cerebellum, this must be cut before the skull roof comes free. Now continue to remove bone around the sides of the skull. Save as much of the dura mater as you can. As you progress, lift the brain from the floor of the the cranial cavity. Try to see the cranial nerves and cut them as far from the brain as possible. Also watch for the PITUITARY GLAND on the midventral surface of the brain and ease it out of the hypophyseal fossa of the sella turcica. The brain should now be free from the cavity and can be cut from the spinal cord and removed.

Study the superficial features of the brain. If a human brain or other mammalian brains are available, compare them with that of the cat. The description which follows is adequate for most mammalian brains. Refer to Plates 11-12 through 11-14.

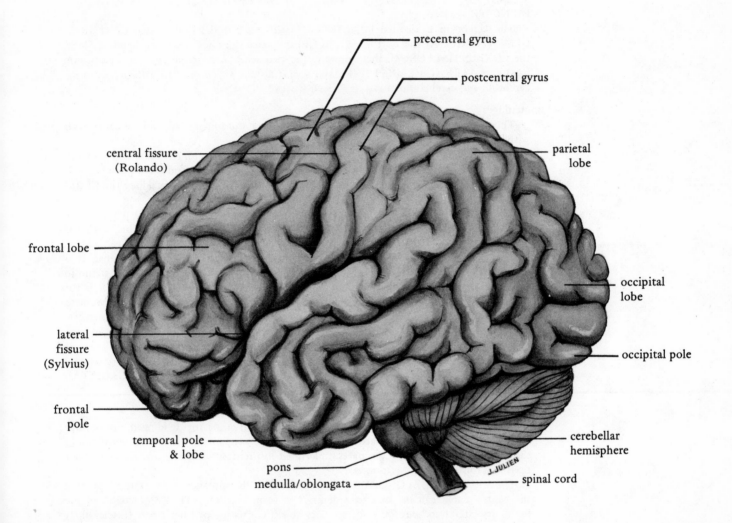

precentral gyrus

postcentral gyrus

central fissure
(Rolando)

parietal
lobe

frontal lobe

occipital
lobe

lateral
fissure
(Sylvius)

occipital pole

frontal
pole

temporal pole
& lobe

cerebellar
hemisphere

pons

medulla/oblongata

spinal cord

J. JULIEN

Plate 11-12. Human Brain—Lateral View

A. General

The brain is composed of three main parts: the BRAIN STEM, CEREBRUM, and CEREBELLUM. The cerebrum and cerebellum are large DORSAL EXPANSIONS which pretty well obscure the brain stem from that view. The cerebrum is the largest single part of the brain. From the VENTRAL SIDE, the brain stem can be seen as a continuation of the spinal cord and the point of attachment of most of the cranial nerves.

The brain stem is divided into four main parts, named from the spinal cord upward: MEDULLA OBLONGATA, PONS, MESENCEPHALON (MIDBRAIN), and DIENCEPHALON.

The cerebrum is divided by a LONGITUDINAL FISSURE into two CEREBRAL HEMISPHERES. At the bottom of this fissure notice the thick transverse band of fibers, the CORPUS CALLOSUM, that connects the two cerebral hemispheres. The cerebellum has two LATERAL HEMISPHERES and a central lobe called the VERMIS. Between the cerebrum and cerebellum is a deep TRANSVERSE FISSURE.

B. Meninges

These follow the same general pattern as those of the spinal cord, and are continuous with them.

The PIA MATER is highly vascular. It is in close contact with the brain and dips into its sulci and fissures. It is perforated by the blood vessels entering and leaving the brain. It gives rise to structures, the CHOROID PLEXUSES, which in turn produce the CEREBROSPINAL FLUID.

The ARACHNOID is a loose investment of the brain separated from the pia mater by the SUBARACHNOID CAVITY. It does not dip into the sulci and fissures, with the exception of the LONGITUDINAL FISSURE of the cerebrum.

The CRANIAL DURA MATER differs in a number of ways from the spinal. It is composed of TWO LAYERS. The outer one serves essentially as an internal periosteum to the skull bones and is referred to as the ENDOSTEAL LAYER. The inner one is the MENINGEAL LAYER. It pushes down into the longitudinal fissure of the cerebrum to form the FALX CEREBRI and in between the cerebrum and cerebellum (transverse fissure) to form the TENTORIUM CEREBELLI. At the FORAMEN MAGNUM it is continuous with the SPINAL DURA MATER.

The ENDOSTEAL and MENINGEAL LAYERS of the dura mater lie in close contact except where they separate to form SINUSES for the VENOUS BLOOD. The SAGITTAL and TRANSVERSE SINUSES are examples of this.

C. Midsagittal section of the brain (Plate 11-13).

The longitudinal fissure of the cerebrum is a good guide for dividing the brain into equal right and left halves. Place a sharp scalpel in this fissure and divide the brain. Study these sections and identify the parts underlined in the description below. Refer to your textbook for detailed descriptions.

The MEDULLA OBLONGATA is continuous with the spinal cord. In its upper portion the central canal can be seen to widen out to form the FOURTH VENTRICLE of the brain. Its lateral and ventral walls are very thick, consisting of fiber tracts (fasciculi). It gives rise laterally to cranial nerves. Some of the "crossing over" fibers, the PYRAMIDAL DECUSSATION, may be seen on the ventral medial side of the cut surface. The medulla has its upper limit at the PONS.

The PONS is a heavy bridge of fibers connecting the two halves of the cerebellum and joining the medulla and the midbrain. It is in the floor of the fourth ventricle. It contains important nerve centers. Name one.

The MIDBRAIN (mesencephalon) is a short section of the brain stem above the pons. In its floor are the CEREBRAL PEDUNCLES which are bundles of fibers leading into the cerebrum. Above the peduncles is the CEREBRAL AQUEDUCT (aqueduct of Sylvius) which passes through the midbrain to connect the fourth with the third ventricle. The roof of the midbrain is the TECTUM and contains rounded eminences, the CORPORA QUADRIGEMINA. These are the relay centers for visual and auditory reflexes.

The DIENCEPHALON is the uppermost part of the brain stem. It may be considered with the cerebrum under which it lies. The cerebral aqueduct of the midbrain expands

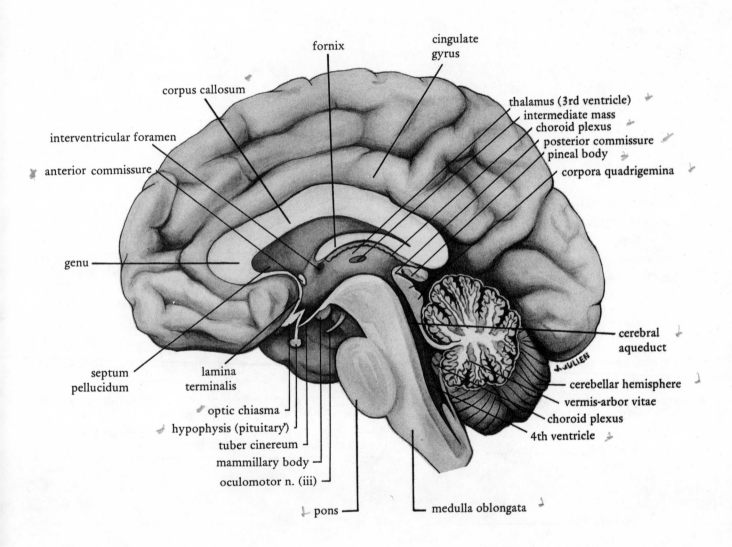

fornix

cingulate
gyrus

corpus callosum

thalamus (3rd ventricle)
intermediate mass
choroid plexus
posterior commissure
pineal body
corpora quadrigemina

interventricular foramen

anterior commissure

genu

cerebral
aqueduct

septum
pellucidum

lamina
terminalis

cerebellar hemisphere
vermis-arbor vitae
choroid plexus
4th ventricle

optic chiasma

hypophysis (pituitary)

tuber cinereum

mammillary body

oculomotor n. (iii)

pons

medulla oblongata

Plate 11-13. Midsagittal Section of Human Brain

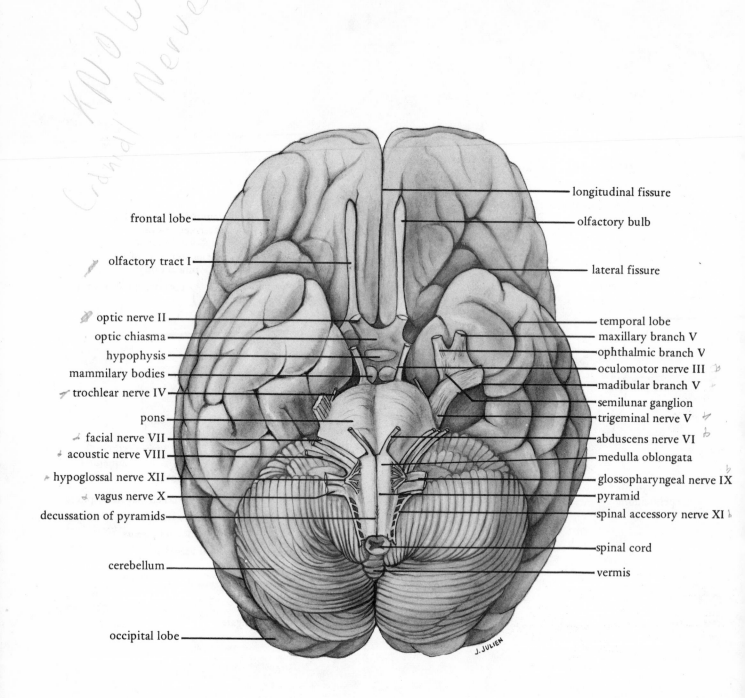

frontal lobe

olfactory tract I

optic nerve II
optic chiasma
hypophysis
mammilary bodies
trochlear nerve IV
pons
facial nerve VII
acoustic nerve VIII
hypoglossal nerve XII
vagus nerve X
decussation of pyramids

cerebellum

occipital lobe

longitudinal fissure

olfactory bulb

lateral fissure

temporal lobe
maxillary branch V
ophthalmic branch V
oculomotor nerve III
madibular branch V
semilunar ganglion
trigeminal nerve V
abduscens nerve VI
medulla oblongata
glossopharyngeal nerve IX
pyramid
spinal accessory nerve XI

spinal cord

vermis

J. JULIEN

Plate 11-14. Human Brain and Cranial Nerves—Ventral View

into the narrow deep THIRD VENTRICLE of the diencephalon. Two large nuclear masses make up most of the side walls of the diencephalon. They are called the THALAMI, and are important relay stations in the sensory pathways to the cerebrum. They are centers also of crude consciousness. The thalami are connected across the third ventricle by a bridge of gray matter, the INTERMEDIATE MASS. This is easily demonstrated in your brain sections.

The floor and part of the lateral walls of the third ventricle are formed by the HYPOTHALAMUS. It contains temperature-regulating centers and possibly a sleep center. It is also involved in the regulation of water, fat, and carbohydrate metabolism. Notice the PITUITARY GLAND (HYPOPHYSIS) which hangs from the floor of this part of the brain and rests in the hypophyseal fossa of the sella turcica. The pituitary arises from a rounded eminence, the TUBER CINEREUM. Back of the tuber cinereum are the paired MAMMILLARY BODIES. The OPTIC CHIASMA lies in front of the stalk of the pituitary.

The roof of the diencephalon is marked by the presence of a PINEAL BODY and a CHOROID PLEXUS extends from it toward the ventricle. The FORAMEN OF MONRO (interventricular) connects the third ventricle to the lateral ventricles which lie within the cerebral hemispheres.

Above the roof of the diencephalon are two semicircular masses of nerve fibers which connect the two CEREBRAL HEMISPHERES across the midline. These masses connect posteriorly, but are separated anteriorly. The larger of these is the CORPUS CALLOSUM, the smaller the FORNIX. The thin membrane between the fornix and corpus callosum anteriorly is the SEPTUM LUCIDUM; it represents the wall between the lateral ventricles of the cerebral hemispheres.

Finally, identify the CEREBELLUM in your brain section. The fourth ventricle is the ventricle of the cerebellum, but it does not extend into the hemispheres. The section is cut through the vermis; you should see the tree-like branching of the white matter known as the ARBOR VITAE. The cerebellum and the cerebrum have an outer covering of gray matter, the CORTEX.

Study slides of the cerebrum and cerebellum, and sketch some of the cells. The cerebral cortex contains pyramidal cells, the cerebellar cortex, the distinctive Purkinje cells, and other types (Figure 11-6 through 11-8).

D. Cerebrospinal fluid

The CEREBROSPINAL FLUID is formed by the CHOROID PLEXUSES located in the walls of the four brain ventricles and in the ependymal layer lining the central canal of the spinal cord. It is emptied into the ventricles and central canal. In the roof of the fourth ventricle are three foramina which carry cerebrospinal fluid into the subarachnoid spaces. These are a single median FORAMEN OF MAGENDIE and two lateral FORAMINA OF LUSCHKA. Cerebrospinal fluid may be formed in other areas of the

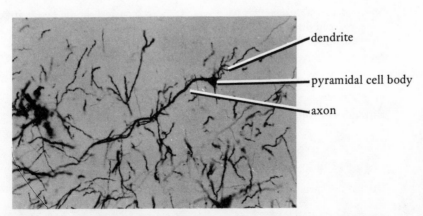

dendrite

pyramidal cell body

axon

Figure 11-6. Photomicrograph of a Section of the Cerebrum of the Cat (Golgi's Method) (120X)

Figure 11-7. Photomicrograph of a Pyramidal Cell of the Cerebral Cortex of the Cat (556X)

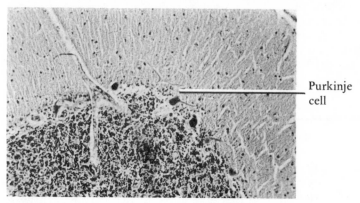

Purkinje cell

Figure 11-8. Photomicrograph of Human Cerebellum

nervous system. It is absorbed through VILLI OF THE ARACHNOID into the large dural venous sinuses and, in a minor way, into the lymphatic vessels.

CRANIAL NERVES (Plates 6-8 and 11-14)

Some of the cranial nerves have already been seen and should be identified with the help of your text and other books. Fill in the spaces in Table IV.

How do cranial nerves differ from spinal nerves?

How does the olfactory nerve differ from the other cranial nerves?

Discuss the crossing-over of the optic nerves.

TABLE IV. Cranial Nerves

Name of Nerve	Motor, Sensory, or Mixed	Origin and Course	Termination and Function
I. Olfactory	Sensory	nasal mucosa cribiform plate	olfactory bulb sense of smell
II. Optic	Sensory	retina optic chiasma	diencephalon sight
III. Oculomotor	Motor	mesencephalon	muscles of the eyeball + upper eye lid movement of eye + blinking
IV. Trochlear	Motor	mesencephalon	
V. Trigeminal	Mixed	① skin, mucous membranes + teeth; ② Pons	① pons; ② muscles of mastication
VI. Abducens	Motor	medulla oblongata	
VII. Facial	Mixed	① skin of ear, tongue floor of mouth; ② medulla	① medulla oblongata; ② glands of mouth, nose + pharynx, muscles of face
VIII. Acoustic Vestibulocochlear	Sensory	ear	medulla oblongata hearing
IX. Glossopharyngeal	Mixed		
X. Vagus	Mixed		
XI. Accessory	Motor		
XII. Hypoglossal	Motor		

AUTONOMIC NERVOUS SYSTEM (Plate 11-1)

This is also called the VEGETATIVE and the INVOLUNTARY nervous system. It includes all those neurons carrying impulses to or from the viscera, blood vessels, and glands. The main divisions are the CRANIOSACRAL (parasympathetic) and the THORACO-LUMBAR (sympathetic).

The THORACOLUMBAR DIVISION as indicated by its name has its efferent fibers carried in the twelve thoracics and the first two lumbar spinal nerves. They go out through the WHITE COMMUNICATING RAMI into the SYMPATHETIC TRUNK OF GANGLIA (also called central or vertebral ganglia). Locate these structures on your cat and label the central or sympathetic ganglia and communicating rami on the appropriate diagram (Plate 11-6). COLLATERAL GANGLIA may also be found which are a part of the thoracolumbar system and which serve as relay stations to the viscera. Fairly obvious examples of these are the CELIAC and SUPERIOR MESENTERIC GANGLIA which you can find between celiac axis and superior mesenteric arteries of your cat. They are the center of the SOLAR or CELIAC PLEXUS. You can easily find also the INFERIOR MESENTERIC GANGLION close to the inferior mesenteric artery of the cat.

Neurons going from the spinal cord to either central or collateral ganglia are called PREGANGLIONIC, those going from either of these types of ganglia to the viscera are called POSTGANGLIONIC. Using red pencil or ink, place on Plate 11-6 these two types of neurons to show them in their proper relationships.

The CRANIOSACRAL DIVISION of the autonomic system will be only partially explored. Its fibers are carried by certain of the cranial nerves; namely, the OCULOMOTOR, FACIAL, GLOSSOPHARYNGEAL, and VAGUS, and by the FIRST THREE OR FOUR SACRAL NERVES. The ganglia of this division are TERMINAL lying directly on or in the organs supplied. Hence the preganglionic fibers are long, the postganglionic are very short.

As an example of a craniosacral division nerve, locate the vagosympathetic trunk where it lies along the common carotid artery, and follow it back toward the heart. Just above the level of the first rib it divides and the sympathetic branch goes off to the middle cervical ganglion while the vagus goes on to send branches to the heart, trachea, lungs, and esophagus, and then to continue caudad to other viscera. The lower viscera are supplied by the sacral autonomics.

It should be apparent that each visceral organ receives nerves from both the thoraco-lumbar and the craniosacral divisions.

Where are the superior (cranial), middle (caudal), and inferior (stellate) cervical ganglia? Try to find them in your cat.

GLOSSARY — Chapter 11

anastomosis (a̍ nas´to mō´sis): G., anastomoein, cause to communicate.

aqueduct (ak´wē duct): L., aqua, water; duco, to lead.

arachnoid (a̍ rak´noid): G., arachne, spider; eidos, shape or likeness.

autonomic (äw to nom´ik): G., autos, self; nomos, law.

axillary (ak´si lēr i; ak sil´ēr i): L., axilla, armpit.

axon (ak´son): G., axon, axle.

brachial (brā´ki a̍l, brak´i a̍l): L., brachialis, pertaining to the arm.

callosum (kal lō´sum): L., callosus, thick-skinned.

carotid (ka̍ rot´id): G., karotides, pl. of karos, heavy sleep.

caudal (käw´da̍l): L., cauda, tail.

cerebellum (ser´e bel´lum): L., cerebrum, brain (a little brain).

cerebral (sēr´e bra̍l, se rē´bra̍l): L., cerebrum, brain.

coeliac (celiac) (sē´lē ak): G., koilia, belly, stomach.

commissure (kom´i shoor): L., commissura, a joining together.

crural (kroor a̍l): L., crus, leg.

decussation (de ku sā´shun): L., decussatio, intersection of two lines.

dendrite (den´drīt): G., dendrites, of a tree; from dendron, a tree.

diencephalon (dī´en sef´a̍ lon): G., dia, between; enkephalos, brain.

dura (dū´ra̍): L., dura, hard.

falx (fa̍lks): L., falx, falcis, sickle.

fasciculus, pl. fasciculi (fa sik´u lus, fa sik´u lī): L., a little bundle.

filum (fī´lum): L., filum, thread.

fornix (fôr´niks): L., fornix, vault, an arch.

funiculus (fu nik´u lus): L., funiculus, a cord, small rope.

glial (glī´a̍l): G., glia, glue.

hypophysis (hī pof´i sis, hi–): G., hypo, under; physis, growth.

hypothalamus (hī po thal´a̍ mus): G., hypo, under; thalamos, couch, chamber.

meninx, pl. meninges (mē ningks, mē nin´jēs): G., meningx, membrane.

myelin (mī e lin): G., myelos, marrow.

neurilemma (nū ri lem´a̍): G., neuron, nerve; lemma, husk, sheath.

pia (pī a̍, pē a̍): L., pia, pious, kind.

pineal (pi´nē a̍l): L., pinea, pine cone.

pituitary (pi tū i ter i): L., pituita, slimi, phlegm, mucus.

pons (ponz): L., pons, bridge

popliteal (pop lit´e a̍l, pop li tē´a̍l): L., poples, the ham.

pyramidal (pi ram´i da̍l): L., pyramis, –dis, pyramid.

ramus, pl. rami (rā´mus, rāy´mē): L., ramus, a branch.

saphenous (sa̍ fē´nus): L., saphenes, clear.

sciatic (sī at´ik): G., ischion, hip joint.

sella (sel´a̍): L., sella, a seat or saddle.

sulcus, sulci (sul´kus, sul´si): L., sulcus, a furrow or groove.

tectum (tek´tum): L., tectum (tego), roof, to cover.

tentorium (ten tō´ri um): L., tentorium, tent.

thalamus (thal´a mus): L., thalamos, chamber, couch.

vagus (vā´gus): L., vagus, wandering.

vermis (ver´mis): L., vermis, worm.

villus, villi (vil´us, vil´ī): L., villus, shaggy hair.

SENSE ORGANS

GENERAL

Living cells in general are irritable; that is, they respond to stimulation. The SENSE ORGANS are the RECEPTORS of the nervous system, and each is strikingly specific in its sensitivity. The ear is responsive to sound waves, the retina of the eye to light, the taste buds to chemical constituents of the mouth contents, the olfactory epithelium to chemicals in the air, the various sense organs in the skin to heat, cold, and pressure. There are also the PROPRIOCEPTIVE SENSES with receptors in ligaments around joints which enable us to know the position or orientation of our body parts without the use of the eyes.

It will not be possible to study all of these receptors in this laboratory. It should be noticed, however, that the receptors mentioned range from very complicated organs such as the eye, to relatively simple ones as the taste buds on the tongue or simple nerve endings in the skin. We shall study the eye, the ear, the nasal (olfactory) epithelium, and the taste buds.

We should remember that these are no more than receptor organs, and that stimulation of them merely sets up impulses in afferent (sensory) nerves which are transmitted to conscious areas in our brains. We see, hear, taste, smell, etc., with our brains.

THE EYE

The eye of the cat may be used for this study, or pig's or sheep's eyes may be obtained from a slaughter house. Models and charts of the human eye should be available.

1. With the use of a mirror, examine your own eye and identify such structures as the eyelids and eyelashes, the caruncle, the cornea, iris, and pupil. Move the eye in its socket and notice the range and versatility of its movement. What muscles are used in these movements, and where are they attached? They get their nerve supply from cranial nerves III, IV, and VI. Label Plates 12-1 and 12-2.

2. Study the coats of the eyeball and label them and related structures on Plates 12-1, figure 2, and 12-2.
   a. Fibrous coat of sclera and cornea.
   b. Choroid coat.
   c. Ciliary body (ciliary muscle, ciliary process).
   d. Iris.
   e. Pupil.
   f. Retina.
   g. Optic disc (blind spot).
   h. Macula lutea.
   i. Optic nerve.
   j. Lens.
   k. Anterior chamber.
   l. Posterior chamber.

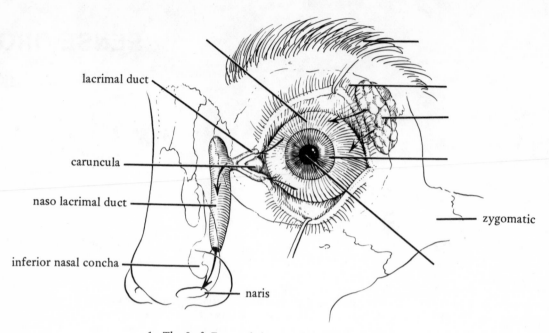

lacrimal duct

caruncula

naso lacrimal duct

inferior nasal concha

naris

zygomatic

1. The Left Eye and the Nasolacrimal Apparatus

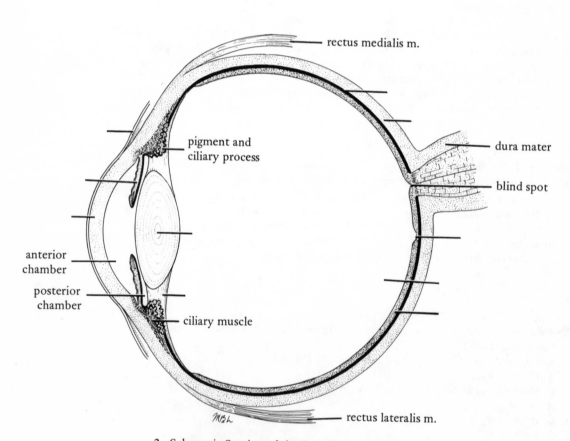

rectus medialis m.

pigment and
ciliary process

dura mater

blind spot

anterior
chamber

posterior
chamber

ciliary muscle

rectus lateralis m.

2. Schematic Section of the Eye—Horizontal Plane

Plate 12-1. The Human Eye and Related Structures

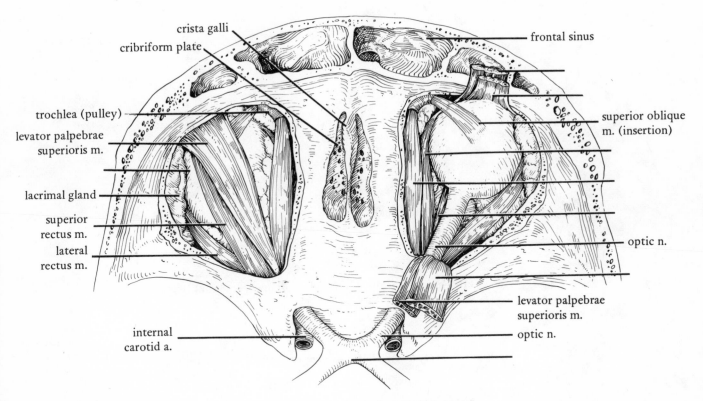

crista galli

cribriform plate

frontal sinus

trochlea (pulley)

superior oblique
m. (insertion)

levator palpebrae
superioris m.

lacrimal gland

superior
rectus m.

lateral
rectus m.

optic n.

levator palpebrae
superioris m.

internal
carotid a.

optic n.

1. Superior View of Eyeballs and Their Muscles

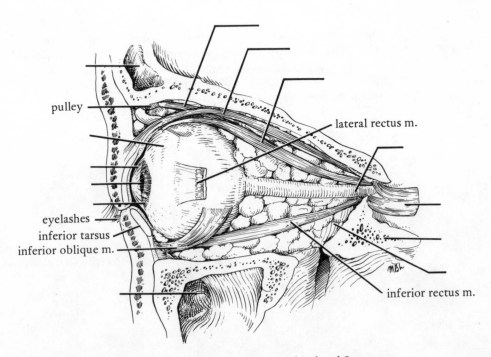

pulley

lateral rectus m.

eyelashes

inferior tarsus

inferior oblique m.

inferior rectus m.

2. Lateral View of the Left Orbit, Eye, and Related Structures

Plate 12-2. The Human Eye and Its Muscles

m. Vitreous body.
n. Suspensory ligament.
o. Conjunctiva.
Where is the aqueous humor?

What are the structures used in focusing the image on the retina of the eye? Define nearsighted, farsighted, astigmatism.

Where is the lacrimal gland?

Where is the secretion of the lacrimal gland drained, and what is its function?

Study the slide of the RETINA and compare it with the illustration in your text.

THE EAR

We shall limit our study of the ear to the use of models, charts, slides, and demonstrations. If a sectioned temporal bone is available, it can be used to advantage.

1. Using the models and charts available, identify the external ear, the middle ear, and the internal ear. Label Plate 12-3, using the guidelines provided.
   What is the function of the external ear?

   Where is the tympanic membrane or eardrum?

2. Recall the position and relationships of the middle ear and the ear ossicles which it contains. What is the relationship of the middle ear cavity to the mastoid cells? Label Plate 12-3, figure 1, using the guidelines provided.
   What function is served by the auditory tube?

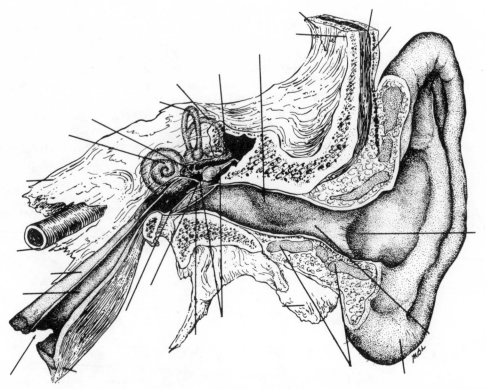

1. General View of a Section of the Left Ear

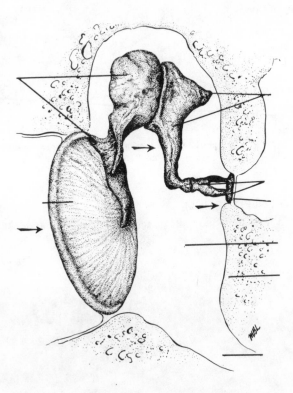

2. Middle Ear and Ear Ossicles

From Crouch, *Functional Human Anatomy*,
courtesy of Lea & Febiger

Plate 12-3. The Human Ear

3. The internal ear is the most complicated of the ear components. It consists of the small shell-like COCHLEA, the VESTIBULE, and the SEMICIRCULAR CANALS. Inside of these bony structures (bony labyrinth) are membranous counterparts which we call the MEMBRANOUS LABYRINTH. This is filled with a fluid, the ENDO-LYMPH. Between the bony labyrinth and the membranous labyrinth is a fluid, the PERILYMPH. The cochlea contains the essential hearing structures, THE ORGANS OF CORTI. The vestibule and semicircular canals serve the function of equilibrium or balance.

4. Label the following on the diagrams provided (Figure 12-1; Plate 12-3, figure 1).
   a. Semicircular canals.
   b. Vestibule.
   c. Cochlea.

5. Study the slide of a section of the cochlea, and sketch an organ of Corti and label Figure 12-1.
   a. Basilar membrane.
   b. Outer hair cells.
   c. Inner hair cells.
   d. Tectorial membrane.
   e. Cochlear nerve.

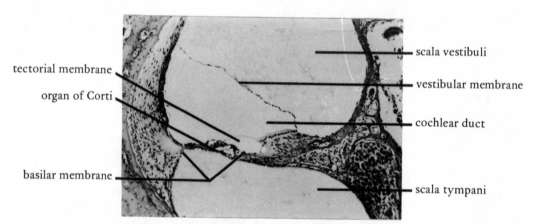

Figure 12-1. Photomicrograph of the Internal Ear of the Kitten (80X)

OLFACTORY EPITHELIUM

Study a prepared slide of olfactory epithelium, and sketch a few cells and label Figure 12-2.

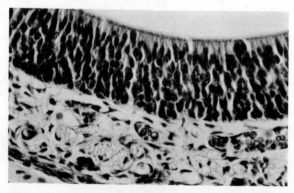

Figure 12-2. Photomicrograph of the Olfactory Epithelium of the Mouse (80X)

Where is this olfactory epithelium found?

These olfactory cells go into the olfactory bulb of the brain. Through what bone do the olfactory cells pass in reaching the brain?

GUSTATORY (TASTE) ORGAN

Study a prepared slide of a section of the tongue, and find a taste bud.

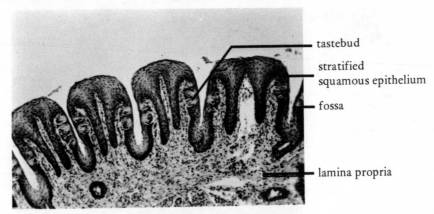

tastebud

stratified
squamous epithelium

fossa

lamina propria

Figure 12-3. Photomicrograph of a Section of Rabbit's Tongue Showing Tastebuds (80X)

GLOSSARY — Chapter 12

caruncle (kȧr ′ung-k'l; ka rung ′k'l): L., caruncula, dim. of caro, flesh.

chorioid (ko ′ri oid, kō ′roid): G., chorion, membrane.

ciliary (sil ′i er i): L., cilium, pl. cilia, eyelash.

cochlea (kok ′le ȧ): L., cochlea, snail.

cornea (kôr ′ne ȧ): L., corneus, horny.

humor (hū mēr): L., humor, moisture, fluid.

lacrimal (lak ′ri mȧl): L., lacrima, tear.

macula (mak ′ū lȧ): L., macula, spot, stain.

ossicle (os ′i k'l): L., ossiculum, small bone.

proprioceptive (prō ′pri o sep ′tiv): L., proprius, one's own; copere, to take.

retina (ret ′i nȧ): L., rete, net.

sclera (sklē ′rȧ): G., skleros, hard.

vitreous (vit ′re us): L., vitreus, of glass, transparent.

REFERENCES

Arey, L. B. DEVELOPMENTAL ANATOMY, Ed. 7. Philadephia: W. B. Saunders Co., 1965.

Balinsky, B. I. INTRODUCTION TO EMBRYOLOGY, Ed. 3. Philadelphia: W. B. Saunders Co., 1970.

Basmajian, J. V. CATE'S PRIMARY ANATOMY, Ed. 4. Baltimore: The Williams and Wilkins Co., 1960.

Best, Charles H. and Norman B. Taylor. THE HUMAN BODY, Ed. 3. Philadelphia: W. B. Saunders Co., 1956.

Bloom, William and Don W. Fawcett. A TEXTBOOK OF HISTOLOGY, Ed. 9. Philadelphia and London: W. B. Saunders Co., 1968.

Booth, Ernest S. and Robert B. Chiasson. LABORATORY ANATOMY OF THE CAT. Dubuque, Iowa: Wm. C. Brown Co., Inc., 1967.

Crouch, James E. FUNCTIONAL HUMAN ANATOMY, Ed. 2. Philadelphia: Lea and Febiger, 1972.

Crouch, James E. TEXT-ATLAS OF CAT ANATOMY, Ed. 1. Philadelphia: Lea and Febiger, 1969.

Cunningham, D. J. TEXTBOOK OF ANATOMY, Ed. 10. Edited by C. J. Romanes, Oxford University Press, London.

Di Fiore, M. S. H. ATLAS OF HUMAN HISTOLOGY, Ed. 3. Philadelphia: Lea and Febiger, 1967.

Duvall, Ellen Neall. KINESIOLOGY—THE ANATOMY OF MOTION. Englewood Cliffs, N. J.: Prentice-Hall, Inc., 1959.

Finerty, John C. and E. V. Cowdry. A TEXTBOOK OF HISTOLOGY, Ed. 5. Philadelphia: Lea and Febiger, 1960.

Gardner, Ernest. FUNDAMENTALS OF NEUROLOGY, Ed. 5. Philadelphia: W. B. Saunders Co., 1968.

Goss, C. M., Ed. GRAY'S ANATOMY OF THE HUMAN BODY, Ed. 29. Philadelphia: Lea and Febiger, 1972.

Horsburgh, David B. and James P. Heath. ATLAS OF CAT ANATOMY, Ed. 2. Stanford University Press, 1939.

Jepson, Maud. ANATOMICAL ATLAS. New York: Rinehart and Co., Inc., 1957.

Kimber, Diana C. and Carolyn E. Gray, Caroline E. Stackpole, and Lutie C. Leavell. ANATOMY AND PHYSIOLOGY, Ed. 15. New York: The Macmillan Co., 1966.

King, Barry G. and Mary J. Showers. HUMAN ANATOMY AND PHYSIOLOGY, Ed. 6. Philadelphia and London: W. B. Saunders Co., 1969.

Korzybski, Alfred. MANHOOD OF HUMANITY, Ed. 1. New York: E. P. Dutton & Co., 1921.

Leach, William James. FUNCTIONAL ANATOMY OF THE MAMMAL, Ed. 3. New York: McGraw-Hill Book Co., Inc., 1961.

Lopez-Antunez, Luis. ATLAS OF HUMAN ANATOMY. Philadelphia: W. B. Saunders Co., 1971.

NOMINA ANATOMICA, Ed. 3. Amsterdam: Excerpta Medica Foundation, 1966.

NOMINA ANATOMICA VETERINARIA. Vienna: Adolf Holzhausen's Successors, 1968. (Available in the U. S. through the Department of Anatomy, New York State Veterinary College, Ithaca.)

Romer, Alfred S. VERTEBRATE BODY, Ed. 4. Philadelphia: W. B. Saunders Co., 1970.

Stiles, Karl A. HANDBOOK OF HISTOLOGY, Ed. 5. Philadelphia: Blakiston, McGraw-Hill Book Co., Inc., 1968.

Truex, Raymond and M. B. Carpenter. STRONG AND ELWYN'S HUMAN NEURO-ANATOMY. Ed. 5. Baltimore: The Williams and Wilkins Co., 1969.

APPENDIX

The examinations which follow are those used during one semester in my own course in Human Anatomy at California State University at San Diego except that the diagrams have been deleted. These sample examinations together with the questions asked in the text of the laboratory manual and at the ends of the chapters in your textbook give a sound basis for preparation for the regular examinations in this course.

Additional examination materials are included following the four complete examinations.

EXAMINATION 1

INTRODUCTION / SKELETAL SYSTEM

Let's begin our exercise with some completion type questions. After all, this is a course in language. Place on the numbered lines to the left the words or phrases which correctly complete the statements to the right. Be sure you match the numbers in the statements with the numbered lines on which you place them.

Example:

0 _____toward_____   When placing the microscope on the table before you the arm should be (0) you.

1. _____   The unit of structure and function in the body is the (1).

2. ___*Mammalia*___   Man, possessing hair, belongs to the Class (2). Other <u>diagnostic</u> characteristics of members of this class are (3 and 4). Other

3. ___*mammary glands*___   classes of vertebrate animals are the (5, 6, 7, and 8). Man also belongs to the Phylum (9) and its diagnostic characteristics are

4. _____   (10; 11, and 12).

5. _____

6. _____

7. _____

8. _____

9. ___*Chordata*___

10. ___*notochord*___

11. ___*gill slits*___

12. ___*neural tube*___

13. ___*anatomical position*___   When describing man's anatomy we assume him to be in the (13). In this position the palms are directed (14).

14. ___*forward*___

15. _____   Tissues are composed of (15 and 16). They fall into four groups (17, 18, 19, and 20). The outer skin is called the (21) and is a

16. _____   (22) tissue. The inner skin is called the (23) and is composed of a (24) tissue. The outer skin, when thick, shows the following strata

17. _____   (25, 26, 27, 28, and 29). The cells in the innermost stratum divide by (30) and push outward toward the skin surface.

18. _____

19. _____

20. _____

21. _____

22. _____

23. _____

24. _____

25. _____

26. _____

27. _____

28. _____

29. _____

30. _____

31. _papillary_____

32. _reticular_____

33. _____

The inner skin is divided into two layers, the (31 and 32). It is used, from some animals, to produce (33).

34. _epidermis_____

35. _____

36. _____

37. _____

The accessory structures of the skin, the hair, glands, and nails are all developed from the (34) of the skin though they push into the deeper layers of the skin and even into the (35) which is under the skin. This under-the-skin layer is a (36) tissue. It is also called (37).

38. _sebaceous_____

39. _____

40. _____

Glands of the skin entering the hair follicles are called (38). Those emptying their products on the skin surface are (39) glands. They are, in form, called (40).

41. _erector villi___

There are muscles in the skin, related to the air follicles, called (41).

42. _dermis_____

43. _epidermis_____

The blood supply of the skin enters through the (42) but the vessels do not penetrate the (43).

44. _Pacinian corpuscle_

45. _free nerve ending_

Two kinds of nerve endings sometimes seen in the skin are (44 and 45).

46. _anterior_____

47. _posterior_____

The belly side of the human body is called (46). The back side of the human body is called (47). These parts in a four-legged animal like the cat would be called (48 and 49) respectively.

48. ventral

49. dorsal

50. superior

The "upper" end of the human body is called (50), the "lower" (51). The two parts could be separated by cutting the body through the (52) plane.

51. interior

52. transverse

53. frontal

The "front" part of the body could be cut from the "back" part through the (53) plane. A cut through the (54) plane would divide the body into more or less equal right and left halves.

54. mid-sagital

55. distal

The foot is at the (55) end of the leg. The humerus is the (56) bone of the upper extremity. The knee joint involves the (57) end of the femur and the (58) end of the tibia. The fibula is on the (59) side of the leg; the ulna on the (60) side of the forearm.

56. proximal

57. distal

58. proximal

59. lateral

60. medial

61. meiosis

Eggs and sperms have half the number of chromosomes as the body cells. This comes about by a process called (61) which takes place in the (62 and 63).

62. testes

63. ovaries

64. support

Important functions of the skeleton are (64, 65, 66, and 67).

65. protection

66. blood formation

67. _____

68. _____

The tissues which make up most of the skeleton are (68 and 69). There are two kinds of bone on the basis of development (70 and 71).

69. _____

70. _____

71. _____

72. periostcum

The fibrous membrane covering bone is (72). It takes part in bone formation and repair by action of its (73) cells. The medullary or marrow cavity of a bone is widened during growth by action of (74) cells. Cells occupying the lacunae of bone tissue are called (75).

73. _____

74. osteoclasts

75. osteocytes

76. sinus

An air cavity in a bone is called a (76). A groove in a bone is a (77); and a whole in a bone is a (78). A hamulus is shaped like a (79).

77. _sulcus_

78. _foramen_

79. _hook_

80. _____   Bone formation is called (80); calcium deposition is called (81).

81. _____

82. _connective tissue_   Tendons and most ligaments are formed of (82) tissue.

83. _____   The cartilage which precedes bone formation is called (83). The
                           cartilage in the external ear auricle is (84); that between bodies of
84. _elastic_   vertebrae is (85).

85. _____

Modified True-False. In each of the statements to the right below, there is an underlined word(s). If the statement is true as it stands, place <u>nothing</u> on the numbered line to the left. If the statement is false, change the statement to make it true by substituting a word(s) for the underlined word(s). <u>Place this correct word on the line at the left</u> of the statement.

Examples:

_____Republican_____   Reagan is a member of the <u>Communist</u> party.

_____   Nixon is a <u>Republican</u>.

1. _____   The dens is derived embryologically from the <u>atlas</u>.

2. _____   The cervical vertebrae may always be identified by the <u>bifid spinous processes</u>.

3. _____   The mandible articulates with the temporal bone by its <u>coronoid</u> process.

4. _____   The mandibular foramen is on the <u>medial</u> side of the ramus of the mandible.

5. _____Yellow_____   <u>White</u> fibers are elastic.

6. _____   <u>Fibroblasts</u> are among the most common of connective tissue cells.

7. _____   The radius rotates around the <u>humerus</u> to pronate the hand.

8. _____   To supinate the hand is to turn it <u>upward</u>.

9. _____   The bone forming the heel is the <u>calcaneus</u>.

10. _____fibula_____   The lateral malleolus is a part of the <u>tibia</u>.

11. _____   The elbow joint allows movement in only <u>one</u> plane.

12. _____   The sella tucica is a part of the <u>ethmoid</u> bone.

13. _____   The cribriform (horizontal) plate has foramina for the <u>optic</u> nerves.

14. _____ The hard palate in the roof of the mouth is formed by the <u>maxillae</u> and palatine bones.

15. _____ The patella is a <u>sutural</u> bone.

16. _____ The <u>talus</u> joins the tibia and fibula to form the ankle joint.

17. _____ The cartilages in the knee joint are the <u>cruciate</u>.

18. _____ The tubercle of a rib articulates with a transverse process of a <u>cervical</u> vertebra.

19. _____floating_____ Ribs 11 and 12 are <u>false</u> ribs.

20. _____superior_____ The jugular notch is on the <u>inferior</u> border of the manubrium.

21. _____ The sternal angle marks the point of joining of the manubrium and <u>body</u> of the sternum.

22. _____ The part of the scapula which is parallel to the vertebral column is the <u>axillary</u> border.

23. _____ The <u>true</u> pelvis lies above the arcuate (iliopectineal) line of the bony pelvis.

24. _____ In the male the bony pelvis has a <u>subcostal</u> angle of less than 90 degrees.

25. _____ The <u>coracoid</u> process of the scapula articulates with the clavicle.

What three bones contribute to the wall of the acetabulum?

1. _____ilium_____ 2. _____ischium_____ 3. _____pubis_____

Briefly describe and compare the articulations of the pectoral and pelvic girdles to the axial skeleton and indicate their functional significance.

Name three abnormal curvatures of the vertebral column and list a few probable causes of such deformities.

What are the primary and secondary curvatures of the vertebral column? Name them--please.

Diagram and label a synovial joint containing a fibrous disc.

Comment if you wish on the content, philosophy, presentation, and organization of the course.

APPENDIX

EXAMINATION 2

MUSCULAR SYSTEM / COELOM

Three types of muscle tissue are recognized. One of these smooth muscles is found in the walls of the visceral and other hollow organs. Please diagram a smooth muscle cell and label it.

Skeletal muscle tissue is characterized as follows:

1.

2.

3.

4.

Cardiac muscle tissue is best distinguished from skeletal muscle by the following characters:

1.

2.

3.

Skeletal muscle and connective tissues form the muscle organs of the body. Describe the belly of a muscle indicating the relationship of muscle tissue to connective tissue components. Use the appropriate anatomical terminology.

Define (1) tendon of origin, (2) aponeurosis, (3) deep fascia, (4) linea alba, (5) sphincter.

The skeletal and muscular systems are often referred to as the skeletomuscular system. In this relation-ship the bones serve as levers, the joints as fulcra, and the muscles as the source of power in performing bodily movements. What kind of leverage is represented by the diagram below? Give one example.

$$\boxed{W}\underline{\hspace{5cm}}$$
$$\Delta \quad +$$
$$F. \quad P.$$

What other type of leverage is commonly seen in the human body? Diagram this type and give one example.

Muscles do not commonly function as single units but in groups. Define the following in terms of their roles in a movement such as the flexion of forearm on the arm. Prime mover, synergist, antagonist, fixator.

APPENDIX

Complete the table below by filling in the numbered blank spaces.   (15 points)

Muscle	Origin	Insertion
Biceps brachii	1. _____ _____	2. _____ _____
Rectus femoris	3. _____ _____	4. _____ _____
5. _____	on humerus; lower half of anterior surface	on ulna; coronoid process
6. _____	on body of humerus and on infraglenoid of scapula	on olecranon process of ulna
7. _____	on tibia; medial side of proximal end	on anterior superior spine of ilium
Biceps femoris	8. _____ _____	9. _____ _____
Sternocleidomastoideus	10. _____ _____	11. _____ _____
Deltoid	12. _____ _____	13. _____ _____
14. _____	on tuberosity of ischium	on medial surface of body of tibia
15. _____	on medial and lateral condyles of femur	on calcaneus

Explain the fact that the biceps brachii both flexes the forearm and supinates the hand.

What muscles are called "hamstrings"?

What is muscle tonus and why does it fail to fatigue the muscles?

Describe briefly the subserous fascia. (10 points)

Comment if you wish.

APPENDIX

EXAMINATION 3

CIRCULATORY / DIGESTIVE / RESPIRATORY / EXCRETORY SYSTEMS

_____

What is a closed system of circulation?   (5 points)

What is the functional importance of the preponderance of smooth muscle tissue in the tunica media of small arteries and arterioles?   (10 points)

Trace the course of a drop of blood from the renal vein to the right vertebral artery naming all structures (vessels, chambers, valves, etc.) through which it would pass. Name the structures in logical sequence and use the following form: renal vein ⟶ thoracic aorta ⟶ left atrium ⟶ tricuspid valve, etc., etc. (16 points)

Trace the course of a drop of blood from the <u>hepatic portal vein</u> to the right atrium naming in proper sequence all of the structures through which it would pass. Answer in the following form: hepatic portal vein ⟶ aorta ⟶ inferior vena cava, etc., etc.   (4 points)

Where are valves found in the circulatory system?   (6 points)

Make a simple diagram to show the intrinsic conducting mechanism of the heart. Label and use arrows to show the direction of passage of the impulse.   (10 points)

The digestive and respiratory systems are closely related structurally and functionally. This is well demonstrated in voice production and articulate speech. Explain this indicating the parts of the two systems involved.   (10 points)

APPENDIX

In the blank space before each term in the left-hand column place the number of the phrase, definition, or homologue from the right-hand column which best matches the term. They may not match out evenly; therefore, don't be alarmed if you have extra terms and phrases.   (22 points)

_____ papillary muscle	1. epicardium
_____ sinoatrial node	2. an opening between atria of fetal heart
_____ atrium	3. lining membrane of heart
_____ endocardium	4. pacemaker of heart
_____ Purkinje fibers	5. artery to heart
_____ visceral pericardium	6. a lymph capillary
_____ trabeculae carneae	7. contraction phase of cardiac cycle
_____ A-V node	8. ear-like fold of atrial wall
_____ foramen ovale	9. returns venous blood to right atrium
_____ tunica interna	10. muscular layer of arterial wall
_____ ductus arteriosus	11. attach to edges of cusps of heart valves
_____ portal vein	12. transmit impulse from atrium to bundle of His
_____ lymph node	13. muscular ridges in wall of heart
_____ chordae tendineae	14. vessel connecting aorta and pulmonary artery
_____ auricle	15. produces lymphocytes
_____ foramen rotundum	16. carries blood away from liver
_____ coronary artery	17. receiving chamber of heart
__6___ lacteal	18. muscles holding heart valves
_____ coronary sinus	19. special muscle fibers conducting impulses to ventricular walls
_____ systole	20. vessel connecting viscera with liver
_____ diastole	21. inner layer of arterial wall
_____ ventricle	22. an opening into the greater omentum

What is the signifiance of the presence of smooth muscle in the walls of bronchioles?   (6 points)

In the blank spaces to the left of each term below, place the number of the definition or phrase which best defines or describes the term. Do not expect a perfect matching.   (19 points)

_14_   cecum   1. a downward projection from the soft palate

_3_   Peyer's patch   2. opening into larynx

_12_   ampulla of Vater   3. aggregate of lymph nodules

_15_   tunica adventitia   4. the hardest substance in the body

_2_   glottis   5. a hyaline cartilage of the larynx

_4_   enamel   6. tonsils

_5_   cricoid   7. band of longitudinal muscle on colon

_____   alveolus   8. papillae with sharp points

_1_   epiglottis   9. composed of elastic cartilage

_____   fungiform   10. endocrine in function

_____   dentine   11. the final subdivision of a lung

_13_   villi   12. the opening of the common bile duct and pancreatic duct

_6_   palatine   13. an adaptive feature of the small intestine which increases
                                          efficiency of absorption

_10_   islets of Langerhans

_16_   crypts of Lieberkuhn   14. at inferior end of ascending colon

_7_   taenia coli   15. outer coat of esophagus

_8_   filiform   16. intestinal glands

_____   uvula

_____   respiratory bronchiole

All organs of the digestive system, from the esophagus to the rectum, are similar in the histology of their walls. Name one characteristic of each of the following which would serve to distinguish it from the others (histologically).   (10 points)

a. esophagus – has skeletal mm.

b. stomach – gastric pits

What are the functions of the urinary system?   (6 points)

What kind of epithelium lines each of the following organs?   (6 points)

1. Proximal convoluted tubule — *low cuboidal*

2. Collecting tubule (of kidney) — *cuboidal*

3. Urinary bladder — *trans*

4. Trachea — *pseudostratified columnar*

5. Duodenum — *columnar (simple*

6. Anal canal — *stratified squamous*

Please draw and label fully a kidney tubule (nephron) with its blood supply. Draw a line across your drawing to indicate what parts are in the cortex and which in the medulla of the kidney.   (15 points)

Comment if you wish.

EXAMINATION 4

REPRODUCTIVE AND NERVOUS SYSTEMS/SENSE ORGANS

What is accomplished by the process of fertilization? Name three.   (6 points)

The placenta is often referred to as a structure of double origin.   What makes up the placenta?   (6 points)

What is mesenchyme and where does it come from in the embryo?   (6 points)

What constitutes the umbilical cord?   (6 points)

Which germ layer gives rise to each of the following?   (6 points)

a. dermis

b. heart

c. epithelium of stomach

d. brain

e. smooth muscle

f. most connective tissue

The items in the right-hand column below define, describe, or otherwise suggest the terms or phrases at left. In the blank spaces, please place the numbers which make the best match. Use only one number--<u>the best--in each case, and <u>don't expect to fill all blanks or use all definitions or descriptions.</u> I just can't seem to make these things match out evenly. There is always something left over. (23 points)

_____ epididymis	1.	the lining of the uterus
_____ corpus cavernosum	2.	homologue of scrotum
_____ primary follicle	3.	a tissue which lines the ureters
_____ urethra	4.	the "neck" of the uterus
_____ testes	5.	encloses the egg cell
_____ stroma	6.	connective tissue of ovary
_____ perineum	7.	produces a hormone progestin
_____ vulva	8.	homologue of clitoris
_____ epithelium	9.	a gland formed around the urethra
_____ hymen	10.	external genitals of the male
_____ labia majora	11.	empties a lubricating fluid into lower urethra
_____ endometrium	12.	a highly coiled tubular structure which lies on posterior side of the testis
_____ prostate	13.	small skin folds--pass around clitoris anteriorly
_____ ejaculatory duct	14.	the region of "outlet of the pelvis"
_____ labia minora	15.	a funnel-shaped opening to the uterine tube
_____ uterus	16.	a membrane covering the upper end of the vagina
_____ penis	17.	fill with blood and cause erection of penis and clitoris
_____ Cowper's glands	18.	lies between seminal vesicles and the prostate gland
_____ corpus luteum	19.	the counterpart (homologue) of the ovary
_____ cervix		
_____ transitional epithelium		
_____ infundibulum		
_____ fornix		

The ovaries and testes belong to two body systems. Name them.

1.   2.

Name in logical sequence the structures a sperm would pass through in traveling from its origin in the testis to its exit from the penis. Anwer as follows: testis $\longrightarrow$ ovary $\longrightarrow$ oviduct $\longrightarrow$ uterus, etc., etc. (10 points)

What is the relationship of the vesicular (Graafian) follicle to the corpus luteum?   (8 points)

Define the following: (12 points)

a. synapse

b. ganglion

c. vulva (pudendum)

d. falx cerebri

e. mesometrium (broad ligament)

f. thalamus

Diagram a cross section of the spinal cord and place on it the meninges and the space or cavities between them. Label only the meninges and the spaces.   (10 points)

Matching Question.   The items in the right-hand column below define, describe, or otherwise suggest the terms or phrases at the left.   In the blank spaces please place the numbers which make the best match. Use only one number--the best--in each case, and don't expect to fill all blanks or use all definitions or descriptions.   (2 points each--42)

_____	neuroglia	1. the terminal branches of an axon
_10_	myelin	2. the spinal nerves in the vertebral canal below the spinal cord
_20_	filum terminale	
_2_	cauda equina	3. the central part of the cerebellum
_____	sympathetic ganglia	4. the meningeal layer in the longitudinal fissure of the cerebrum
_14_	choroid plexus	5. the nerve to the diaphragm
_____	vermis	6. allows escape of cerebrospinal fluid from 4th ventricle
_____	tentorium cerebelli	7. a bridge of white matter between cerebral hemispheres
_12_	optic nerve	8. an outgrowth of the roof of the 3rd ventricle
_____	brachial plexus	9. a relay station for sensory neurons to the cerebral cortex
_____	thalamus	10. a fatty covering around an axon or dendrite
_5_	phrenic nerve	11. connects lateral and 3rd ventricles
_____	falx cerebri	12. form chiasma in front of pituitary
_16_	cervical plexus	13. connective tissue of nervous system
_19_	vagus nerve	14. produces cerebrospinal fluid
_____	pineal body	15. a meningeal partition between cerebrum and cerebellum
_____	foramen of monro	16. formed by the last 4 cervical and the 1st thoracic spinal nerves
_____	corpus callosum	17. a bridge of gray matter connected the thalami across the 3rd ventricle
_18_	arachnoid	18. a web-like meninx
_____	foramen of Luschka	19. provides innervation to heart, lungs, stomach, etc.
_17_	intermediate mass	20. the terminal portion of the spinal cord
		21. a collection of nerves forming the sciatic nerve

<u>Multiple Choice.</u>   Pick out the <u>best</u> answer in each of the following by putting the appropriate letter in the blank space.   The best answer is the most accurate and the most specific.   (2 points each--30)

Example:

___b___   The heart is located in the: (a) abdomen, (b) thorax, (c) left arm, (d) spinal ganglia, (e) central gray matter of spinal cord.

_____   1.   The cell bodies of visceral sensory neurons are found in the: (a) sympathetic ganglia, (b) collateral ganglia, (c) vertebral ganglia, (d) spinal ganglia, (e) central gray matter of spinal cord.

_____   2.   A fold of the meningeal dura mater of the brain dips into the transverse fissure to form the: (a) falx cerebri, (b) tentorium cerebelli, (c) choroid plexus, (d) vermis, (e) corpus callosum.

_____   3.   The myelin (medullary) sheath is lacking on the fibers of neurons of the: (a) central system, (b) cranial nerves, (c) spinal nerves, (d) preganglionic pathways, (e) postganglionic pathways.

_____   4.   An example of a pure sensory nerve is the: (a) posterior root of a spinal nerve, (b) oculomotor nerve, (c) cranial nerve VIII, (d) vagus nerve, (e) afferent neuron.

_____   5.   The vagus nerve which you saw in the <u>cat</u>, in <u>man</u> has centers in the: (a) cervical plexus, (b) brachial plexus, (c) cervical nerves 5 and 6, (d) heart, (e) medulla oblongata.

_____   6.   The tapered lower end of the spinal cord is the: (a) filum terminale, (b) cauda equina, (c) subarachnoid cavity, (d) conus medullaris, (e) terminal funiculus.

_____   7.   Cerebrospinal fluid is produced in the: (a) central canal of the spinal cord, (b) subarachnoid space, (c) ventricles of the brain, (d) choroid plexuses, (e) villi of the arachnoid.

_____   8.   The supporting and protecting membranes of the spinal cord are called: (a) neurilemma, (b) arachnoid, (c) neuroglia, (d) myelin sheath, (e) meninges.

_____   9.   A structure composed of fibers (commissural) connecting the two halves of the cerebellum is the: (a) fornix, (b) cerebral penduncle, (c) tuber cinereum, (d) foramen of Monro, (e) corpus callosum, (f) pons.

_____ 10.   A relay station in the brain for the neurons of the sensory pathways from the cord is the: (a) thalamus, (b) cerebral penduncles, (c) fornix, (d) corpora quadrigemina, (e) superior colliculi.

_____ 11.   The thalami are connected across the third ventricle by the: (a) corpus callosum, (b) fornix, (c) intermediate mass, (d) posterior commissure, (e) septum lucidum.

_____ 12.   The superior cervical ganglion is a part of the: (a) central nervous system, (b) sympathetic nervous system, (c) autonomic nervous system, (d) parasympathetic nervous system, (e) sympathetic trunk.

_____ 13.   Endolymph is found in the: (a) bony labyrinth of the ear, (b) the middle ear, (c) the membranous labyrinth of the ear, (d) the endoderm.

_____ 14.   The hypophysis is located in the: (a) floor of the mesencephalon, (b) floor of the diencephalon, (c) roof of the third ventricle, (d) cerebellum, (e) medulla oblongata.

_____ 15.   Cerebrospinal fluid escapes through the roof of the fourth ventricle by way of the: (a) interventricular foramina, (b) villi of the arachnoid, (c) foramina of Luschka, (d) foramina of Magendie and Luschka, (e) foramen of Magendie.

List one function for each of the following: (20 points)

a. cochlea

b. ear drum

c. semicircular canals

d. trochlear nerve

e. ciliary muscles of eye

f. iris of eye

g. lens of eye

h. rods (of eye)

i. ear ossicles

j. posterior root ganlion

k. olfactory nerve

l. extrinsic eye muscles

Name the diagram on the opposite page using the numbered spaces below.   (20 points)   This was a mid-sagittal section of the human brain.   See Plate 11-13.

1. _____

2. _____

3. _____

4. _____

5. _____

6. _____

7. _____

8. _____

9. _____

10. _____

11. _____

12. _____

13. _____

14. _____

15. _____

16. _____

17. _____

18. _____

19. _____

20. _____

Label the external and internal organs of the human female.   See Plate 10-1 in this manual.

Please label the following on the lines at the bottom of the page. (30 points)   These were drawings of a sensory neuron and a cross section of the spinal cord with a spinal nerve attached showing its relationship to the sympathetic nervous system.   See Plates 11-2 and 11-6 of this manual.

Comment if you wish.

APPENDIX

ADDITIONAL EXAMINATION MATERIALS

1. SKELETAL SYSTEM

_____

Filling blank space. Surface anatomy.

What bones or parts of bones are involved in each of the following "surface" features of the human body?
Be specific in your answers.   (16 points)

A. sygomatic arch: 1. _____   2. _____

B. jugular or suprasternal notch: 1. _____   2. _____

C. bone just above thyroid cartilage: 1. _____

D. prominence on midline of neck posteriorly: 1. _____

E. the tip of the shoulder: 1. _____

F. three bony prominences at the elbow: 1. _____

    2. _____   3. _____

G. bony structure on which we sit: 1. _____

H. projecting structure between costal margins: 1. _____

I. lateral and medial prominences at distal end of the lower leg: 1. _____

    2. _____

K. bone of the heel: 1. _____

Diagram and label fully a synovial joint--one without a fibrocartilage, please.   (15 points)

Matching Type. Place the number of the words in the first column before the statements of which they are true. Don't expect an even matching of blanks and numbers.   (21 points)

1. Hyoid bone

2. Diaphysis

3. Scoliosis

4. Atlas

5. Great trochanter

6. Humerus

7. Epiphysis

8. Femur

9. Lordosis

10. Talus

11. Axis

12. Foramen magnum

13. Calcaneus

14. Cochlea

15. Coronoid process

16. Patella

17. Palate bones

18. Kyphosis

19. Zygomatic

20. Glenoid cavity

21. Malleus

_____ is a flat bone.

___11___ is the bone around which the head rotates.

_____ is part of the mandible.

_____ is the name given to the ends of bones.

___6___ articulates with the scapula, radius, ulna.

_____ is called the "ankle" bone.

___4___ is the bone upon which the head rests.

_____ is the name given to the center or the shaft of long bones.

_____ forms the heel.

___5___ is located on the femur.

_____ is a lateral curvature of the spine.

___1___ lies between the lower jaw and the thyroid cartilage.

___19___ form the promontories of the cheeks.

___17___ are found in the roof of the mouth.

___12___ is the large opening at the base of the occipital bone.

___9___ is an increase in the lumbar curve.

_____ is found in the middle ear.

___20___ is an articulating surface of the scapula.

_____ is found in the internal ear.

True-False Type. Place a plus sign (+) after each statement that is true. Place a zero (0) after each statement that is false.   (50 points)

1. The peritoneum is a serous membrane.   _____

2. Ligaments are composed of epithelial tissue.   _____

3. Hyaline cartilage is found in the nose.   _____

4. Marrow contains blood vessels.   _____

5. If the periosteum is destroyed, bone fails to regenerate.   _____

6. Cartilage is found at the ends of bones. _____

7. The radius is on the medial side of the forearm. _____

8. Cartilage is freely supplied with blood vessels. _____

9. The humerus is an example of a long bone. _____

10. The carpus is an example of a flat bone. _____

11. The tarsus is an example of a short bone. _____

12. The sternum is an example of a flat bone. _____

13. A vertebra is an example of an irregular bone. _____

14. The upper extremity of the femur has two condyles. _____

15. The humerus articulates with the scapula, radius, and ulna. _____

16. The pelvis is made up of the two innominate bones. _____

17. The cavity of the pelvis of the female is more shallow and wider than that of the male. _____

18. Articulations are always movable. _____

19. The femur is the longest bone of the body. _____

20. There are twelve pairs of ribs. _____

21. All the ribs articulate with the sternum. _____

22. The foramen magnum is the large opening in the pelvic bone. _____

23. The humerus articulates with the scapula and tibia. _____

24. The fibula is on the lateral side of the upper leg. _____

25. A bursa is a piece of bone between joints. _____

26. The clavicle is a double-curve bone. _____

27. In a ball-and-socket joint, the shallower the cup, the greater is the extent of motion. _____

28. Man is a vertebrate. _____

29. The shaft of a long bone is called diaphysis. _____

30. The periosteum is thicker in children than in adults. _____

31. The head of the humerus articulates with the glenoid fossa. _____

32. The dens is a part of the axis. _____

33. The sacrum is made up of five vertebrae. _____

34. There is a joint between the sacrum and ilium. _____

35. The olfactory nerves pass through the ethmoid bone. _____

36. The ethmoid bone lies in the center of the skull.   _____

37. The sphenoidal sinuses drain into the throat.   _____

38. The frontal and ethnoid sinuses are the only ones which drain into the nasal cavities.   _____

39. In a dislocation, the bone is either fractured or bent.   _____

40. The palatine and mandible form the hard palate.   _____

41. The thorax is rounder at birth than in adult life.   _____

42. The coracoid process is a hooked projection of the scapula.   _____

43. The ulna articulates with the wrist.   _____

44. The bones of the wrist are called tarsals.   _____

45. The patella protects the knee joint.   _____

46. Only long bones are covered with periosteum.   _____

47. Alveolar processes are found on both the mandible and maxilla.   _____

48. The antrum of Highmore is in the maxilla.   _____

49. The scapula is called the collar bone.   _____

50. The pisiform is on the lateral side of the wrist.   _____

Selection Type.   Place the number of the correct word or words on the line at the right side of the statement.   (16 points)

1. The tissue of which bone is composed is called (1) epithelial, (2) connective,
   (3) muscular, (4) nervous, (5) vascular.   _____

2. The membrane covering cartilage is called (1) perichondrium, (2) periosteum,
   (3) perineum, (4) endosteum.   _____

3. The bones of children do not break as easily as those of old people because they
   contain more (1) organic matter, (2) inorganic matter, (3) periosteum, (4) marrow.   _____

4. The largest part of the sternum is called (1) manubrium, (2) gladiolus, (3) xiphoid
   process.   _____

5. The clavicle articulates with the (1) sternum, (2) humerus, (3) scapula, (4) cartilage
   of the second rib, (5) cervical vertebrae.   _____

6. Connections of bones are called (1) muscles, (2) aponeuroses, (3) articulations,
   (4) cartilage, (5) synovial membrane, (6) tendons.   _____

7. The head of the femur articulates with the (1) patella, (2) tibia, (3) fibula, (4) acetabulum.   _____

8. A medullary cavity is found in the (1) spinal cord, (2) shafts of long bones,
   (3) Haversian systems, (4) short bones.   _____

9. The bone in the upper part of the arm is the (1) femur, (2) clavicle, (3) scapula,   _____
   (4) humerus, (5) tibia.

10. Ossicles are found in the (1) cranium, (2) pelvis, (3) inner ear, (4) middle ear,   _____
    (5) mandible.

11. The mastoid cells open into the (1) external ear, (2) middle ear, (3) inner ear.   _____

12. The upper jaw is formed by the (1) maxilla, (2) mandible, (3) malar, (4) ramus,   _____
    (5) zygoma.

13. The soft spaces between the bones of the skull in infants are called (1) sutures,   _____
    (2) fontanels, (3) Wormian spaces, (4) fossae, (5) processes.

14. The anterior fontanel normally closes at about the (1) tenth month, (2) twelfth   _____
    month, (3) eighteenth month, (4) twenty-eighth month.

15. The acetabulum is located in the (1) shoulder, (2) ankle, (3) wrist, (4) cranium,   _____
    (5) hip, (6) thorax.

16. Sinuses communicating with the nasal cavities are found in the following bones: _____
    (1) maxilla, (2) mandible, (3) frontal, (4) occipital, (5) parietal, (6) malar,
    (7) temporal, (8) ethmoid.

---

2. MUSCULAR SYSTEM

Please give the name of a muscle, the complete name, for each of the following brief descriptions.

1. _____ It is a flexor of the elbow joint and inserts on the ulna.

2. _____ A muscle of varied action which has insertions on the spine of the scapula, the acromion and clavicle.

3. _____ It inserts on the humerus and abducts the arm.

4. _____ It has its origins on the upper nine ribs and inserts on the vertebral border of the scapula.

5. _____ It has its origin on the 3rd—the 5th ribs and inserts on the coracoid process of the scapula.

6. _____ It has its origin in the supraspinous fossa and its insertion on the top of the greater tubercle of the humerus.

7. _____ It compresses the abdomen and has its origin on the lower eight ribs.

8. _____ A muscle of the quadriceps femoris group which extends the leg and flexes the thigh.

9. _____   A muscle which flexes the knee and also the hip joint.

10. _____   Has its origin on the head of the fibula and the median
                                        border of the tibia and inserts on the calcaneus.

Please fill in the blank, numbered spaces in the following table. If a space is not numbered, leave it blank.

Name of Muscle	Origin	Insertion	Action
sternocleido-mastoideus	1. _____	2. _____	
3. _____	infraspinous fossa	4. _____	5. _____
6. _____		olecranon of ulna	7. _____
8. _____	coracoid process of scapula	9. _____	flexion and adduction of humerus
10. _____	lower rim of thorax	11. _____	increases vertical diameter of thorax
12. _____		13. _____	flexion of forearm and supination of hand
gastrocnemius	14. _____	15. _____	16. _____ _____

You fill in the blank spaces to the left of the page with appropriate words or phrases each time I use a
number in the narrative.   (30 points)

Example:

0 _____epiphyses_____   The ends of long bones are called (0).

1. _____   The muscle organs of the body, which make up about 40% of our
                               body weight, are composed of (1) muscle tissue and connective
                               tissue.

2. _____   Cardiac muscle tissue is found only in the (2), while (3) muscle
                               tissue is found in the walls of blood vessels, intestine, etc.
3. _____

4. _____   All muscle tissues are specialized in the physiological (functional)
                               property of (4).

5. _____   Muscles are in a condition of partial and sustained contraction
                               called (5) during our working hours. Muscles are capable of
6. _____   graded or measured responses because they are made up of (6)
                               all or a few of which can be called into action to meet a specific

7. _____   need or challenge. The muscle gives a maximal response when
                              (7) of the motor units are called into action.

8. _____   A muscle which is most directly involved in a movement is called
                              a (8). One which causes an opposite movement is a (9). One which
9. _____   aids movement by steadying the joint is a (10).

10. _____

11. _____   A single muscle most directly involved in flexing the elbow and
                              supinating the hand is the (11). The action of the triceps brachii
12. _____   muscle across the elbow joint is an example of leverage of class
                              (12). In terms of action it is called an (13) of the forearm.
13. _____

14. _____   The four important muscles of the abdominal wall are the (14, 15,
                              16, and 17). All of these muscles serve to (18) the abdominal wall;
15. _____   one of them, the (19), also flexes the trunk.

16. _____

17. _____

18. _____

19. _____

20. _____   Three muscles insert on the calcaneous through the (20) tendon.
                              They are (21) action of the foot. One of them, the (22), is also a
21. _____   flexor of the leg on the thigh.

22. _____

23. _____   A muscle which adducts the thigh and flexes the leg is the (23).
                              Three other adductors of the thigh are the (24, 25, and 26).
24. _____

25. _____

26. _____

27. _____   The individual fibers of a muscle organ are grouped into bundles,
                              the (27), and are enclosed in a connective tissue sheath, the (28).
28. _____   It is continuous with a similar sheath around each muscle fiber,
                              the (29), and also with a covering of the whole "fleshy" part of the
29. _____   muscle, the (30).

30. _____

Place checks in the appropriate spaces to properly characterize each kind of tissue.

	Smooth	Cardiac	Skeletal
1. intercalated discs			
2. voluntary action			
3. striations			
4. nuclei small, peripheral			
5. cells spindle-shaped			
6. branching fibers			
7. involuntary			
8. in walls of stomach			
9. myocardium			
10. nuclei numerous			

When one goes to sleep in class, why does one's head and mandible drop? (5 points)

3. COELOM AND VISCERA

Name five organs found in the mediastinum. (5 points)

Double serous membranes support and connect the various viscera of the peritoneal cavity. On the basis of their positions and relationships to certain organs they are of three types--<u>mesenteries</u>, <u>ligaments</u>, and <u>omenta</u>. Define each of these--carefully and critically. (9 points)

---

4. RESPIRATORY / DIGESTIVE / EXCRETORY SYSTEMS

List the adaptive features of the nasal passageways which make it more comfortable and healthful to breathe through the nose than through the mouth. (10 points)

What processes are involved in the formation of urine by the kidney? Name them only. (6 points)

Name the valves of the digestive system from esophagus to anus. State which of these are under voluntary control. (8 points)

Distinguish between elimination, absorption, and excretion by giving good definitions of each.   (9 points)

In the numbered blank spaces to the left below, place a word or phrase which is appropriate from the statements at the right. Be sure your numbers match.   (30 points)

1. _____   The air in passing through the nose is (1, 2, and 3). The shelf-like
                                 structures in the nose are supported by the (4, 5, and 6). The
2. _____   recesses beneath the "shelves" are called the (7, 8, and 9). In
                                 addition to serving as an "air conditioner" the nose is a receptor
3. _____   for (10).

4. _____

5. _____

6. _____

7. _____

8. _____

9. _____

10. _____

11. _____   There are (11) openings in the walls of the pharynx.

12. __palatine arches__   The mouth is bounded posteriorly by the (12) which divides medially
                                 into two "pillars," the (13 and 14), between which are located the
13. _____   (15) tonsils. From the middle of the (12) "hangs" a small projec-
                                 tion, the (16).
14. _____

15. __palatine__

16. __uvula__

17. _____   The larynx is supported by cartilages the largest of which are the
                                 (17 and 18). The larynx contains the (19), which are used
                                 for voice production.

18. _____

19. _____

20. _____   The trachea is lined with (20) epithelium and is supported by (21)-shaped cartilages to prevent collapse.

21. _____

22. _____   From the terminal bronchioles the air passes in sequence through the (22, 23, 24, and 25) to the terminal structures of the respiratory tree, the (26).

23. _____

24. _____

25. _____

26. _____

27. _____   The bronchioles of the lungs contain (27) tissue in their walls which is involved in asthma. The lungs contain also considerable (28) tissue which is important in expiration of air.

28. _____

29. _____   The outer surface of the lung is covered by the (29) and the chest wall is covered internally by the (30).

30. _____

Please list four ways by which the small intestine is adapted <u>by structure and action</u> to make the <u>absorption</u> process an efficient one.   (8 points)

1.

2.

3.

4.

INDEX